Millennial Hospitality

By

Charles James Hall

This book is a work of fiction. Places, events, and situations in this story are purely fictional. Any resemblance to actual persons, living or dead, is coincidental.

ISBN: 1-4033-6873-2 (E-book)
ISBN: 1-4033-6874-0 (Paperback)
ISBN: 1-4033-7670-0 (Dustjacket)

This book is printed on acid free paper.

1stBooks – rev. 04/25/03

Forward

I have enjoyed telling family, friends, and the wonderful people whom I have met at book signings the story of how the Millennial Hospitality series came into being. I thought other readers might like to hear it as well.

Over the last 18 years, from time to time when I entered the room where my husband sat at the computer, I noticed that he would quickly shut the screen that he was working on. When I asked him what he was doing, sometimes he would answer, "Nothing" or "Just relaxing".

Other times, he would say that he was working on a book. In May of 2002, he became unemployed. After he was a month into unemployment, this scenario repeated itself. He said he was working on his book. I said, "Well, you know, if you die tomorrow, there is no way I am going to go hunting through the many files you have, to look for any book. I suggest that you print some of that out right now; I would like to see it."

Charles said, "Which book did you want to see?"

"What do you mean, which book? How many books do you have in there," I asked?

He said, "Oh, a couple, three."

Naturally, when I saw some of the chapters, I was determined that we should publish it. I felt it was excellent material and it should be picked up by one of the major houses, but I knew that would take time and since no income was coming into our house, we decided to self publish.

The manuscript needed editing badly, partially because he had started the books on an old Tandy 2000 and there were technical difficulties in retrieving it. The major problem I had with the book was the macho language he thought he needed to use. My daughter and I were up to the task of editing the material and Charles was much in agreement when we told him that the story was so good, the swear words added nothing and furthermore, deleting them would make the book appropriate for mid-schoolers.

Well, Charles worked hard implementing all of our corrections, but then, inadvertently used older unedited files to compile the CD to send to the publisher. I will leave out some of the drama that followed. It slowed things down considerably, and because we were so anxious to start marketing our books, I had ordered 500 copies of *Millennial Hospitality* before I saw one bound copy. We decided to re edit immediately and Charles sat for days and hand edited some of the worst mistakes from the 500 copies we already had in our house. If you have one of those copies, they have already become collector's items.

That was then and this is today, the day it is that you are beginning to read *Millennial Hospitality*. We both hope that you will enjoy reading it and if you have not already read *Millennial Hospitality II The World We Knew* and *Millennial Hospitality III The Road Home*, we know that you will want to read them as well.

14 February 2003
Valentine's Day
Marie Therese Hall

This book is dedicated to the greater honor and glory of God
Who created us all, aliens included.

Acknowledgements

Millennial Hospitality is in print only because of my wife's support and encouragement. She is also responsible for the books title the design for the cover, and was my chief editor. I am also grateful to the young men whom it was my privilege to serve with during the Vietnam War years.

Table of Contents

My Place

As for man, his days are like grass,
he flourishes like a flower of the field;
The wind blows over it and it is gone,
And its place remembers it no more.

...Psalm 103 15:16

The train station in downtown Las Vegas was beautiful beyond description that Friday morning when I arrived. It was an early spring day in the mid 1960's. I was 20, an enlisted man, just out of training school, a weather observer in the United States Air Force. Homesick, I stood for a long time on the platform in my dress blue uniform, out in the bright, hot, beautiful desert sunshine. I watched the train as it pulled slowly away from the station and headed out into the brown desert to the southwest toward Los Angeles. I stood there watching silently, alone. As the train disappeared far away into the heat waves and into the distance, it seemed as if the world I had known disappeared with it. At last I turned around to view my new world. It was a world full of flashing lights, ringing bells, money-filled slot machines, blackjack tables, and scantily clad waitresses, for which the city was already famous. I could hardly have been more eager to enter this world, by way of its doorway at Casino Center. It seemed as if I had nothing to fear except, perhaps, getting my dress blue uniform muddy from the grass in front of me. The grass was half covered with water from the nearby natural springs. It

1

formed the beautiful well-watered set of meadows for which Las Vegas had been named. "What a nice relaxing touch of Las Vegas hospitality," I thought to myself. "My life now has it all. It has beautiful, scantily clad women, grass green money, and money green grass." Little did I know at the time, my life would very soon have desert afternoons spent in desperate life or death struggles and moonlit desert nights filled with white terror. For the next two and a half years, my assigned place would alternate between the base at Desert Center, and the gunnery ranges at Mojave Wells.

As I stood watching, an Air Force master sergeant in his early 30's got out from a dark blue USAF van parked nearby. He greeted me as he approached, "I'm Master Sergeant Walters. You're Airman Charles Baker, aren't you?"

"Yes," I responded. "I'm Airman 2nd Class Charles Baker, reporting for duty."

"Place your duffel bag in the van, and we'll get started," he responded. "We have a mighty long drive down to the southwest to get to the Desert Center Air Base. It's several hundred miles. We'll have to make good time if we intend to arrive before the chow hall closes."

"I got off at the right place, didn't I?" I asked.

"Oh yes, yes. Of course yes," he insisted. "Even though Los Angeles is closer, the drive into the train station in downtown L.A. is such a headache, we'd all rather come the extra miles up here to Las Vegas."

"If the Air Force had permitted it, I could have taken the bus from the train station here, down to Desert Center," I volunteered.

"Oh, no! Of course, not!" exclaimed the sergeant. "Those bus connections are confusing and the bus ride takes forever. Only someone who really knows his way around the southwest should ever attempt that. The long drive up here to Las Vegas in a government van is no trouble at all. We're happy to do it. It's fun coming in to Las Vegas. We even get to play the slot machines as we wait.

"First of all, I have to make sure that you know your boundaries. I have to make sure that you know your place. As soon as we arrive at Desert Center this evening, you'll sign in and be issued a bunk in the barracks. Then Monday, when you report for duty at the weather station, we'll issue you an off-duty pass. Your pass will permit you to travel as far as 450 miles away from the Desert Center base whenever you are not on duty. So when you have the time and money and you are not on duty, you will be able to travel in to L.A., San Diego, Yuma, Las Vegas, or to any town in-between. You can only travel outside of those boundaries if you have been issued special leave papers."

"I understand," I responded.

"Tonight, our commander, the major, has invited everyone in the detachment to attend his birthday party at the Desert Center officers' club. Today he turned 42. Of course, enlisted men such as you and I are normally not allowed in the officers club. Like all enlisted men, we have to learn our place. Tonight's party is special. It starts at 9:00 p.m. Put on your dress uniform, and be sure to attend."

"I'll be there, sergeant," I answered.

The drive down to Desert Center was a long one. I was quite tired by the time we arrived. I signed in, found my bunk, and just barely made it to the chow hall before it

3

closed. Then I slept for 3 hours or so, before getting dressed and heading over to the officers' club for the party.

The weather detachment was typically small. It contained barely 18 officers and men. I paid no attention when master sergeant Walters stated, "Not everyone is here. Sullivan from Mojave Wells couldn't make it," or when Dwight responded, laughing, "Maybe tonight, Sullivan's partying with Range Four Harry."

It was a wonderfully carefree party with loud music, several young women in attendance and lots of dancing. I was finishing my third glass of beer when a middle-aged lady came up to me and asked me to dance. Without thinking I responded, "No. I don't want to dance with you because you're too old." She became quite upset and stomped off. The party, the drinking, the dancing, and the laughter continued late into the night until closing time.

Monday morning came. I reported for duty at the weather station. Master sergeant Walters took me outside to the parking lot for a short fatherly talk. He explained that the older woman at the party, who had asked me to dance, was the major's wife. Everyone else had spent the evening dancing with her. Everyone, that is, except the major and I. He recommended that the first thing I should do, this morning, was to apologize to the major for turning down his wife. As we were going back inside the weather station, the major summoned me into his office and had me sit down.

He closed the door and began in fatherly tones, chuckling as he did so, "You know airman Baker, you're the first military man that has ever known his place and has also shown my wife her place. You're the only man here who doesn't want to dance with my wife. I can see right off that you and I are going to be great friends. Yes sir, airman.

You're the only man here I can trust around my wife. I can see that you're going to fit right in around here. This is definitely your place."

Wind Song

What is man that you are mindful of him,
the son of man that you care for him?
You made him a little lower than the angels,
you crowned him with glory and honor
and put everything under his feet.

…Hebrews 2:6

Springtime was beautiful at Desert Center. It had rained a few days earlier and the sagebrush was covered with beautiful purple flowers.

It was just past 2:00 in the afternoon on this breathtaking spring day. I was sitting in my barracks with the door open, looking out across the distant sea of purple sage flowers. I was quite homesick and I was wondering how things were back in Wisconsin. The winds on this Monday afternoon had been modest, but the gusts were quite high. The door to my room opened to the lee side of the barracks. Watching the winds periodically blow huge patches of desert sand across the sagebrush, I found it to be a relaxing, almost musical experience.

I was sitting there, quietly engaged in humming tunes to the music of the winds when my melancholy world was shattered by the ringing telephone. Answering the phone, I said, "Barracks four. Airman Baker speaking."

The voice on the other end was the operator at the Desert Center tower. He sounded terrified. "Baker! Thank God you're there!" he exclaimed.

I didn't have the faintest idea how to respond, so I responded humorously, "Well, I have so many impostors that I've taken to introducing myself as the real Airman Baker," I laughed.

Without laughing, the operator continued in the same terrified tone of voice. "We're in desperate trouble here. We need you at the weather station immediately."

"I don't understand," I responded. "McIntyre is working the day shift today. I haven't heard of any problems. Certainly the major and sergeant Walters know where to find me if they decide I'm needed down at the station."

"I know that Charlie. I can't officially ask you to relieve McIntyre down at the weather station, but I'm asking you as a friend to do whatever you can to help us. I have six F105 fighters trapped aloft in this wind. They're down to less than 30 minutes of fuel and we're all desperate. They can't land in this wind and they can't parachute out. Nobody knows what to do. McIntyre has kept them circling for hours. I've already tried asking the major and sergeant Walters to ask you to come in but they refuse. They say that McIntyre is the assigned duty observer and they won't relieve him of his duties just because I request it. If you just go down to the station, you'll see immediately what the problem is. Look, my captain is coming and I don't want him to know I called you. I'm breaking all of the regulations and he'll be mad as a hatter."

Then the operator suddenly hung up the phone. Curious now, I quickly put on my uniform and hurried the mile to the weather station. Since I didn't want to raise any eyebrows, I quietly entered using the back door. Inside McIntyre was working happily in the teletype room. He was humming a pleasant tune as he typed up another one of his weather reports.

"How's things going, McIntyre?" I asked pleasantly.

"Oh, just fine, old man." he replied happily. "I can't talk right now, though. I'm right in the middle of typing up these reports."

"I see some F105s circling around out there. I suppose they probably need to know what your latest wind report is," I continued.

"Yes, I just gave it to the tower," responded McIntyre in his same happy warrior tone of voice. "I just closed the base again you know, old man. They'll just have to wait until this wind lets up. The winds should be letting up pretty soon. See, these latest winds that Sullivan just phoned in from Mojave Wells? See they are light and variable, all the way up to 20,000 feet. Both the forecaster and I figure the winds here at Desert Center are sure to let up real soon."

One glance at the weather reporting forms showed the problem immediately. McIntyre had opened and closed the base more than 250 times since the inversion broke at 10:00 a.m. this morning. Every time a gust of wind started, he closed the base. Every time the gust ended, he opened the base. The flight of six F105s was obviously mouse trapped by his indecision. I could see why the tower had phoned me. Yet, strictly speaking, McIntyre was actually conforming to all of the rules and regulations. The major and sergeant Walters had no reason whatever to relieve him of his duties. McIntyre and the weather forecaster were basing their decisions on the Mojave Wells wind reports. Likewise, every report from Mojave Wells supported the weather forecast and McIntyre's decisions. Yes, I could see the problem immediately.

Guessing the planes to be down to less than 20 minutes of fuel, I entered the teletype room where McIntyre was working. There in the privacy of the small room, I gently said to McIntyre, "You know, McIntyre, I owe you a lot of favors. You've helped me out so many times. Remember just last week you worked a double shift, yours and mine too?"

"Oh, think nothing of it, old man." responded McIntyre.

"Well, today, I thought I would do something nice for you to show my appreciation. I see the afternoon movie at the base theater will start up at three o'clock. It's that latest spy adventure movie that you have wanted to see. I know you're probably short on cash because I know that you help out your mother back home, so I tell you what. Here's five dollars. I'll relieve you for the rest of the afternoon. You go see that movie you like so much, and I'll have a clear conscience. It really meant a lot to me, McIntyre, those times you've worked my shifts for me, and didn't tell the Major. You remember how I was so sick you had to help me back to the barracks that one morning. I just need to say thanks."

McIntyre's face lit up as he took my five dollars. "Gee, thanks, old man. That's really nice of you. I'll take you up on that. First though, I better finish typing this up."

"I'll be happy to do that for you, McIntyre," I said. "You'll just barely have time to make it over to the theater as it is. Here, I'll sign in showing I'm relieving you. You head out the back. No sense in the major and others asking too many questions. They have their problems. You and me, well, we have ours. You be sure to have fun now."

"Thanks old man," happily exclaimed McIntyre as he signed out and exited through the back door.

I quickly signed in as the duty observer. I picked up the emergency phone to the Desert Center tower. The tower operator answered with that same desperate tone in his voice, "Desert Center tower"

Speaking quietly and clearly into the phone, I said, "This is airman Baker. I'm the duty observer for the rest of the afternoon and also for this evening's swing shift. I want to make sure you guys know that the base is closed."

"Charlie, it's you!" exclaimed the operator. "Where's McIntyre?"

"He's doing me a favor and checking out the women in the latest spy film over at the base theater," I answered, nonchalantly. "What's the status on those six F105s I see circling out there."

"Unless you can think of a way to get them onto the runway, they're going to have to crash into the desert in 15 minutes," responded the operator. "We have all of the fire trucks and ambulances deployed along the runway. Nobody knows what to do about those winds and that blowing sand out there. Five of them are young pilots and need winds less than 20 miles an hour and at least one mile of visibility to land. The sixth one is the flight leader. He can take higher winds but he still needs the visibility to see the runway."

I could see the problem immediately. They'd all taken off in the calm winds of the morning while the base was still covered with a bubble of cold air. They had all taken on a full load of fuel in case the winds started up before they could return from Mohave Wells. When they returned from the gunnery ranges, they discovered that McIntyre wouldn't permanently close the base. Had he done so, they could have all just headed off for some other place with no wind, like Yuma Arizona. Yet, when McIntyre opened the base, the weather wouldn't actually let them land. They had therefore been mouse trapped into circling over Desert Center for several hours. Disaster was now threatening all of them.

"How long would these pilots spend in the landing approach, if they did it as fast as they could?" I asked the tower operator.

"Two minutes," was the answer.

Checking the wind recorder, I said to the tower operator, "That's too fast for these new guys to adjust to these changing winds. Have all six airplanes use a longer, more gradual approach. If you can, make it last exactly five minutes. That'll give them more time to adjust to the changing winds when they're turning and landing.

"Have them make the entire approach with their gear down. That way, when they're flying blind in the sand on the end of the approach path, their planes will handle the same as when they were flying in the clear."

"Roger. Copy," responded the tower operator.

I continued, "The wind gusts have been very regular, almost musically timed. The wind has had gusts to 50 miles per hour lasting almost exactly one minute, then the wind has let up to 15 miles per hour for almost exactly one minute. When the wind is gusting, the blowing sand obscures everything, but when the wind lets up, the pilot can see for miles. I'll go outside on the tarmac where I can feel the wind and still see my wind recorder. Don't have the planes enter the approach path until I give the word. I'm going to have them enter the approach path while the wind is gusting. Remember, they'll be entering the approach path blind. Have them lower their gear while they're still in the clear.

"I'm going to time it so the gust lets up just before they reach the end of the runway. That way, they'll be able to land in that nearly calm period which happens in between gusts. I'm going to have them enter the approach path two minutes apart, so you may have as many as three on final approach at the same time."

"Roger," responded the operator. "That's no problem. There are three of us up here."

"Have the fire trucks and ambulances re-deploy so they're marking the exit ramps from the runway. That way, once a plane lands, he can clear the runway even if the sand starts blowing again," I continued.

"Roger, copy." responded the tower.

"Remember, each plane enters the final approach one at a time, and each plane waits for me to say go," I reminded them.

A short pause followed as the tower explained the instructions to the F105s. "Roger," said the tower. "Right about now they're ready to agree to anything."

I watched the wind recorder carefully. I also studied the sand carefully as the wind blew it past me in an almost musical fashion. Then, twenty seconds into the blowing sand, I had timed the gust carefully, I told the operator, "Start the first F105."

"Roger, copy," responded the tower.

Two minutes later, I ordered the second F105 to begin his approach. I timed the wind gusts carefully. Four minutes later, I ordered the third F105 to begin his approach. As my watch was coming up on the five-minute mark, to my great relief, the existing gust let up on schedule and the first F105, 1000 feet over the end of the runway as expected, was now able to land. After dropping onto the runway as requested, he let his fighter roll to far end of the runway and exited immediately onto the taxiway.

Amid the cheers from the tower operators, I continued timing the wind gusts carefully. Now, six minutes from my starting point, I ordered the fourth F105 to begin his approach. In like fashion the second fighter landed in between gusts after seven minutes. It became almost like playing the piano. After eight minutes I ordered the fifth F105 to begin his approach, and after nine minutes I watched the third F105 land in between gusts. After ten minutes I ordered the flight leader - the sixth F105 - to enter the approach path. After eleven minutes I watched the fourth F105 land. Having no more F105s to order into the approach path, there was nothing else for me to do but time the gusts and watch as the fifth F105 landed after 13 minutes. The last two minutes seemed to pass like hours as I waited for the flight leader to complete his approach path. Right on schedule, after a total of fifteen minutes had passed, the latest wind gust let up. As the sand cleared, the flight leader's F105 could be seen 1000 feet up, over the end of the runway. As his F105 was just touching down on the runway, his engine flamed out. His fuel tanks were absolutely dry. As the next gust of sand overtook him, his plane rolled safely to a stop in the middle of the runway.

It took several minutes for the cheering to calm down in the tower. The operator came back to me shouting, "Charlie! You did it! I don't know how you were able to time it that perfectly, but you did it!"

"Oh, it wasn't that hard." I shrugged. "It was sort of like playing the piano. Well, I better let you guys handle the airplanes. I need to get things cleaned up around here. Remember, the base is closed until at least midnight."

13

With that I said good-bye and hung up the phone. Then I busied myself with my routine duties. As I was filing the weather reports on the forecaster's viewing board, I wondered, "Why are the winds reported from Mojave Wells so different from the winds blowing outside?"

A short time passed, probably twenty minutes. As I was working I noticed an Air Force maintenance truck drive up in front of the weather station. A bird colonel stepped angrily out of the truck and strode forcefully up to the door of the weather station. As I watched, he grabbed the outer screen door with both hands. Wearing one of the most brutal expressions that I have ever seen a man wear, he proceeded to tear the screen door from its hinges. Then, once the door had been thrown to the ground, he proceeded to stomp all over it, kicking and tearing at it, until nothing but pieces remained.

"Ah, the flight leader," I said to myself quietly. "I wonder if he's brought his napalm with him."

He proceeded to forcefully kick in the door to the weather station - it wasn't locked at the time - all the time screaming, "Where is he? Where is McIntyre? I swear I'm going to strangle him with both my hands."

Both the major and sergeant Walters were shocked into action. The major and the sergeant came running in to the observer's section and began shouting, "Where's McIntyre? Where's McIntyre?"

Just then the bird colonel succeeded in breaking through the front door, physically kicking it into pieces as he smashed through its last remains. I could see that the colonel had some pretty definite ideas regarding the rest of the station's interior decorating as he stomped into the observing portion of the station - violently smashing a wooden chair on the floor as he did so.

Gripping a piece of the broken wooden chair leg in his right fist, he turned to the major, who was still shouting at me, "Where's McIntyre?" and pointing to me. The colonel screamed, "He's not McIntyre, you idiot! He's the only reason that any of us are still alive! He's the one getting the medal I'm demanding the Air Force deliver for this fine mess! Now where is that scrawny little weather observer that kept me and my men trapped up there for the last four hours?"

I could see the colonel was a fine man - created a little lower than angels, I suppose - but all in all, still a pretty fine man.

The major turn to me in surprise and shouted, "I thought McIntyre was the duty observer today."

Interrupting the major, the colonel screamed, "He was, until thank God, this airman sent him packing! Now where is he hiding?"

"I'm not sure." I responded pleasantly. "My attention was focused on the aircraft emergency we just had, so I have no idea where he might be right at the minute." Having just saved six lives, I decided that I might as well continue the trend for a seventh.

Range Four Harry

"What did you go out into the desert to see?
A reed swayed by the wind?"

Luke 7:24

"Well, Charlie," said Dwight, putting down his thermos of coffee, "You're going to get your chance to solve the mystery of Range Four Harry. I talked the major into sending you up to Mojave Wells for a temporary tour of duty – a TDY - starting next Monday. A TDY up there lasts six weeks. You'll love it. You'll be relieving Sullivan. His four years are up, and he'll be getting discharged in ten days."

It was another beautiful spring morning at Desert Center Air Force base. The music of the '60's was so enchanting. I was still proudly wearing two stripes. I was just finishing the last weather report for the night shift. The station clock was showing 8:00 a.m. and Dwight had come to relieve me for the day shift.

"You talked the major into what?" I asked. Dwight was one of my closest friends. Surprisingly, Dwight and his lovely young wife and children had few other friends in the Desert Center area. Dwight and I were like brothers. I knew that whatever he'd done, he must think it was good for me.

"Mojave Wells, Charlie," laughed Dwight. "You know, the Air Force gunnery ranges up that desert valley northwest of us. You'll be up there the full six weeks.

You'll get extra TDY money. You'll have your own Air Force pickup truck to drive wherever you want. There won't be any officers around! You'll have a wonderful time."

"Thanks, Dwight," I responded. "But why me?"

"To tell the truth, Charlie," responded Dwight. "You're the only man we have who can handle it. Summer is almost here, and the ranges are going to be very busy. There'll be a lot of airplanes flying around up there, so you'll have plenty to do. The major agreed with me, but I tell you Charlie, you're so good that the major was a hard man to convince. He wanted to keep you here to help out on airplane emergencies. Those six F105s you saved last spring really impressed him. I was afraid he'd say "No". I almost couldn't talk him into it. I really had to work on him, Charlie."

"Man, Dwight, that was really nice of you," I responded.

"Oh, think nothing of it," replied Dwight. "Really, I did it for myself. First, I got his curiosity up. I told him that you'd solve the mystery of Range Four Harry. The major wasn't going to agree. That afternoon, he had to go over to the Desert Center base commander's office. When he came back, he agreed with me.

"You see, Charlie, summer is coming on. Old Harry likes it hot. He is certain to start coming out again. Harry hides up in the mountains during the wintertime, but he always comes out on warm summer evenings. He likes to run around out on that dry lakebed up on range four. You're sure to see him. Both the major and I, we really want to know what he is."

"Range Four Harry?" I asked. "You got me there, Dwight. I've never heard of him."

"Never heard of him, Charlie." answered Dwight, using that same calm voice which was his hallmark. "Range Four Harry is supposedly a horse that got too close to an atomic bomb blast that was set off way up at Frenchman flats back in 1954. It was right after the blast that people started seeing him. He's been down here, out on range four ever since. The radiation burned him real bad, so usually he hides up in the mountains. But on warm summer nights, he comes down into the valley and roams the number four range up at Mojave Wells.

"One side of him glows a soft fluorescent white. No one knows what the other side of him looks like. Everyone who has tried to walk around him and look at him from the other side, has gotten burned pretty bad, or attacked. Either way, they've all come back scared stiff.

"If you see him, don't ever try to walk up in front of him and look in his face. Harry doesn't want anyone to see his face. The few people who have seen him from the front, say his face is human-like, but very unusual. He is said to have large blue eyes and his head is real large. They say his face looks sort of like the face of a horse, and his tail is made of long blond hair."

Dwight's story was so outlandish that it made me chuckle. Dwight acted as if he actually expected me to believe him.

"A radioactive horse that glows in the dark?" I asked, almost breaking into open laughter. "With large blue eyes? That ran away from an atomic bomb blast back in 1954?" It certainly sounded like the kind of make-believe story that a veteran would pull on a new guy just for fun.

"Honest, Charlie, I've seen him myself, and so has the major." replied Dwight.

"You and the major have actually seen this Range Four Harry?" I asked humorously.

"Yes, Charlie," replied Dwight, appearing to be entirely serious. "It used to be that the wind measurements were always taken from the range four weather shack. Range four is the one that is so far out there. But, every weather observer that went out there, returned terrified. They refused to go out there again because of Range Four Harry. The situation came to a head three summers ago, when Rigby and Anderson were up there. The Air Force was flying night training missions at both range three and range four. They wanted Anderson to handle the winds at range three and Rigby to handle the wind measurements at range four. Rigby and Anderson wouldn't do it. They wouldn't split up like that. They insisted that it was just too dangerous, and insisted that a second team of two weather observers come up and help them."

"They wouldn't do it, even as a two man team?" I asked.

"That's right," said Dwight. "Neither Rigby nor Anderson would go out to range four. Anderson would never go out there at all, and Rigby wouldn't go out there alone. Neither of them would even consider going out there at night, even if someone else went along with them. They insisted that Range Four Harry made it too dangerous.

"That's not the half of it. Rigby and Anderson would never agree to do a TDY at Mojave Wells unless they were both together. By the time they were discharged, they'd both done three tours of duty up there, and they were both absolutely terrified of Range Four Harry. When they were out there on the ranges, they wouldn't even go to the bathroom alone.

"When the Air Force wanted to do the night missions, both Rigby and Anderson came down here and begged the major to send more men to help them. They said they'd cover range three because Steve and the range maintenance men would be there with them. The range maintenance men are known as 'The Range Rats'. They're the Air Force enlisted men who pick up the practice bombs, maintain the gunnery ranges, build roads, and stuff. They all insisted that the major send two more men to cover range four. To a man, they said one man couldn't cover range four on account of Range Four Harry. Well, the major decided that he and I would go up there together to be with Rigby and Anderson for a couple of weeks. He wanted to see what was going on. The major was determined to get to the bottom of it, so he decided that he and I together, would cover range four.

"One night on our second week, just after darkness had set in, the major and I were sitting in the range four lounge. All of the lights were turned out. We were out there alone, just the two of us. We had Wayne and Steve, the leaders of the range rats, take us out there while it was still daylight. They left us there, and they went back in to range three. Steve said they'd come back out for us in the morning.

"Well, in between wind measurements, the major and I would lock ourselves in the range four lounge, as Steve had said. We sat there as quiet as we could. We didn't even say anything to each other. Steve said that if we wanted to see Harry, we couldn't talk above a whisper. Well, we were sitting there, looking out the window towards the west when we saw him.

"Harry was just up the valley to the northwest of the buildings at range four. He was out over that dry lakebed which is so open. He was out where there isn't any sagebrush or anything. He must have a real smooth gait, because it looked almost like he was drifting or floating over the dry part of the lakebed.

"Anyway, he came south, right past the window. He was only about a quarter of a mile away. I tell you, Charlie, the major and I both got a real good look at him. He looked just like a large glowing fluorescent white horse.

"The major was so surprised, he grabbed my arm, pointed out the window, and said, 'Look, it's Harry!' in a real excited voice. Well, just as Steve had said, Harry has near perfect hearing. Maybe the radiation improved Harry's hearing or something, because as soon as the major said that to me, Range Four Harry figured out we were there. Old Harry turned around real fast and took off.

"I tell you Charlie, when it was over, I was scared stiff. You should have seen the major. He was more scared than anyone I've ever seen. We didn't take any more wind measurements. Neither the major nor I were fit for duty. We stayed locked in the range four lounge the rest of the night. We had the door locked and barricaded. We used the chairs and anything else we could find. When Steve and the range rats came out to get us in the morning, I thought the major was going to kiss them all. Then the major decided that because of the danger from Range Four Harry, the routine wind measurements would no longer be taken from range four. Starting that morning, all future wind measurements would be taken from range three. Wind measurements from range four would be taken only under very special circumstances, and only if the TDY observer agreed that it was safe to do so."

21

After hearing Dwight's story, I had a real problem. I really didn't know what to believe. On the one hand, his story was so outlandish. It couldn't possibly be true - a radioactive white horse that floats, terrifying grown men at night in the desert? It seemed as if I should respond by laughing until my sides ached. Yet, the problem I faced was very simple. Dwight had told other outlandish stories which I believed to be true. His outlandish story of the famous lady singer who had fallen in love with him at the USO, had survived my cross-examination. According to a biography authored by her close relative, Dwight was the only man the singer had ever been in love with. The biography included a picture of the singer sitting with Dwight at a table in a USO.

Then, there was Dwight's apparently unbelievable story about one of the American presidents keeping the Russian ambassador waiting while talking with him and his father. On close inspection, it too, had survived my cross-examination, complete with a picture in another widely published book.

Thus, Dwight's story about Range Four Harry caused me quite a problem. Why would Dwight, so honest in the past, be making up such an outlandish story now. We both knew that all I had to do to check up on Dwight's story was to ask the major.

After thinking about Dwight's stories carefully, I decided to ask Dwight some more questions. "What did Harry's face look like?" I asked.

"I don't know, Charlie," responded Dwight. "I never got to see it. Anderson said he saw Harry in the daylight one time. He said he had a large head with chalky white skin and large blue eyes."

"You say that Harry has blonde hair?" I continued.

"I never actually got to see his hair," responded Dwight. "But Anderson said that the day he saw Harry out in the sunlight, Harry had nearly transparent white blonde hair."

"But you said you actually saw Harry?" I inquired.

"Yes, yes, I actually saw him," said Dwight seriously, "So did the major."

"Tell me again what you saw." I said.

"Well," said Dwight, "He gave off a soft fluorescent white light. The light hurts your eyes when you look into it, even though the light isn't very bright. He didn't make any sound when he moved. He was about a quarter of a mile off when he was close. He came from the northwest, up along the mountains. Then, when he left, he went back up there from where he came."

"But the lakebed is dry. Is there any grass or water up that way for a horse to live on?" I asked.

"No. None for at least forty miles," said Dwight. "But Harry doesn't need grass and water to live on."

"He doesn't?" I responded.

"No," said Dwight. "At least that's what Steve says. Steve says Harry gets his food and water from some place real far away, so he doesn't need any when he's around here."

I thought about things for a minute, trying hard not to laugh. Then I continued. "Rigby and Anderson, they got their discharge from the Air Force a couple of years ago, didn't they?"

"Yes, they're long gone," said Dwight. "Sullivan has been up there the longest of anyone since then."

"When did they first start seeing Range Four Harry?" I asked.

"Well," said Dwight, "Rigby was on his first tour of duty at Mojave Wells when Harry first terrified him. He went out to range four before dawn every morning in order to take the morning balloon run. One warm summer morning, Harry came down from the mountains and part way across the dry lakebed. Rigby said Harry stopped about a quarter of a mile off. He said Harry just stood looking at him while he released the balloon and took the wind measurements. He said that Harry stood about six feet tall. He said that Harry's face looked similar to that of a horse. Rigby said that at first he thought he was dreaming. Then, as Rigby was finishing his balloon readings, old Harry gave out a short whinny, sort of like a horse. That's when Rigby suddenly realized that whatever it was out on the dry lakebed, it was real. Alone in the desert night, unarmed, and forty miles from anywhere, Rigby panicked. That morning, Rigby barely made it back into Mojave Wells. By the time he made it back into the barracks area, he was so terrified he could hardly drive anymore.

"After that, Rigby was so terrified of Harry that he'd never go out into the desert until after sunup. Even then, he'd always take a range rat, or one of the cooks with him for protection. He always carried a loaded pistol with him when he went out there. Sometimes he couldn't find a cook or range rat to go with him, so he wouldn't take the winds at all. He'd just hide in the base area. That's why the Major decided to send Anderson to be up there with him. The very first day that Anderson was up there with Rigby, Harry came again. So they informed the Major that they would take the winds from range three only, and never from range four. Range three is only 20 miles out in the desert instead of forty.

"On one morning Rigby was sick, so Anderson decided to drive out there alone. Like Rigby, Anderson came back absolutely terrified. He claimed that Harry had snuck up behind him. He said when he finished taking the balloon readings, he turned around suddenly and Harry was standing there, no more than ten feet from him. He became terrified and panicked instantly. He dropped everything and ran for his truck. Then he drove the truck full bore back to base. When the range rats got out there, they found the generators still running, and all of the weather instruments lying right where Anderson had dropped them. After that, Anderson, like Rigby, would never go out there alone."

"But, I don't understand," I said. "What about the morning wind measurements? I mean, they're supposed to be taken from the range three weather station. How did they take the wind measurements when they were hiding in the barracks?"

Dwight responded, "Lots of times when Range Four Harry was in close, the winds they sent in weren't worth the time it took to write them down on paper. On those days, they just made up the winds and phoned them in from the barracks."

I paused to think over Dwight's story for a few minutes. Dwight waited patiently. Then, after mulling it over, I asked Dwight, "How did Range Four Harry get is name?"

"That happened before my time," responded Dwight. "As I understand it, back in the fifties, a weather observer was stationed up there, named Jackson. They stationed him up there because he had a drinking problem. Lots of the times he'd have two or three beers before he was willing to drive out onto the ranges alone, especially at night. He was a good observer, though. The winds he turned in were usually dependable. Well, one day he was out at range four. He always swore that he was stone sober at the time and that he'd been dry and on the wagon for several weeks. It was in the late afternoon. He claimed that he saw something white over along those mountains northwest of the range four lounge. Even though he was stone sober at the time, he decided that he'd been drinking for so many years that he'd started hallucinating. So he wanted to see if the white patch was real. He'd been taught in alcoholic rehab to handle his halllucinating that way. Jackson got into his truck and drove over there. The white patch just stayed where it was.

"When he got there, he stopped the truck, got out and walked up to it. He was certain that he was hallucinating. He said that it was sitting on a large rock, ten feet or so above him. He said it looked like a thin human, all white - chalk white. It had blonde hair and blue eyes. It looked down at him sort of the way a horse might look down at him. As I understand what happened next, Jackson looked up at it and said, 'Go away. I know I'm having a drinking problem, and I know that you're not real.'

"The white thing looked back and said to him in English, 'I'm as real as you are.'

"Then Jackson said, 'Well, I'm real, and I have a name. My name is airman first class Jackson. If you're so real, what's your name?'

"The white thing responded, 'You may call me Range Four Harry.'

"Jackson found it all very funny. Jackson began laughing and laughing. Then he turned around and walked back to his truck, laughing, 'I've been drinking way too much. Now my hallucinations even have names.'"

I spent the next several minutes laughing myself. Then, teasing Dwight slightly, still in total disbelief, I asked, "There's one thing I don't understand, Dwight. If Range Four Harry makes it so dangerous to go out on the ranges alone at night, why am I being sent up there alone? Won't I have to drive out there at 3:15 a.m. in the morning to measure the winds, too?"

"Right now, Sullivan always takes some cooks and range rats with him when he goes out there. He never goes out there alone. You'll be up there with Sullivan for the first week. You decide what to do after that. If you need help, like Rigby and Anderson needed help, just phone me up. I'll explain it to the major." Then Dwight became very serious, and said, "Remember, Charlie, when you're up there, you can tell me anything. I'll believe you. You can call me up any time, even at home. You can tell me anything. Don't go taking any risks. I really did see Harry. He's perfectly real. If you go out there after him, he really will burn you, just like he burned John Zimmerman two years ago. Zimmerman got a medical discharge because of it. If you decide to make up the morning winds like Rigby and Anderson used to, when you phone them in to me, use the word 'very'. Just say they're the very early morning winds. That way I'll know they're made up. Then I'll go look at the wind charts and make sure they look right, just like I used to do for Rigby and Anderson. If the winds haven't been made up, then don't use the word 'very'. Just say they're the morning winds."

"That's really nice of you Dwight. I'll remember that in case I ever need it," I said sincerely. With that I told Dwight I'd be seeing him later and signed out as duty weather observer.

Letting the station screen door slam behind me, I began the long hike back to my barracks. I was walking across the parking lot when my friend Michael drove up beside me. Michael was still in training. So, he was also working the day shift.

"Hi, Charlie," exclaimed Michael, happily. "It's good to see you."

"Michael," I answered. "How are you?"

Michael, as usual, couldn't miss an opportunity to mention his beautiful younger sister Pamela. He and Pamela were alone in this world. They had no other living blood relatives. Their natural parents had both been killed in separate car accidents when Michael was six. They were both determined to stay together, even after they were both married. It would all work out so simple if Pamela could arrange to marry one of Michael's friends. One of Michael's worst kept secrets was his hope that Pamela and I would get married. "I'm running late this morning, Charlie. I had to drop my wife and sister off at work downtown. That traffic down by the courthouse is terrible. What's happening with you?" he responded. He was obviously happy that he had arrived in time to talk with me.

"Well, according to Dwight, I'll be starting a TDY up at Mojave Wells next week," I said. "Dwight was telling me all about Range Four Harry."

"Oh, you mean that old prospector and his burro that people see hiking around the ranges at night?" answered Michael.

I was quite surprised. Michael and his sister had grown up in Palm Meadows, and had lived in the city all of their life. He'd certainly heard all of the desert legends many

28

times over. "A prospector and his burro?" I asked. "Dwight said it was a horse that glowed in the dark."

"Whatever it is, it does glow in the dark" said Michael. "That much I'm sure of. Both Pamela and I have seen it from a distance. When I was in High school, the place where I used to park with my girl friends is on that road that goes up the northeastern side of Mount Baldy. There's a romantic parking spot up there, just above the tree line. From up there you can see all up and down Mojave Wells valley. You can see the stars, the moon, everything. We've never been close enough to see very much. He must have been 15 or 20 miles away at the time. What I saw was a bunch of soft white lights that would float around the Mojave Wells valley. They weren't just up by range four, though. Range Four Harry would prospect all over the place. Besides range four, he'd take his burro all over range three. Then he and his burros would go down by ranges one and two. Pamela said that several times she saw them come right up into Mojave Wells itself, even into the barracks area. She said she saw them float right into the barracks. Sometimes they would float right into the house trailers."

"But if the lights were so far away, why do you say that Range Four Harry is a prospector?" I asked.

"That's what my stepfather and my stepmother told Pamela and I," answered Michael. "When we were children and our step parents were dating, they said that one warm summer night they saw him next to the road going up towards Death Valley. That was back in the spring of 1954. They didn't see much of him. I guess he was prospecting in the Joshua trees along the road. They didn't actually see his burro. I guess he was in a tent or wearing a sheet. He must

29

have had his lantern underneath it to light it up, because there was white fluorescent light all over the place."

"Well, Michael," I stated, "I see it's getting pretty late. I better let you go. Thanks for the information about Harry. I'll be sure to ask Pamela about him, the next time I see her."

Michael, looking pleased, said mischievously, "She'll love showing you that place up on Mount Baldy, Charlie. Be sure to ask her." With that Michael said goodbye and reported to work.

As I walked back to my barracks, the whole thing seemed so immensely humorous. I wasn't long out of sight of Dwight and Michael before my sides were aching from laughter. My friend Dwight, I thought, wanted so much for me to receive the extra TDY pay that Mojave Wells duty paid, that he would tell both me and the Major anything to get the Major to send me there. Then there was my friend Michael. Obviously, he would tell me anything just to get his sister Pamela and I, parked in a romantic spot out on the slopes of Mount Baldy. Yes, I thought to myself, Jesus had certainly provided me with two of the best friends a man could have. That had to be the case, I thought. After all, how could all of those outlandish stories possibly be true?

Yes, I thought, laughing until my sides ached. "How could all of those outlandish stories be true?" As I walked slowly back to my barracks, I laughed until I thought I had pulled a muscle in my left side. Soon I found myself laughing too hard to walk, so I had to rest a while, sitting on a concrete bench that marked the bus stop near my barracks.

Two days later I was still laughing. I found the whole experience tremendously humorous. "A radioactive white horse that floats around at night in the distant deserts and scares grown men who venture out in the moonlight?" I laughed. How could there possibly be a shred of truth to the whole story. Still, I did have that one problem. Neither Dwight nor Michael had ever told me anything wrong in the past. The outlandish stories that they had both told me had survived my cross-examination.

That second afternoon, I reported to the Desert Center base hospital for a routine checkup before heading out for Mojave Wells. Sitting in the reception area, I still found myself laughing. The receptionist was a young single girl named Sandra. She was my age. We were good friends. I had danced with her a few times at some Air Force enlisted men's dances and taken her to a movie once. As I sat there, Sandra wondered why I was so amused. I was laughing so hard that I was unable to recite the entire Range Four Harry story. However, between laughs, I blurted out Zimmerman's name. At the time I expected that Sandra too, would break out laughing with me. I could hardly have been more off the mark. Instead, Sandra responded seriously, "Oh, him. Here, Charlie, because we're friends, I'll show you his file. We keep it in a special place with the other files of airmen who have received special medical discharges."

As I tried to still my laughter, Sandra got up, went into a room in the back, opened a safe, and returned with a folder of medical records. My laughter turned to shock as she opened Zimmerman's medical folder to a series of four pictures. Each picture clearly showed bone deep burn marks on Zimmerman's upper left arm and shoulder. The doctor's report stated the burns were similar to deep radiation burns. According to the report, Zimmerman claimed that a white radioactive horse had burned him. Zimmerman stated he

31

had encountered the horse out in the desert north of range four. It also stated that Zimmerman had just barely gotten back into Mojave Wells alive, collapsing from his wounds just as his truck rolled to a stop in front of the motor pool.

Too much in shock to finish reading the entire report, I turned to Sandra and asked, "You mean it's actually true? You mean there is actually something out there calling itself Range Four Harry?"

"Yes," Sandra responded. "Or at least, that's what Zimmerman swore as they were treating him with morphine for his burns. He was in such agony at the time, the doctor doesn't see how he could possibly have been lying."

"You mean that's what I have to face when I go out on the ranges?" I asked, stammering in disbelief.

"Yes," she continued. "And remember, Zimmerman claimed it came only when he was out there - alone."

Four - The Government's Number

Under three things the earth trembles,
Under four it cannot bear up.

...Proverbs 30:21

"Sullivan," I whispered quietly. "Wake up. It's Monday morning. We're late. It's already four a.m."

Sullivan lay in his bunk for few seconds. Then, suddenly wide-awake, he quickly jumped from his bunk, taking care not to wake the other six airmen who shared his barracks. He slipped smoothly into his new green fatigues. He took his new working shoes out of their box, and quickly put on the new brogans. Grabbing his new fatigue cap, he silently led the way to the weather truck parked outside. His new car was parked next to the truck. As I carefully brushed past it, I noticed that the car engine was still warm.

This was the first time I had ever met Sullivan in person. He hadn't been on base when I arrived the day before. On this, my first morning at Mojave Wells, I stood in awe of him. He was the same height as I was. His charismatic personality, athletic build and graceful manner all left me green with envy. His uniform was brand new, immaculate, pressed, in perfect order, and polished. Sullivan was the very picture of perfect military discipline.

As I followed him to the pickup truck, I felt ashamed of my fatigues. Although clean, and only one year old, mine were already faded, showing ragged edges, paint spots, and an occasional loose button. I wondered how he had

33

managed to keep all of his uniforms perfect and spotless. The desert is a harsh working environment. He had, after all, at his own request, been assigned here for the past several months. Sullivan made it all seem so simple. He had, he explained, bought all new fatigues so he would look military when he was discharged at the end of this week. I pointed out to him that the dress blue uniform is the required uniform for the discharge ceremonies, not the work fatigues that he was currently wearing. He thought about that for a minute, and answered, "You know, I never thought of that."

We were very late getting started. The first balloon run was supposed to be taken while it was still nighttime out on the ranges. However, sunrise was already well under way by the time we began walking towards the weather station's pickup truck. It was parked some distance away in front of the cook's barracks. The truck was nearly new, and painted a nice relaxing blue with a white roof. Sullivan, for all of his perfect military spit and polish, didn't seem to be the slightest bit eager to actually head on out to the ranges or to arrive on time. It was only my gentle persuasion, "There's nothing out there to be afraid of", I chided, that finally got him started, although he did seem to take issue with the way I had phrased my statement. It seemed odd to me at the time. However, Sullivan had spent many more nights out on the ranges than I had.

The drive out to range three was uneventful. It was a beautiful early morning. The rising sun bathed the sagebrush meadows that stretched north up the Mojave Wells valley. The warm desert valley glistened in the soft beautiful golden rays of sunshine. Sullivan, however, obviously did not consider the valley to be beautiful. He seemed awfully nervous. He seemed distantly fearful of something. I found it surprising. I believed that a man who had made the drive every morning for the last several months, would learn to calm himself down and to see the desert in all of its beauty. How else I wondered, could a man find the courage to drive out onto the ranges every morning, every day, every night, out into the darkness alone. Sullivan, however, just gave the engine more gas. Soon, at speeds exceeding seventy miles per hour, we were flying out towards range three. I felt a little worried at the time. You see Sullivan didn't seem to know the road very well.

Soon, the range three gate fell behind us. The buildings of range three loomed out of the darkness. Arranged to form a large open square, the buildings, some 22 miles out in this remote desert valley, exuded feelings of unbelievable solitude, intense loneliness, and a human lifetime of neglect.

The truck glided past the generator building on the right and, after making a sharp right turn, Sullivan skidded the truck to a stop in front of the weather shack. Jumping from the truck, he strode quickly and powerfully towards the locked front door of the weather shack. In total awe of his professionalism, I followed slowly along behind.

Reaching the front door, Sullivan grasped the lock firmly in his left hand. With his right hand, he quickly felt all of his pockets. Then, turning towards me, he said firmly, "Give me the key!"

In surprise, I responded, "What key?"

"Didn't the cook give you the key?" He asked firmly.

"No," I responded timidly.

Without another word, Sullivan released the lock, swiveled smartly on his right boot, and strode quickly and powerfully through the beautiful moonlight, back to the truck. I followed timidly behind. As I climbed in on the passenger side, Sullivan started the motor, and said to me, firmly, and pleasantly, "The first thing you'll want to do, Charlie, is to get a copy of the key."

While I hung on for safety, Sullivan gave the engine some gas and soon we were speeding back down the range three road, back towards the barracks area. As the truck sped on through the early dawn, Sullivan took out a new piece of paper and a new pencil from one of his shirt pockets. Handing them to me, he said authoritatively, "Here, record these winds."

Taking the pencil and paper, I began recording as Sullivan continued, "One thousand feet, southwest at three. Two thousand feet, southwest at five." Then, thinking for a minute, he continued, "No! Make those two thousand foot winds, out of the southwest at four. Four is the government's number, you know."

"The government's number?" I asked, in surprise.

"Yes," Sullivan responded. "The government's number. Anytime you're making up the morning winds, you want to be sure they believe you down at Desert Center. You see, Charlie, you're up here this morning, so everyone down there is expecting the winds to be especially accurate. That's why this morning we'll go with the number four."

"The number four?" I asked still in surprise.

"Yes, the number four." Sullivan said simply. "Three doesn't have any power associated with it. The number three always seems incomplete. The number five is a suspicious number, you know. Nobody ever believes five.

But four, now, that's a number you can trust - that's the government's number.

"You know, Charlie, those people down there really believe in you. They're depending on you to straighten this thing out. What those people really want from you is the number four. We have to be careful not to disappoint them."

I could see that Sullivan was a man who had everything well thought out.

Sullivan continued with more numbers for me to record. As we drove on towards base, he proceeded to make up the wind and the weather report, apparently showing the wind speed and direction for every altitude up to 20,000 feet. Yes, all in all, it was a very educational Monday morning.

Soon, we were entering the barracks area. Sullivan pulled the truck into its parking spot at the front of his barracks. Turning to me, he stated simply, "Wait here. I'll call these in."

While the truck engine idled, I waited patiently in the passenger seat. Sullivan climbed the steps to the barracks. Once inside he strode to the barracks phone. Through the open windows, I listened as Sullivan dialed the Desert Center weather station and read the winds to my friend Dwight. Then, hanging up the phone, he returned quickly to the waiting truck. As he climbed in, he announced simply, "It's time for breakfast. We'll be just a little early."

Sullivan's personality had a powerful effect on me. I had spent the time waiting in the truck, sitting in envy. I kept wishing I were more like him. I wondered why the Chief Observer down at Desert Center, Sergeant Walters, considered him to be a man of very little character. Through it all, one question never occurred to me. I never once wondered why a weather observer completing an extra long tour of duty of the gunnery ranges, wouldn't have the key to his own weather station - or have learned the road out there by heart.

As we headed towards the chow hall, I couldn't resist asking him some questions. "Where are you from?" I asked.

"Long Beach, California." He answered pleasantly. "I was born in Los Angeles. I'm attending Long Beach State." Then he thought for a minute, and added quickly, "At least I will be when I get out of the Air Force. How about you, Charlie?"

"Wisconsin." I returned. "I fell in love with the University of Wisconsin at Madison. I sure get homesick for that place."

"I know how you feel." said Sullivan. "I can hardly wait to get back to California."

Right then, I guess, I knew that God had intended for Sullivan and me to be friends. I knew that God had some special purpose in mind when he had sent me to relieve Sullivan. The fact that my commander, the major, stated that he had received special orders signed by the Pentagon, sent by way of the Desert Center base commander, never once entered my mind. God works in mysterious ways.

My mind drifted back to all of those mornings I worked at Desert Center, all of those mornings when Sullivan had phoned in the winds. On a few mornings he had actually been on the other end of the line. However, most mornings the voice reading the winds would be that of a randomly chosen cook or the air policeman, or an occasional range maintenance airman known as a range rat. Sullivan was a natural born leader. Every man at Mojave Wells liked him. He made it seem so natural to protect him, and to do whatever he asked.

As I sat there, in awe of Sullivan, I remembered some stories that the Chief Observer Master Sergeant Walters had told me. Walters claimed that one morning Sullivan had wrecked the weather truck while driving back to base. Walters believed that Sullivan had been giving an all night beer party for his friends, out on the ranges, and had been driving drunk at the time. According to Walters, Sullivan was so likable that all of Sullivan's friends at Mojave Wells had covered up for him. They claimed that someone else whose name they would not divulge had been driving the truck and wrecked it. According to Walters, the Major had sat down with Sullivan alone, and had privately asked him for the truth. Sullivan claimed that two men, whose names he did not know, had been in the truck. One of them had been driving. Sullivan claimed that both men in the truck were in a panic and trying desperately to get away from Range Four Harry. The Major, himself, claimed to have actually seen Range Four Harry out on the ranges. For that reason the Major ordered that no action be taken against Sullivan. Looking at Sullivan, I could see why all of the men at Mojave Wells had backed him. He was so likable. Turning him in would have been like turning in your own brother.

After thinking in silence for a few minutes, I turned to Sullivan, and said, "Sergeant Walters wants you to show me all of the different ranges.'"

Sullivan looked visibly afraid. After a short pause, he said, "OK, Charlie. After we finish the one o'clock balloon release, I'll take you down to range one. The range rats tell me they're going to be out at range two this afternoon. If we see them out there, I'll show you range two also. Now as for range four, you'll have to have the air policeman and the

39

range rats take you out there and show you around. I never go out there." Then, thinking for a minute, he continued, "Whatever you do, Charlie, never let the range rats take you out to range Four after dark." Then, thinking some more, he continued, "Even in the daytime, never let them take you up into those mountains northwest of range four - not even up close to those mountains. It's just too dangerous."

"You mean because of Range Four Harry?" I asked.

"No!" responded Sullivan emotionally. "No! There's no such thing as Range Four Harry! I don't care what anyone says!"

With that, Sullivan slipped into an emotional silence. The truck bounced up into the chow hall parking lot. As Sullivan turned off the engine, I jumped out on the passenger side. I understood why Sullivan had gotten so emotional over range Four Harry. After all, he had been stationed up here completely by himself. He had been expected to drive alone and unarmed, out into a very big desert every morning for months. I could see that he had found a lot out there to be afraid of.

Breakfast was surprisingly good. I was just finishing my eggs and bacon when Sullivan, at last, joined me at my table. Retrieving the keys and saying good-bye to the cooks had taken him some time. Introducing me to the head cook who had followed behind him, Sullivan stated, "This is Smokey. If you have any questions or if you ever need someone to help you in the mornings out on the range, just tell Smokey."

Somewhat off balance I stood up and shook hands with Smokey.

Smokey greeted me; "Sullivan will be going back down to Desert Center tomorrow after breakfast, Charlie. You'll be completely in charge of the wind measurements starting tomorrow. That includes the morning run. My friend Sullivan likes you, Charlie. Don't be afraid to ask me if you need help. I've scheduled Steve to help you on tomorrow morning's run."

For some reason Smokey's words didn't seem to be sinking into my brain. "But there's only seventeen or so airmen up here. Sooner or later I'm going to have to stand on my own two feet," I protested. "Sullivan showed me range three. It's only a one-man weather station. It's really nice of you guys to want to help me, but honest, I can handle the morning wind measurements myself. My friend Dwight told me all about it. What would I need a second airman for?"

Smokey glanced towards Sullivan. Then, choosing his words carefully, he responded, "Well, you know, you might need some help for something. Like you might need someone to keep watch outside while you were inside the weather shack, finishing the calculations. Steve is really good at that, you know, maybe even the best. He's been here the longest. You should take him with you and let him show you the ropes. You need to know how to stay hidden when you're out there, how to park your truck behind the generator shack so that no one can see it. You need someone to show things like that, at least for a couple of days."

Smokey's words weren't sinking into my coffee starved brain. "If I'm all alone out in a deserted stretch of government owned desert, why would I want to stay hidden?" I wondered to myself. Still, trying to be sociable and hoping to make Smokey happy - chow hall cooks make wonderful friends - I responded, "OK. I'll wake Steve up and take him with me when I get up in the morning." It seemed to make both Smokey and Sullivan much happier.

The late morning and early afternoon balloon runs passed quickly. Desert Center needed only four more wind measurements that day. The sagebrush meadows of range three were as beautiful in the noonday sun as they had been under the morning sun. Sullivan was an excellent, understanding teacher and the time passed quickly. I remember feeling honored that Sullivan was there to teach me - even though Sullivan didn't seem to know where any of his tools were. It is strange how much a few short hours can mean to a man.

The noon meal and the one o'clock run passed quickly. Then, our duty day completed, Sullivan and I got into the weather truck. Together for the last time, we began the long drive down to range one. I closed the door and locked the weather shack behind us as Sullivan started the truck.

With Sullivan at the wheel, we retraced our route back down the range three road. When we were still three miles from base, we reached the junction with the road to range one. Leaving the paved range three road, Sullivan made the left turn at the gravel-covered junction. Now heading east on a gravel road, we began the long drive down the valley to range one. Many miles down the valley we passed another road junction. Speaking at last and pointing to the gravel road heading across the valley to the mountains on the other side, Sullivan stated simply, "That's the road to range two. It's at least 22 miles from here back to town."

As we continued on towards range one, I noticed that Sullivan was driving much slower now. Slowing to 25 mph, then 10, he seemed afraid to close the distance between us, and the buildings in the sagebrush up ahead. Stopping, finally, on the edge of the graveled area between the control tower and the weather shack, his hands visibly trembling, it was obvious to me that he wanted only to turn around and head back into base. Still sitting in the driver's seat with the engine running, he locked his door and rolled up his window. Then, despite the heat on this hot summer day, he insisted that I do the same. He stared intently through the windshield, looking out across the beautiful sunlight sagebrush meadows in the distance. In near terror, he asked me quietly, "Do you see anything out there?"

Except for the gentle breezes and beautiful purple sagebrush flowers, there was little else to be seen. "No, Sullivan," I said, "There's nothing out there. Do you see anything out there?"

"No, not today," said Sullivan, obviously still terrified of something. "But one Sunday afternoon last fall, I came down here to clean the weather station. There was an angry white coyote out there in the sagebrush. I didn't see it until I got out of my truck and I was walking towards the weather shack. Then I saw it stand up on its hind legs, out there, about a quarter mile out in the sagebrush. It was growling at me. I became afraid. I began running towards the weather shack in order to get inside. As I came around the corner, standing there, hiding from me, was a little white boy. I almost tripped over him."

"A little white boy?" I asked in disbelief. "But Sullivan, we're at least 25 miles from town. All of this land is part of the Desert Center gunnery ranges. How could a little boy get way out here?"

Sullivan's fear still gripped him as the terror of that bygone day flooded through his mind. "I went to grab him to protect him from the coyote and he clawed me" said

Sullivan. Then he raised the shirtsleeve on his lower left arm until it exposed a long deep scar. He continued, "That's how I got this. I started bleeding all over myself and all over him. I became struck with panic. I ran back to my truck but it wouldn't start. The little boy went running out into the sagebrush towards the coyote. The two of them went running down into the valley. I watched them until they disappeared in the sagebrush way down there, maybe five or seven miles down on the other side of that dry lakebed. I was hysterical at the time, but I was able to bind my wounds and get the bleeding stopped. Then I was finally able to get my truck started. Charlie, I shouldn't have brought you down here. It's just too dangerous. I just can't come down here anymore. We need to leave right now."

"Wait, wait, Sullivan." I said. "I haven't seen the weather shack yet."

Sullivan was already starting to turn the truck around. Convincing him to stop and let me inspect the weather shack was no easy matter. However, after several minutes of near begging, he agreed. Turning to me he said, "OK, Charlie, but I want you to close the truck door behind you when you get out. I'll stay in the truck and keep the engine running. You must understand. If there is anything hiding around the other side of the weather shack where the door is, I won't wait for you to get back in. I'll stop just long enough for you to jump into the back of the truck, and then I'm heading out of here. I want you to know that if I have to leave you, I'll go back into base and get help. Then I'll come back with the air policeman and the rest of the range rats."

"That's fair enough," I said. "But, really, there's nothing out here, Sullivan. Look and see. There's really nothing out here."

Sullivan seemed to relax a little as we both scanned the beautiful and obviously empty stretch of desert that lay before us. I carefully opened the truck door and got out. Closing the truck door behind me, I slowly and carefully walked across the graveled area between the control tower and the range one buildings. Turning the corner of the weather shack, I stopped, still in full view of Sullivan. There was simply nothing hiding there. There was no coyote, no lost little boy with claws, not even an insect. I stood there for a minute, hoping Sullivan would relax. Then I took out the key to unlock the lock on the door. I walked slowly over to the door. I was fearful that Sullivan would panic over nothing and leave me stranded out there. I gingerly opened the locked door and peered inside. The dust inside said it all. It was as plain as the nose on my face. No one had so much as opened the door to this weather shack since the previous fall. According to the entries in the logbook, no one had been here for months.

Sullivan began racing the truck engine and began slowly moving the truck toward the exit road. I quickly closed the weather station door and locked it. Then, hurrying back to the truck, I grabbed hold of the door handle and attempted to get inside. Sullivan was so terrified, I had to pound on the door handle to get him to stop the truck and let me in. In just the short time I had been out of the truck, Sullivan had locked the door for safety.

Once I was safely back in the truck and the door locked, Sullivan floored the gas petal. At speeds exceeding 50 mph, he headed back towards base. Once range one lay two or three miles behind us, he seemed to calm down and I began to talk some sense to him.

"There really wasn't anything whatever out there, Sullivan." I said calmly. "Nothing whatever. Not a bird. Not a coyote. Not a snake. Nothing."

"Did you look out in the sagebrush?" He demanded emotionally. "Did you look way out in the sagebrush, right above the flowers? Was there anything out there?"

"I looked all over, Sullivan," I said. "There wasn't anything out in the sagebrush. Nothing, there was absolutely nothing. The coyote you saw. How did it look?"

"It had light colored or blonde hair. It looked almost like an albino. Maybe it had gotten exposed to some atomic bomb radiation or something because it was so thin. It was standing about a quarter mile out in the sagebrush, looking at me," replied Sullivan, calming somewhat.

"But a quarter mile is quite a ways out in the sagebrush, Sullivan." I replied. "The sagebrush down here is pretty tall and healthy. Doesn't the sagebrush stand a lot higher than a coyote? I don't understand why you could see the coyote at all."

"You're right," said Sullivan, "But you don't understand. This coyote was standing upright on his hind legs. This let him see over the sagebrush. He could stand up that way, walk that way, run that way, and everything."

I really didn't know what to do. Sullivan obviously needed time to calm down so I sat quietly and thought for a few minutes. Nothing seemed to be making any sense. An albino coyote that runs on his hind legs and protects a little lost white boy with claws seemed to be little more than somebody else's make-believe nightmare. Yet the scar on

Sullivan's arm was as real as his terror. I really didn't know what to think.

Sullivan drove on some more. Finally he seemed to conquer his fears. He started to get back to his old self. Sullivan continued, as though he wanted to confess something. "You have to understand, Charlie. Nobody believed me. They sent me out here, alone - always alone. I didn't have a gun, a club, or anything. Lots of nights my flashlight wouldn't work, even with new batteries. The mornings were dark and cold. I'm not like you. You know what to do when you're alone. You know how to handle it when things happen and you're by yourself. You know how to scare off the coyotes. You know how to make friends with little kids. You know how to make a stand, how to place your back to the wall and face, alone, whatever it is that's coming towards you at night. My mother died when I was young. I never learned things like that. Then when they happened, I didn't know what to do. They nearly killed me. I did the only thing I was able to do, Charlie, I broke and ran. It was all I knew how to do."

Meaning to calm Sullivan, I replied, "I understand Sullivan. I understand completely. I thought you handled it very well. If that claw-mark on your left arm had cut an artery, you would have died out here. You really handled it well, Sullivan. You really did."

Up ahead was the turnoff to range two. Sullivan remembered his promise to take me out there if the range rats were there. He stopped the truck at the road junction and pointed the truck down the range two road. With the truck stopped and the engine idling, he gazed intently at the range two buildings some five miles distant. Because of the afternoon haze, the desert heat waves, the glare from the

47

bright sunlight, little if anything could be seen. Sullivan obviously was unwilling to leave the range one road unless he was certain that the range rats were already over at range two.

Suddenly Sullivan saw something move in the sagebrush, out along the range two road. He seemed to be looking along the tops of the sagebrush at a spot about a half-mile down the road. Near panic gripped him. Throwing the truck into reverse, he backed the truck back onto the range one road. Then, using the forward gears and speeds reaching the very limits of the truck's endurance, he headed us back toward the barracks area. Shouting at me in terror, he screamed, "Did you see it? Did you see it? It was out there! It's still out there! After all these months, I tell you, it's still out there. You must have seen it. You must have seen it!"

I had to confess that I really hadn't seen anything. It didn't appear to me that there was anything out there to be seen. It wasn't until several miles had passed under our tires that Sullivan started to get hold of himself. This time, calming Sullivan required all of my energy and attention. The whole experience had left me feeling disconnected and confused. I honestly didn't know what to think. Sullivan's scar proved that something had happened several months earlier and he was obviously still terrified.

I remembered that only three months earlier Desert Center had requested some wind measurements from range one and Sullivan had apparently provided them. On one occasion at Desert Center I, myself, had recorded the numbers while Sullivan calmly read them to me over the phone. At that time, he could hardly have sounded happier. Yet, there was no mistaking the records in the range one weather shack. No one had unlocked the door for several months.

I thought things through carefully as we sped back toward base. I decided to wait until after the evening meal to ask Sullivan the questions that were forming in my mind. Yes, I decided to wait. However, I had misjudged the depths of his terror. As soon as he had finished parking the truck next to the barracks, he turned to me and said, "Here Charlie, here are the keys to the truck and to the weather shacks. They're yours now. I really can't go back out there, ever again. I'm so glad it's over. I'm so glad they sent you to relieve me. I hope you understand. I like you Charlie, I really do. I don't know why they sent you up here all alone, but they did. You must be careful. When I get back to Desert Center, I'll tell them. I'll tell them you shouldn't be up here alone. It's too dangerous. I'll tell them for you, Charlie. It's just too dangerous.

"I'm going to pack my things in the car I own, now, and go back to Desert Center. I'll be leaving you here by yourself. I hope you understand. I like you, Charlie, I really do, but I just can't spend another night here. I just can't. Even in the barracks, it's just too dangerous. You must take care of yourself, Charlie. You must take very good care of yourself."

With that, Sullivan, unlocked his door, got out of the truck, and rushed into the barracks. Without waiting for the evening meal, he hurriedly packed his few belongings into his car. Within fifteen minutes he was gone, never to return. I was still in awe of him and his near-perfect personality. I hadn't even gotten a chance to say good-bye.

The next morning came. Certain that I could take the morning run by myself, I saw no reason to wake Steve. So, by myself, at 3:15 a.m., I started the weather truck and headed out towards range three. Except for the sagebrush, the shadows, the moon and the stars, there was little else to look at. The balloon release, taking the readings, and phoning Desert Center with the results, all proceeded in an uneventful routine manner. The radio that I had brought with me received all of the best Palm Meadows radio stations. Soon, the nighttime air was filled with the latest rock sounds, and I was ready to phone Desert Center with the results of my computations. I was just hanging up the phone when Steve arrived, driving his own truck. Tall, lanky, and a near-perfect stranger, I was really touched when he explained that he had driven the many miles out to range three, just to make sure I was all right. It took the longest time for me to think of anything, other than to thank him and tell him how thoughtful he had been. Immediately, Steve and I became as close as any two brothers.

The next few days passed uneventfully. By Friday the days were beginning to fall into a pattern. I drove out by myself in the morning and drove in for breakfast. I drove back for more wind measurements until noon and drove in for the noon meal. I went out for the last run and locked up at 2:00 in the afternoon and headed back into base. Through it all I was alone.

On this first Friday, though, I was sitting quietly in my range three weather shack, listening to the radio. It was a beautiful summer day. I had opened my front door and my side door to let the summer breezes in. It had just turned 9:00 a.m. when the phone rang. Picking it up, I answered, "Range three, Charlie."

The male voice on the other end asked, "Can I speak with Sullivan?"

"Sullivan?" I answered. "I'm sorry, he's not here. Perhaps I can help you."

The voice continued, "Well, ah, who am I speaking to?"

Before answering, I thought for a minute. Sullivan's new car, the confusion over the keys, suddenly, it all fell into place. "This is Sullivan's friend, Charlie." I said. Then, I continued with an innocent lie, "We went to high school together. We work together on our cars, here at this machine shop on the edge of town. What can I do for you?"

The voice, sounding relieved, continued, "Well, I'm the manager at the apartment house, here where he lives. I was afraid he'd be angry because I'm breaking the rules by calling him at this number. I'm only supposed to use this number if it's an emergency."

"Oh, don't worry about that." I reassured him. "He's quite understanding. He won't be angry that you called."

"I just wanted to tell him the delivery boy brought some packages for him on Monday. I still have them here." The voice continued. "He can pick them up at my apartment. I was going to tell him this past Wednesday when I saw him, but I got interrupted. I called him down at his regular work number but they said he was on vacation today. I know he said never to bother him at this number but these packages are large. They look like they might be the auto parts he ordered."

"Yes," I answered, continuing my innocent lie, "The heat in Long Beach was really getting to him so he took the week off. I'm sure you'll probably see him tomorrow.

"When I see him, I'll be sure to tell him about his packages." I continued. "Let me make sure I know your apartment number so I get the directions right. Which apartment are you in?"

The voice responded, "I'm right here in apartment seven, same as always. It's the same apartment he comes to when he pays his rent. He can stop by any time."

"That's right there on the edge of Long Beach, right. The same place he's lived in for the last several months?" I continued.

"Yes, that's right," the voice answered. "You know, that same place he moved into several months ago, right after he got discharged from the Air Force. I tell you he's been just the best tenant, never any loud parties or anything. We're just as happy as we can be with him."

"Yes," I answered calmly. "His nerves sure were shot when he got out of the Air Force last fall, weren't they?"

"Oh, they sure were," the man answered. "I tell you, something out there in that desert scared him bad. You know, for the first three months he was here, he wouldn't answer his door even if he knew it was me. I tell you, he sure was terrified by something out there.

"Boy, that's the truth." I answered. "Well, I'll be sure to tell him about his packages. I wonder if you would do a favor for me the next time you see him." I asked

"Sure," responded the voice. "What would you like?"

"When you see him, tell him that his good friend Charlie figured out the puzzle he was working on." I said. "Tell him Charlie understands. Then tell him not to worry. I want to make sure he knows that his secret puzzle is safe with me."

"Sure," the voice responded. "No problem whatever. I'll be sure to tell him the very next time I see him."

With that, we bid each other good-bye and hung up.

Yes, I had seen it clearly. Sullivan had been terrified by whatever had happened out at range one. Sullivan believed that his life was at stake. He had done the only thing he knew how to do. Yes, I was sure of it, now. Months before, after nearly dying out on range one; Sullivan had trained the cooks, the policeman, and the range rats to take the weather reports for him. He had drilled them carefully to always go in pairs for safety. Between his likable personality and the gifts he gave them, they had all banded together to help him. How could any man, myself included, have refused him? Then, with all of his bases covered, he simply packed his belongings and left for the safety of his hometown, Long Beach, California. Once there, he found a job and rented an apartment. He told everyone that he had already been discharged from the Air Force. Then he proceeded to live a very quiet life until his real term of enlistment was up. Naturally, he hadn't bothered to tell anyone at Desert Center. They'd have called it desertion from the Air Force - a federal crime.

The following Monday morning came. It was 4:30 a.m. Alone as usual in the range three weather shack, I was just filling the balloon when the phone rang. Turning off the helium supply, I answered the phone, "Range three, Charlie."

The voice on the other end was Sullivan's. Speaking quietly, pleasantly, and humbly, he said, "Charlie, I just had to tell you thanks. I don't know how to thank you. I don't even know how you figured it out. It's just like Sergeant Walters said when my discharge was being processed. He said he'd never met anyone as intelligent as you. I also want you to know that I told them down at Desert Center. I told them you shouldn't have been sent up there alone. I told them they should have sent two observers so that you wouldn't always have to be begging favors from the range rats, just so you could have someone else with you when

53

you go out onto the ranges. I don't know what else to say, Charlie, but I just had to call you and say thanks."

"Thanks for remembering me, Sullivan." I said happily. "Don't worry, I understand completely. Your secret is safe with me."

Then Sullivan continued, "Who else is working with you this morning?"

"Oh, no one." I replied honestly. "As usual, I'm out here alone."

Upon hearing this, Sullivan immediately became agitated. Terror began surging through his voice. "You shouldn't do that, Charlie. It's too dangerous. It's just too dangerous. They'll come, Charlie. They always do. Even in the barracks, they always come! They're curious, Charlie. They're curious about everything. They come in the darkness! How they love the darkness! They come just to look! They'll come for you just like they came for me. You should always have someone out there with you, to keep watch - to warn you so you can leave before they come!"

"Who, Sullivan?" I interrupted in surprise. "Who'll come? Who is it that comes in the darkness?"

"The Creatures!" screamed Sullivan, his voice breaking into terror. "The White Creatures!! The White Creatures, Charlie! They'll come! They always come!"

"The Creatures? Who are The Creatures? Do you mean Range Four Harry?" I responded in surprise.

"NO!" Sullivan continued, now screaming in terror. "NO! NO! GET BACK FROM ME!! GET BACK!! YOU CUT ME!! YOU CUT ME DOWN ON RANGE ONE!! I WASN"T DOING ANYTHING TO YOU!! YOU'RE NOT HUMAN!! YOU CAN'T BE SORRY!!" Then Sullivan apparently began reliving some more of the awful nights of terror that he'd spent alone, out in the empty darkness of the desert ranges, so many months ago. He could be heard dropping the phone and screaming hysterically, "No! No! There's no such thing! NO! There can't be! I don't believe it! I don't believe in you! No matter what you say. I have to get out of here! I have to run! I don't believe in you! Whatever I see ... Whatever you show me! I don't believe... There can't be anything out there!! There just can't be anything!! There just can't be!!"

Then, more hysterical screaming could be heard as he broke down in terror. Someone in the background apparently began pounding on his front door shouting, 'Are you OK, Sullivan? Are you OK in there?' while he continued screaming, trying desperately to get control of himself, screaming, "NO! GET BACK FROM ME! PLEASE!! GET THEM BACK FROM ME!!" In the background, the front door could be heard slamming open, and an older man talking to him calmly. After many long minutes, Sullivan finally calmed down enough to pick up the phone and talk. He continued, emotionally, "I have to go now, Charlie. You must leave immediately. Never go out there alone - NEVER - NEVER - NEVER! Just make up those winds, and phone them in from the chow hall – just give them the number four! When you make up those winds, just give them the number four. Think of yourself, Charlie. They'll believe you. They'll always believe you! Charlie! They expect it from you!

"I don't know if we'll ever see each other again, but I have to go. Thanks, Charlie. Thanks for understanding. Thanks, for understanding. I'm so glad that God sent you to relieve me, instead of someone else. No one but you would have understood. Remember, Charlie, never go out there alone. NEVER! It's just too dangerous!"

With that, he hung up.

I stood thinking about what had just happened for a while before hanging up the phone. Then, my growling stomach reminded me that I had to finish my work before I could have breakfast. I turned the helium supply back on and continued with the business of taking the morning run – alone.

Requisition Roulette

Therefore, since we are surrounded
by such a great cloud of witnesses,
let us throw off everything that hinders
and the sin that so easily entangles,
and let us run with perseverance
the race marked out for us.

Hebrews 12.1

"You know, Charlie, you're the first observer from Desert Center who's ever checked out this two and a half ton truck in the two years I've been here." Mark stated matter-of-factly. Mark was in charge of the Mojave Wells motor pool. He pushed the clipboard holding the motor pool truck sign-out sheet across the counter at me, and continued in friendly tones, "It's a fine truck. It'll get you down to Desert Center and back with those helium cylinders you need. But what surprises me is that you say you need so many. Twelve helium cylinders is a lot of helium. Each one of those cylinders must weigh 200 pounds, but don't worry. That truck out there can handle the weight. Just the same, you're going in for supplies much sooner than any of those other Desert Center observers used to. This is just your first week up here, and it's still only Wednesday. Your needing the big truck is mighty unusual. According to the motor pool records, none of those other observers ever used the big truck at all."

Mark and I were close friends. He was an exceptionally fine mechanic. Intensely Baptist, he read the Bible daily. When he spoke, he seldom used swear words. "Yes, I suppose I am, Mark." I answered as I filled out the truck request form. "But numbers are numbers. I'm using a cylinder of helium every two or three days. That means in an ordinary month, I expect to need eight or nine just out at Range Three. Then if I keep a couple spare and replenish the supplies down at Range One ... well, twelve cylinders just aren't that many."

"You're the weather observer," laughed Mark, tossing me the keys. "It's got gas in it and it's ready to roll. You're supposed to have someone with you when you take the truck to Desert Center, but none of the range rats are free, so you'll just have to make the long trip in to Desert Center by yourself. Be careful when you're loading those heavy helium tanks. That's usually a two or three man job. Remember, the Sergeant who runs the Airman's club needs the truck first thing tomorrow morning. He goes for club supplies every two weeks."

It was a clean truck, and obviously well maintained. After a short walk across the open motor pool parking area, I started the truck right up. I made a quick trip out to my range three weather shack, picked up my four empty helium cylinders, picked up my log and inventory books, and headed into town. Soon I was off base and heading down the highway towards Desert Center.

It was a long drive. Alone as I was, it left me time to wonder about Mark's words. When I had taken over as the duty observer the week before, none of my weather shacks had much in the way of supplies. The four range weather shacks had only 31 balloons total of all colors - red, white, and black - barely 6 days supply with breakage. Monday of this week, I had reviewed the old wind reports recorded by the range three observers before me. The reports went back 10 years. Hundreds of expected reports were missing, fragmented, or incomplete. Thousands of other wind reports were so unbelievable; they were obviously not worth the paper on which they were written. In addition, the forms and the old logbooks had hundreds of unusual entries. One observer, five years before me, whose name was McPherson, recorded that he had abandoned the range four weather station for his entire six week tour of duty because he was terrified by the fluorescent lights that he stated always came from up the valley to the northwest in the summertime. Then, a week later he recorded that he was abandoning all of the range weather stations and taking his weather reports from his barracks back on base, even if the ranges were in use. He recorded that he had started seeing the same lights out in the sagebrush near range three. He said the lights appeared to be following him around and watching him from a distance. Two weeks of such terror was all he could take.

Then there was yesterday. I had been familiarizing myself with the Mojave Wells base dump. To my surprise, I uncovered more than 1000 old weather balloons, still in their original shipping boxes, thrown away by the observers before me. The dates on the boxes were spread uniformly over the last seven years. It was possible that the dump contained hundreds more, hidden under the landfills and other trash. Yes, it was a beautiful day, and there was much to be considered as I drove along.

Reaching the outskirts of North Palm Meadows, I negotiated the left turn onto the cross road which led across the valley to Desert Center. In those days, the city had not yet grown in the northern direction, and this road, like most roads in Palm Meadows Valley, was a poor quality two-lane road that passed through open desert. The road was lined with yucca and mesquite. Finally reaching the far eastern side of the valley, I entered the main gate to Desert Center. The trip had been hot and tiring. I was eager to finish my business and get something to eat. So it was with great satisfaction that I finally reached the parking lot outside the main Desert Center supply warehouse. It was located at the southern end of one of the north-south runways. Crossing the spur rail line, I parked the truck out front, collected my books and paperwork, climbed the stairs, and strode, finally, into the reception area of the warehouse. A timid, mousy appearing airman first class was manning the counter. He outranked me by one stripe, so I approached him in military fashion and greeted him respectfully. I handed him a copy of my orders that appointed me to be the Mojave Wells Duty weather observer and allowed me to requisition supplies on my own signature. "Hello," I began. "I'm Charlie, and I'm here to requisition supplies for the Mojave Wells weather stations. That's my two and a half ton truck, out front. After we do the paper work, I can back it up to whichever loading dock you want."

The airman's response was friendly enough, but he was obviously unable to project his personality across the width of the reception counter. I felt as though there had been a war and he'd lost. "Yes. It's nice to meet you Charlie," He answered. "What supplies do you need?"

I handed him the requisition sheet that I had brought with me, and responded, "Here's my paperwork. As you can see, I'm requesting one month's worth of supplies. I need 120 neoprene balloons, 12 cylinders of helium, two dozen batteries with bulbs, 6 rolls of twine, some pencils, tablets, office supplies, and 300 blank weather reporting forms. I'd like those balloons to be 20 black, 50 red, and 50 white."

The airman opened the supply record books in front of him. Then he scanned my requisition sheet and reacted as though he'd taken a bullet in the chest. Straightening back up slowly, he stated, "The other weather observers didn't request supplies for an entire year, like this. They used to come in once a month, or every few weeks, and just pick up a month's supply at a time. That's what our delivery schedule is based on."

"Well, that's what I'm doing," I answered simply. "I'm practically out of supplies up at the Wells. As my orders show, I've just been stationed up there, and all of the weather stations are nearly empty. I need to lay in supplies for the coming month up at range three. That's what this is, the supplies I need for the coming month."

"No," he responded, shaking his head, slowly. "Not with numbers like these. There's something screwy going on. There's no problem with the office supplies, twine, extra plastic measurement tools, and weather forms. The forms come in packages of 250. We have thousands of them in the back, so you can have all you want, but 12 tanks of helium? We have only 3 in stock, and we're expecting that to last until our next shipment in November. For batteries we have only 7 in stock, and we won't be ordering any more of those for another three months. But look at those balloon request numbers - 120 balloons? That's simply ridiculous. I have 37 in stock. The other observers considered that to be a year's supply. There's a box of 10 black, a box of 10 red, and a box of 10 white. I also have a partial box of 7 white. It was a box of 10 that broke during delivery. You can have them all, but we don't have another balloon shipment scheduled until late next month, and that shipment is expected to be only 30 balloons, 10 of each color. That's going to have to hold you."

"But that isn't anywhere near what I need in the way of balloon and helium supplies," I protested respectfully. "That's little more than a week's worth, and I use the different colored balloons at a rate that is based on the weather conditions at release time. The white balloons are of no use against a cloudy sky. They get lost against the background of white cumulus clouds every time. Really, I should be requesting 120 whites, 120 reds, and 120 blacks. Why is the shipment rate so low?"

"Now don't you go trying to blame us," the airman responded defensively. "That shipment schedule is based on the rate at which the observers before you requisitioned supplies. They were experienced, highly trained weather observers. They knew the job way better than you appear to. You can check out all of the supplies which I have in stock, but you'll have to make them last, just like the other observers before you did. I can't change the shipment schedule unless you're willing to sign an emergency request form, and describe the nature of the supply emergency. That'll be processed through our Chief Master Sergeant, our commanding officer, and the Desert Center Command Post. That's a lot of work, so think about it. Don't make the request unless you actually need the supplies."

"Well, that's what I'm going to have to do then," I answered simply. "I'll check out all of the helium, balloons, batteries and bulbs which you have, and submit an emergency request form for the rest. I would also like to request that you increase the supply schedule because I'll be needing 100, maybe 120 balloons every month, not just the 30 which you've been ordering."

"If that's what you want to do, then I'll fill out the paper work for you to sign," responded the Airman. "How soon will you be needing these supplies?"

"Well, 37 balloons will cover me for only 6 or 7 working days," I answered, "and the color mix isn't very good. Can I pick them up next week at this time?"

The airman looked aghast and exclaimed, "Oh no, no. That's way too soon. I'll probably have to get the helium from Kelly Air Base in San Antonio, Texas 'cause the helium comes from wells in Texas. The first train shipment I can get out of Kelly is 10 days from now. I can get the extra balloons out of March Air Base in Los Angeles. I can probably have a Herky bird fly them up here, but that will take at least 8 days. The extra batteries are of a special military design. They have to come from the factory in Madison, Wisconsin. Those I could get trucked out here in a week, but they're of no use without the balloons. On the form, I'll state they're needed as soon as possible, and we'll increase the shipping schedule accordingly. You can take whatever I have now and plan on returning with your truck exactly two weeks from today. The supply shipments usually arrive before noon, so just to be on the safe side, don't come before 2:00 in the afternoon. That's the best I can do."

"Ok," I responded. "Let's do it that way. It leaves me mighty short of balloons for the next two weeks. I'll just have to live with it. But remember, two weeks from now I expect to be totally out of balloons and helium, so I'll really be needing those supplies!"

"Right," responded the airman. The tone in his voice said it all. He really didn't believe me. He proceeded to fill out the emergency supply request in the most disinterested, routine manner imaginable.

I signed the emergency requisition, loaded the supplies he had and reminded him as I was leaving, "Remember, I'll be here at 2:00 p.m. sharp on Wednesday afternoon in two weeks. I expect that I'll really be needing those supplies."

The drive back to Mojave Wells was uneventful, and punctuated by my anxiety over my supply shortage. Reaching Mojave Wells, I immediately headed the big truck out towards my range three shack. By now it was the late afternoon. I was hurrying to deliver my supplies and make it back in for the evening meal before the chow hall closed. The ranges were deserted and lay covered with beautiful summertime desert foliage, which glistened in the hot, late afternoon sun. The gentle afternoon winds rustled the dry sagebrush and the tumbleweeds that had collected behind my weather shack. I had no sooner finished backing the big truck up to the south door of my weather shack, when I suddenly felt very uneasy. I immediately became convinced that I wasn't alone out at Range Three and that someone was watching my every move. Still, I couldn't quite place my finger on why I felt that way. I opened only the south door of my weather shack and rushed through the unloading process. I didn't waste any time looking around or stopping to rest. It wasn't until I had returned the two and a half ton truck back to the motor pool and made it in to the chow hall that I started breathing easier. Still, I couldn't quite say why Range Three lying isolated in the late afternoon sun, had been so unnerving. I thought about it for a while over supper. Then, feeling better with a full stomach and friends close by, I shrugged the whole experience off, and decided that my nerves must have just been playing tricks on me.

The next morning, the 4:30 a.m. run went smoothly enough. However, I couldn't find my favorite pencil. This annoyed me greatly. I knew I had used it the day before, so after phoning the wind results in to Desert Center, I went looking for it. It seemed only natural to check the soft dirt out back of my shack. Perhaps it had fallen out of my pocket when I was unloading the truck the day before. I began by checking the soft dirt carefully. The tire tracks of my big truck were clearly visible, as were my own footprints. Then, suddenly, I noticed a second set of footprints. The hair began standing up on the back of my neck. Alone in the night, as I was, I was too stunned to study the prints carefully. Quickly I locked up my weather shack, shut down the diesel, double timed to my pickup truck, and headed back to base. In the chow hall, well fed and far away from danger, I became brave again. Soon I was laughing at myself. The prints were probably just those of one of the young range rats, I laughed to myself. After breakfast I headed back out for the 8:00 a.m. run, and pretended the tracks didn't exist. I ignored them for most of the morning. Then, after finishing the 11:00 a.m. run, I felt brave enough to inspect the prints again. I still hadn't found my pencil, and it annoyed me greatly. In the daylight, the footprints were just as mystifying as they had been by moonlight. Someone who weighed much less than myself had come out from behind the Range Three lounge and stood for a while in behind the mesquite out back of my weather shack. Then, it appeared that they suddenly went running down towards the mesquite to the southeast. One of the boot shaped footprints, however, held my attention for weeks to come. It overlaid the tracks made by the right front tire on my big truck. That set of tracks had been made when I had backed the loaded truck up to my shack the afternoon before. That boot print itself was overlaid by another set of the same tire tracks that I had made after I unloaded the truck and was pulling out the afternoon before. The conclusion was inescapable. Whoever had made the footprints, had done so while I was unloading my truck the day before. It meant that while I was unloading my truck, they had been standing behind the nearby mesquite watching my every move. I was so unnerved by the revelation that for months to come I would force the memory of those days from my mind, and pretend that nothing had ever happened.

The next day, knowing that my supplies were short, I drove my pickup truck out to the Mojave Wells base dump and salvaged as many balloons as I could. The balloons had been in perfect condition when they were originally thrown away, and most of them were still in their original, unopened shipping boxes. Many still had copies of their Desert Center requisition forms taped to their sides. Yet, the recovery rate was extremely disappointing. Of more than 1000 balloons that the observers before me had thrown away, I was able to salvage only 25. The balloons were very fragile. Between the weather, the time, the operation of the dump trucks and the bulldozer, they were all practically useless.

Wednesday, two weeks later, now operating on my last tank of helium, out of batteries, and looking at the end of my balloon supply, once again I checked out the two and a half ton truck from the Mojave Wells motor pool. I loaded my empty helium tanks, collected my log and inventory books as before, and began the long anxious run to Desert Center for supplies. As before, it was a beautiful day, and there was much to be considered. I had been studying the old logbooks left by the observers before me. One observer, three years before me, recorded the starting time for one of his balloon runs as 8:00 a.m. sharp and the ending time, for his 10 minute balloon run, as 9:23 a.m. sharp. In the logbook he swore that he had looked at his watch every minute, but that one hour and five minutes had passed while he walked the 50 feet from the theodolite stand to the front door of the Range Three shack. The following day, his entry stated that he, too, was abandoning the ranges and reporting the weather from the chow hall because he'd experienced another incident of the same type. This time, he stated, some of the items in his pockets had been rearranged during the hour or so during which his mind had gone blank, and he was now experiencing occasional nightmares. Yes, there was much to be considered.

I arrived at the Desert Center main gate at 2:10 in the afternoon. The guard at the gate checked my ID as usual, and stated, "They're expecting you down at the supply depot, Charlie." and waved me through. I hit the gas, wondering why the guard at the gate would be so well informed. As before, I pulled my truck into the gravel parking lot in front of the main supply warehouse, collected my books and forms, climbed the stairs, and strode anxiously into the customer service area. As the door closed behind me, I noticed that two Desert Center Air Policemen in a military police car had pulled into the parking lot behind me.

Approaching the counter, I greeted the timid airman sitting at the other end of the counter, "Hi. It's me, Charlie. I was hoping that my supplies had arrived."

"Yes," he responded timidly. Then he walked back to an office in the back, stuck his head in through the open doorway, and stated quietly, "It's him. He's here now."

I could hear a chair moving, and then the Chief Master Sergeant in charge of supply came out through the open door. He strode authoritatively up to the counter where I was standing. He was carrying several logbooks and supply record books with him. He motioned towards a lower, desk-like portion of the counter to my left. There were chairs vacant on both sides of the counter. He took one and sat down on his side, so I followed suit on my side. Without greeting me, he picked up the telephone, dialed an on-base number, and spoke into the phone, "I got him here now. Have the Air Policemen wait outside. I'll need 20 - 30 minutes or so to get the facts straight, then you can come in and arrest him."

He hung up the phone, turned to me, and stated in an authoritative, sergeant like manner, "Young Airman. You're in big trouble, placing emergency requests for supplies as you've been doing. We got the supplies that you asked for. We met those numbers you submitted 'cause we are the best supply outfit in the entire U.S. Air Force. The supplies are sitting out back in the warehouse. Now I want to know what the real numbers are before I have those two Air Policemen come in here and arrest you. You're one young airman who'll be spending tonight in the brig, just as you deserve. I've been in this man's Air Force for 28 years now, and I won't sit idly by while this goes on right under my nose. I want to know who else is in on this with you, and just what you were expecting to do with 100 or 120 balloons a month that you asked for. I figure you've got to be planning on selling at least 100 of those balloons to some civilian store or something and keeping the money, and that's a federal crime. Now if you cooperate with me in this, we'll go much easier on you. I figure that you're young, and someone else has put you up to this. I want their names... NOW, AIRMAN!"

Taken completely aback, I responded defensively, "Up to what, Sergeant. I've only requested the supplies that I need to perform my duties, as ordered. One month's worth of weather reports from the Mojave Wells Gunnery ranges uses up at least 100 to 110 balloons, and that hasn't changed in years. A tank of helium will fill only 10 or 11 balloons. I've only requested 120 balloons and 12 tanks of helium. I expect to be placing supply requests of that size every month that I'm assigned as the duty observer up at Mojave Wells. I don't see what the problem is, Sergeant."

"What the problem is?" screamed the Chief Master Sergeant in my face in angry rhetorical tones. "What the problem is? Look at me, young airman! Look at me good! Do you see these 8 stripes I proudly wear? Do I look that dumb to you? I've been in this position now for more than 6 years. I have my supply records for Mojave Wells for the last 6 years right here in my hands. Now before I open them up and show you just how badly you're lying...show you to your face just how many lies you've been spreading...I'm giving you one last chance to come clean. Who else is in on this with you?"

"In with me for what, Sergeant?" I asked respectfully. "I'm not up to anything! I'm the duty observer up at the Wells, and I'm performing my military duties, as ordered. I don't understand the problem. We can do the math, and I can show you that I need the balloons I've requested."

"The math!" he screamed angrily. "Yes, young airman. While the Air Policeman are waiting to come get you and all of your lies, let's just do the math!"

Taking a pen from my uniform pocket, and using the clean back of the requisition form, I began slowly, "Well, I'm ordered to measure the winds out on the gunnery ranges, at least 5 times a day. Some days I have to take 6 runs a day. At least one of those runs is at night. For those night runs, I attach a battery and a bulb so that I have a light by which to track the balloon. There are at least 20 night runs a month. I fill the balloon with a preset quantity of helium and release the balloon into the wind. Then I use the theodolite to track the balloon and compute the wind direction and velocity. The balloon is destroyed in the process. It simply rises until it breaks. Usually, this happens about 35,000 feet up. The balloon can never be recovered or reused. Even if it were to come down intact, it would be unrecoverable. It would be miles away from my weather station, off in a canyon or on a mountain peak somewhere.

"I am ordered to do these scheduled runs every weekday… that's five times a day for five days a week. In addition, the balloons are very fragile. Approximately one balloon in every 6 breaks before I can release it. This means that in a single week, I use between 25 and 30 balloons. This means that in four weeks, I am expecting to use between 100 and 120 balloons. See, Sergeant, that's what I've requested for my next month's supplies. I requested 120 balloons. Actually, I should have requested more because the weather conditions determine which color of balloon to release. The red and white balloons are the most useful, but black balloons are needed against high cirrus clouds. As you can see, my request for 120 balloons is a perfectly normal monthly request."

"One hundred and twenty balloons a month is perfectly normal?" screamed the sergeant angrily. "That's 1440 balloons a year, and you're calling THAT perfectly normal? I checked with that Major and that Chief Master Sergeant of yours over at the Desert Center weather station! They agreed with your numbers, but I don't. You may have THEM fooled, young airman, but they'll be shoveling snow in hell the day you fool ME with those numbers!"

Opening his supply records, he continued victoriously, "Here are the REAL numbers! My supply records go back for as long as I've been here at Desert Center. That's 6 and a half years. In that time, 59 different weather observers from Desert Center have been assigned in turn, to the Mojave Wells gunnery ranges. Each one of those airmen had experience and training that would put you to shame! Six of them were already tech sergeants wearing five stripes instead of your two. Another twelve were already four stripe sergeants - the remaining 41 had already made airman first class. That's three stripes YOUNG AIRMAN!! You're the first airman second class, carrying only two stripes whose EVER been assigned up there! Many of those other observers I knew personally. Unlike YOU, THEY knew what THEY were doing! Look at the REAL numbers! Just look at them! Nineteen of those 59 observers did not requisition any balloons or any helium supplies for their ENTIRE six week tour of duty up on the ranges. They requisitioned office supplies and blank forms only! The remaining 41, for the entire six and a half year period, requisitioned a total of only 1853 balloons of all colors.

That's TOTAL for the entire six and a half year period! You're using balloons at least six times faster than all of the other weather observers combined! Now you tell me, YOUNG AIRMAN, just what is going on? Using your own numbers, why weren't you out of balloons at least three days ago?"

Momentarily taken totally aback, I responded, stammering, "But I know my numbers are right, sergeant. Just because all those guys refused to go out on the ranges and perform their military duties doesn't mean anything to me! I intend to go out on the ranges, day or night, whenever my superiors order me to, and to perform my duties as ordered. I went through supply hell last week. I was just barely able to salvage 25 balloons from the dump up at Mojave Wells to cover me for the last few days, but right at the minute, I'm virtually out of supplies. I need all of those supplies to perform my duties, just like I said."

The sergeant paused to think for a minute. "From the dump?" he asked, slowly. "You found 25 useable weather balloons out at the Mojave Wells dump?"

"Yes," I answered honestly. "There are more than 1000 balloons of all colors laying out in the Mojave Wells dump. They had to have been thrown there by the observers before me. Most of them are still in their original boxes. The dates on the boxes are spread uniformly over the last seven years. That dump was started just seven years ago, so it's anybody's guess what happened before that. I salvaged the ones I could, but 25 useable ones were all I could find."

"What are you trying to tell me, Young Airman?" exclaimed the sergeant. "Am I supposed to believe that 41 experienced, highly trained weather observers before you, came in here, checked out 1853 balloons, carried them up to

Mojave Wells, and proceeded to throw away at least 1000 of those balloons without ever so much as opening up the boxes they came in?"

"Yes," I responded simply. "You can drive up to the base dump at Mojave Wells and count the balloons for yourself. You'll probably even recognize your own signature on many of those requisition forms. If you're too busy, then send those two air policemen sitting in the car out there. It's a pleasant drive, and they seem to have spare time on their hands."

The sergeant sat there in deep shock for a few minutes, obviously thinking things through. Then he continued, "If one new balloon is required for each wind measurement, as you say, that would mean that 59 weather observers, over the course of the last six and a half years, could not have taken more than 850 or so actual wind measurements, maximum. That is an average of no more than 13 runs per observer. Using your numbers, that's only two and a half day's worth of wind measurements for each six week tour of duty."

"Yes," I responded. "Of course, I suppose that it varied somewhat from observer to observer."

The chief master Sergeant began paging through his records and supply catalogs. In the catalog describing the requested weather balloons, he found a clearly typed entry that stated each neoprene weather balloon could be inflated and used only once. He looked at me and thought about the entry for a few minutes. Then he picked up the telephone and called the Desert Center command post. After verifying the range schedule, usually five or six runs a day every day for five days a week, he hung up the phone, turned to me, and stated in a quiet, gentler voice, "The Desert Center base

commander, and my supply catalogs verify your numbers."
Then he picked up the phone, dialed security, and stated,
"I'm canceling the security alert. Tell your air policemen to
resume their normal duties. They won't have to arrest
Charlie. He looks clean to me. Tell them to stop by here at
8:30 a.m. tomorrow morning with a camera and some color
film. There are a few things I'd like them to photograph up
at the Mojave Wells dump." Then he slowly hung up the
phone. Through the front glass door, I could see the military
police start their car and pull slowly away, obviously
resuming their normal rounds.

Initiation Rite

"…Ask the Lord of the Harvest, therefore,
to send out workers
into his Harvest Field …"

Matthew 9:38

"Charlie, we have some fresh blood for tonight's poker game," announced Wayne on a warm Sunday night.

"Great," I answered happily. "Who are they?"

"They're two new range rats just in from boot camp at Lackland AFB," responded Wayne. "This one is John. The one over there is Ed."

"Hi guys," I answered. "I'm glad to meet you. I'm the duty weather observer here on the ranges."

Wayne continued, "Guess what? There's even a third guy coming up this Wednesday. He's a new cook named Matt. That means we'll have almost 17 guys stationed up here with us for the next three weeks or so."

Then Ed interrupted. "Yes, but don't get your hopes up. John and I were stationed with Matt in boot camp. He had everybody in the squad angry with him. He's from New York City, on the Jersey side. He acted like he's better than everyone else. As soon as he arrives, John and I intend to kick his butt the way he deserves."

"Well, alright," I answered. "But remember you have to do it fairly. You have to do it one at a time, and give him a day or two to rest in between. Before the fight you have to shake hands, and after the fight you have to shake hands.

ou can't just go jumping him in the barracks, either. We all have to agree on a time and place. First of all Steve, Wayne, Doug, the boys, and I, we need to have our chance to place our bets. We don't get many good fights up here so we can't afford to let one go to waste. And make no mistake, when Steve, or Wayne, or Doug, or I, anyone of us, when we say its over, then its over. You understand. If one of you is down or something, then you have to give the other guy the chance to get up if he wants to. If he doesn't, then the fight's over. Then you all have to be friends. Those are the rules up here. You understand? You have to fight it out until you're all friends!"

"Yes," they both answered meekly.

I finished by stating simply, "Remember, if you break the rules, I'll personally kick both of your butts myself."

Wayne chimed in, "We've all seen Charlie in a good fight. He sure as hell can do it if he wants to."

Now that we were all in agreement, the poker game followed immediately. We were all having fun, and several hours passed. Soon it was past 11 o'clock on a beautiful desert night. The moon had risen, and we were all laughing when Doug, sitting across the table from me, suddenly claimed he'd glimpsed something white out through the window behind me. Getting up from the game suddenly, he strode quickly down the aisle towards the southern entrance to the barracks, and quickly disappeared outside for a few minutes. When he came back, he looked a little scared, and was shaking his head slowly from side to side. Steve, without rising from his chair asked, "Are they out there again tonight, Doug?"

Doug answered simply, "Yes. They're in real close. They posted their guards over by the trees across the highway. They must have parked on the other side of the highway, over in that canyon that goes up into Big Bear Pass, and come into town from there."

Steve continued with his questions, "And you're sure they weren't out there last night?"

"Yes," responded Doug. "I'm sure, I checked everywhere."

Steve thought for a minute and then responded in a calm and serious manner, "It must be the two new guys that are attracting them. They're so curious about everything. When those two new guys showed up, and with this hot weather we've been having, I figured they'd start coming in close again for a while."

Then Wayne joined in, speaking to the new guys, "That's why Steve's having all you new guys bunk alone together in that empty barracks next door. He figured they'd started coming in close again, in order to check out you new guys, go through all of your stuff, and such - like they did to us when we first got here."

"Yes," answered Steve seriously. "I figured if we kept you new guys close to us for a few nights, and had you guys leave your belongings alone in that empty barracks next door, they'd come in close, check you out until their curiosity was satisfied, and then go away. After a few nights of this, they won't want to take the risk of coming in this close again. Then they'll go back to their normal way of doing things. They'll go back to staying out in the desert. They'll just watch you from a distance when you go out there."

Steve paused for a minute, to let his words sink in. Then he continued, "The only person they've ever kept watching, and following around close up, is Charlie, there. He still bunks alone in that long double barracks down by the flight line. Where he gets the guts to do it, I'll never know. He's the toughest airman that any of us have ever seen. But anytime he wants to, he's free to move in here with us. Even now, they still keep coming into his barracks at night, and going through his things when he's sleeping. I don't know why. Maybe, I guess, it's because some of their kids like him. They'll do anything to please their kids, you know."

I had to chuckle a bit, under my breath. I supposed that Steve, Wayne, Doug, and the boys were putting the new guys through a highly polished initiation rite.

Then Wayne added, "When you go back to your barracks tonight, it'll probably look as though someone has carefully gone through all of your belongings. If anything is missing, don't let it frighten you. They never take anything for very long. They always return whatever they take, sooner or later. The longest I've ever seen them take anything is two and a half months. There seems to be some place close by that takes them two months or so, to go to, rest up, and come back. But don't worry. They never take money, or anything valuable. They always return whatever they take."

It was becoming difficult for me to keep a straight face. Wayne continued, "Steve, should I go out, check the new guy's barracks, to see if they're still in there? Maybe ask them to leave if they are?"

Steve thought for a minute, and answered in a calm and serious fashion, "No, they'll keep coming until they're satisfied. There isn't anything we can do to stop them, anyway. As long as they're not hurting anybody, there's no reason to scare them away. No one ever goes up into Big

Bear pass at night, so there isn't any danger to anyone. Even in the daytime, I never take that gravel road up towards those old charcoal kilns alone, any more. It's so deserted, and seeing those old kilns isn't worth the risk. The last time I tried that road, was a hot afternoon last summer. I was only half way up that arroyo when one of those white creatures came out in one of their scout craft and flew along side my truck for a short ways, watching me as I drove. I said to myself, 'Forget this noise.' Even though the arroyo is narrow, I turned my truck around and headed back into town."

I had to chuckle some more under my breath. The two new troops were obviously becoming frightened. They also appeared to be appreciating the absent third new guy, more than before. The idea of having a third guy bunking with them in their empty barracks was definitely looking a lot more attractive.

Despite the fact that Steve, Wayne, and Doug appeared to be completely sincere, I figured they were just putting on an act to frighten the new guys, and get them to stop fighting with the absent third new guy. Thinking I would give Steve and Wayne a chance to have more fun by prolonging the initiation ceremony, I asked Wayne, "What do you think they are? What do you think is out there? Are they friends of Range Four Harry or something?"

Wayne answered the question with a question of his own, "Charlie, You said that one of your hobbies was reading flying saucer magazines and things?"

"Yes," I responded.

Wayne continued, looking me straight in the eye, "Well, Charlie, what do you think flying saucers are?"

Defensive, I responded, "Oh, I don't know. I've never seen one, so I can only guess. I suppose most of them are hoaxes or have ordinary explanations. If they were real, the only logical explanation is that they would be visitors from some other planet orbiting some distant star. But space is so vast. The stars are so far apart. I don't see how they could make the deep space crossing between the stars. You'd have to travel faster than the speed of light or else it would take 1000 years just to get here from the nearest star. Once here, they would be in dire need of food, shelter, fuel, repair parts and other supplies. Alien visitors from space would be in the position of traveling for a millennium, all the while hoping for a little hospitality when they arrived. I don't see how that would be possible, or why they would take the risk that we wouldn't be friendly to them. Anyway, even if flying saucers were real and were coming here from some other star, there's nothing out here in this deserted desert valley to attract them. They wouldn't be out here. They'd be in Washington D.C. or back east, or something."

Wayne became emotional and began disagreeing. Getting up from his chair, he began pointing up the valley towards the north. Pacing back and forth emotionally by the closed barracks door. He continued, "No! No, Charlie! You're wrong! I know you're wrong! I'll tell you what I think flying saucers are. I think they're out there. I think they're right out there in the desert - right out there. I think they're up the valley, up north of here. I think they're dug into those mountains in the distance - out there. They're tall and white. They can make the deep space crossing from one star to another in just a couple of months. Their craft CAN travel faster than light. That's what Range Four Harry is. That's what comes around our barracks at night. That's what you see out in the desert at night. That's what is out there."

Out of respect for our close friendship, I suppressed my intense desire to break out laughing openly. I found something about the idea to be incredibly amusing. "Space aliens build a flying saucer, travel 50 light years in two months, make the deep space crossing, and spend their time here on earth by watching seven American solders playing poker in the desert. Could life get more ridiculous?" I wondered quietly to myself. Getting hold of myself at last, I politely asked Wayne, point blank, "Have you ever personally seen range Four Harry, or anything tall and white - or flying saucers out there in the desert? Have you ever personally seen anything close up or in the daytime?"

I could hardly have been less prepared for his answer. Steve, Wayne, and Doug, all looked at each other. All three of them looked me straight in the eye and answered together, "Yes." Then Wayne continued, "There's a valley at the base of the mountains up to the northwest. It's an easy drive up there. You don't need four-wheel drive so you could probably make it in your weather truck. You take that first pass that you see northwest of here and go up in there, maybe 50 miles. When you've gone maybe 50 miles, look up along the base of the mountains to the north. You can't miss it. They like to park in that valley, down out of sight. There are several springs in that valley. You can see the springs on your weather map.

"One day two summers ago, Steve, Doug, and I were up in there by those springs when we ran into them. They like to go there a lot and rest in the sunshine. Steve asked them if we could see the craft they came in, so they took the three of us over into the next valley and showed it to us. It was about as big as this barracks, only it was more rounded and oval. Steve and Doug had to stay outside. I was the only one they let walk inside."

I was really taken off balance. By now the new guys were becoming terrified. I thought Wayne was just pouring it on to frighten them. "They let you walk into their craft?" I asked, trying to look as if I believed them. "What did it look like inside?"

Wayne continued, "Well, they only let me step just inside the door. It was sort of like a passenger plane inside. On my right was a cockpit like area with seats where they sit when they are flying around. There were lots of gauges and switches and things that they use to control the craft when they're flying. On my left was their living area. They had things like stoves, and food storage lockers, and showers. They sleep in hammocks. Right in front of me, where you first go in the door was this whole panel of switches with hieroglyphs on them. The switches wouldn't move when I touched them. They just discharge electrically. One of them opened and closed the front door. Another turned on the outside lights, another the inside lights."

"Where do they come from?" I asked defensively.

"They wouldn't ever say," responded Wayne sincerely. "But Doug thinks they must come from Egypt because the markings on the switches looked so much like the ancient Egyptian hieroglyphs. Steve doesn't agree, though. He thinks they come here from some other planet orbiting some distant star."

"What did the markings look like?" I asked.

"Here, I'll show you," responded Wayne without so much as a moment's hesitation. Taking out a pencil and a sheet of paper from his nearby locker, he quickly sketched the first five, which he said were larger than the others, and positioned along a top row just inside the door. Then he continued sketching two more that he said were part of a second row, located just below the first. Pointing to the first, which looked sort of like a sketch of the sun, he stated, "This one controlled the outside lights. The next one looked sort of like a door opening upwards. He stated that it controlled the opening of the front door.

Wayne handed me the paper. I took it, more to be polite to my friends than anything. I folded it carefully and placed it in my wallet. I was totally mystified by Wayne's statements. I really didn't know what to say next. Steve, good friend that he was, continued, "Whatever you do though Charlie, don't ever go up there alone. I know they like you, and all. So far they've been treating you way different than the way they treated those other observers that Desert Center used to always send up here. All of those other guys they'd have run off by now. Just remember, they can get angry just as we can. If you ever want to go up there, always take me or Wayne, or Doug with you. It just isn't safe for anyone to go up there alone."

Then Steve turned to Wayne and continued, "You know, Wayne, now that we have these new guys here, don't you think a week from this next Monday would be a good time to take them out to range four and show them Range Four Harry. We have to show them what they are up against when they're out there alone."

"That's a good idea," responded Doug. "Range Four Harry's one of them. They could see him for themselves. How about Charlie here? He should go along too."

"Yes," answered Steve. Then, turning to me he continued, "We'd love to have you along, Charlie. You go

83

out there at night by yourself so much, you've probably seen them more than any of us. I know they think of you as special. If you were along, these new guys wouldn't have to worry about them attacking, 'cause you could just go out there and talk to them."

By now I was really defensive. From Steve's remarks, I supposed that he must just be intending to scare the new guys as part of the initiation rite, so I decided to join in. "Why yes." I answered. I'd love to go along with you. How do you intend to go about seeing this legendary Range Four Harry?"

In obvious sincerity, Steve responded, "Well, we'll do it as we always do. Harry's real easy to frighten so we have to be real careful." Then Steve paused for a moment while he counted on his fingers. He seemed to be counting in twos, "…two active, two sleep,…" Then he continued, "Yes, next Tuesday seems like just the right night to go out there and look. We'll take two power wagons out to range four during the late afternoon on Monday. Doug will drive the first, and I'll drive the second. We'll stay real close together so that the dust from the first one hides the second. That way, if Harry is watching from the mountains, he'll think that only one wagon has come out. We'll take lots of water and we'll take lots of sandwiches and things from the chow hall. Then when we get out to range four, I'll hide the second power wagon out of sight in one of the hangers. The rest of you grab everything and get into the range four lounge before the dust settles. Harry has real good eyesight, so you can't mess around doing anything outside. Doug will keep driving back and forth so there's lots of dust to confuse Harry if he's watching from the mountains. Once you guys are in the lounge, open all of the windows real quick, and then stay away from them. You all have to stay down out of sight, and you can't turn on the diesels, or use the phone, or talk or anything. Harry has real good eyesight and real good hearing, so no one can talk above a whisper. We'll lock the lounge door, and then Doug will drive one power wagon back to base. He'll drive real fast and make lots of dust, so if Harry is watching, he'll think that range four is still deserted. Then we'll all take turns watching, especially those mountains up towards the northwest. If it's a warm night, I guarantee that he'll be out there. We'll see him, you'll see."

It was now way past my bedtime, so I said good night to everyone and went back to my bunk. Soon I was chuckling myself to sleep. Steve and Doug and Wayne sure knew how to frighten the new guys, I laughed to myself.

The next morning, my drive out to range three was uneventful. I was quite tired, and by the time I arrived out at range three, I was happy I hadn't gone to sleep at the wheel. There was some moonlight, and the desert looked beautiful under a warm clear sky. I got a diesel started, and as I walked towards my weather shack, I paused for a few moments to gaze up the valley towards the mountains in the northwest. I was laughing to myself at the time. Steve and Doug and Wayne had been so clever it seemed, at making up the story of Range Four Harry, hieroglyphs, and all, just to scare the new guys. Still, there was one thing I just couldn't quite understand. At least six different times in the past, Steve had taken new guys out to range four at night, and on at least four of those trips, they had all come back in terror. Each of those four times, everyone with Steve had claimed to have actually seen Range Four Harry. On one occasion, to a man they all claimed that Harry had come in

85

around the range four buildings, and had actually looked in through the glass in the front door, into the range four lounge. They all claimed that they had hidden, and prayed, and spent the rest of the night hiding in complete terror. Quietly, I performed my arithmetic. Counting my friend Dwight, the Major, and the other weather observers who had strange experiences out on these ranges, there were more than 30 people who independently claimed to have seen Range Four Harry.

As I stood there, gazing out into the desert and sagebrush which covered the Mojave Wells Valley, I noticed three soft white fluorescent patches floating just off the desert floor down in the valley to the west of me. It was in the same area where the range rats had been working the previous Friday. The chow hall had delivered their noon meal to them. I supposed, therefore, that the white patches must just be the plastic wrappings from their noon meal drifting in the wind. The Range Rats had probably left their sandwich wrappings and other pieces of paper laying around, I supposed, and now the light desert wind must be playing with them in the moonlight. Without giving things much thought, I opened up my weather shack and proceeded with the morning run.

Later, as I was releasing the balloon, I noticed that two of the white patches had floated some 20 miles north and were now opposite the range four buildings. At the time I wondered. The white patches had drifted 20 miles in 30 minutes in a wind I measured at only 5 miles and hour. "That's a pretty good trick." I said to myself. I noticed that the third white patch had floated east up the side of the valley, until it now floated on the range four road, just three miles north of me. I didn't give it much thought. I released my balloon and continued with my wind measurements. Finishing the run, I performed my calculations, phoned them in to Desert Center, shut down my weather shack and my diesel, and prepared to head in to breakfast. Just before getting back into my truck, curious, I decided to check the valley north of me and see where the white patches were. Two of them could be seen up along the base of the mountains, now some 35 miles northwest of me. I wondered how simple pieces of paper and plastic could reflect that much moonlight. After all, I wondered, 35 miles is an awfully long way to see anything. The third white patch still drifted a few inches above the gravel on the road north of me. Curious, and having 45 minutes or so, to spare, I decided to start my truck and drive down the range four road to get a better look at the soft white fluorescent patch which drifted down there.

I started my truck, and eased it onto the gravel range four road. I decided to gently approach the plastic, so I stayed in second gear, and held my speed to 20 mph or so. The fluorescent white patch, however, seemed to know that I was coming. It floated towards me a short distance until it got to a break in the sagebrush. Then it left the road, and floated towards the old ammunition bunker located at the base of the mountains east of me. When it got maybe three quarters of a mile from the road, it stopped and just floated there, as though it were watching me. When I had gotten far enough down the road to be opposite the white patch, I stopped my truck, and set the parking brake. I left the engine running, and the truck in neutral. I got out into the desert evening to get a better look at the white patch, now just over a mile away. It was white, fluorescent, had filmy edges, and appeared to be featureless. However, there was

87

no question that it was solid because it blocked out everything behind it. I was so convinced that it must just be paper or plastic that I thought nothing of walking out into the desert towards it. I also shrugged off the notion that it must be intelligent when it kept retreating from me. Soon I was more than a half-mile out into the desert and getting no closer to it than when I started. My stomach was growling in hunger, so I shrugged off the chase and slowly returned to my truck. The white patch continued drifting on towards the ammunition bunker. Trying to make light of my foolish chase, I laughed, shrugged, and stated aloud to the desert evening, "Such is the nature of plastic."

It took a while for me to get my truck turned around on the narrow range four road. Soon I was headed back to base and hoping I made it before the chow hall closed. Along the way I wondered, "Is that what everyone calls Range Four Harry? First I'd heard that he was a radioactive horse, then a prospector with a burrow. Now I see parachutes or plastic. I wonder what is he really?"

The days passed quickly, and Wednesday came soon enough. By noon it was already necessary for me to break up an argument between the new cook Matt and the new range rats John, and Ed. They were all three, young men with guts and courage. I left the chow hall certain that the American military was still able to control any battlefield it chose to. Then Thursday, I had to keep them from jumping Matt in the shower, and late Friday afternoon Matt was going to take both of them out behind the motor pool. He was quite a fighter, and I believe he could have done it too. After I broke up the scuffle, I impressed on all three of them that Steve, the boys, and I weren't going to be denied our chance to bet on the fight before they had it. Steve and I had scheduled the showdown for two weeks from Saturday and we still needed time to collect all of the wagers.

Late Sunday afternoon, I was walking back to my barracks when I saw Matt driving in from the desert in the chow hall truck. I'd been keeping a close watch on him and the new range rats. I felt they needed time, and a good scuffle, so they could become friends. I wanted to make sure that it was a fair fight when it happened. Anyway, I felt certain Matt could take them both, and I wanted time to place a few more bets before they had it out. I knew where John and Ed were, so I was certain that they hadn't been out in the desert fighting with Matt.

I had watched Matt for some distance. He'd taken the chow hall pickup truck out into the desert valleys northwest of Mojave Wells field - out into the mountains where the spring fed valley lay. Locating all of the places where the range rats routinely asked their noon meal be delivered, was a normal part of the on the job training for chow hall cooks, but he had gone out there alone. Except for me, Matt hadn't yet formed any friendships on base. No one would train him, or tell him anything. Except for me, he wasn't on speaking terms with anybody. I wasn't worried, I just figured that sooner or later he'd get around to having a push-shove match with everyone in turn, and in the end everyone would be his friend. He had grown up in Jersey City, and had been here in the desert for a mere 5 days, so I was surprised that he had the courage to go driving so far out into the desert so soon, and so alone.

He parked the truck in front of his barracks, and was just getting out when I arrived on foot. His binoculars were still hanging around his neck and they banged up against the truck as he climbed out. I stopped him. I noted that he hadn't taken any food or water with him when he went out into the desert, and I cautioned him. The summer heat makes the desert a dangerous place, I said. A man has to think things through before he goes out there. I pointed out that driving with the binoculars around his neck probably wasn't safe, and suggested that he should have removed them and placed them on the seat next to him. Lastly, I pointed out that even though his truck was equipped with a two way radio, he should have told me or someone like the first sergeant where he was going before he went out there. Then he should have checked in when he got back. That way, we'd know where to come looking for him if he didn't make it back.

Matt just stood there, glassy eyed, and speechless. He seemed to be terrified of something, and his mind seemed to be churning inside. Sensing his confusion, I stated, "If there's ever anything you wish to talk about, just drive out to my weather shack at range three. I'm always there. Feel free to come, anytime and talk - just anytime." Then I left him standing there. Later that evening, I looked in on him. He was sitting on his bunk, with the lights at his end of the barracks turned off. His head was in his hands, and he was obviously sitting there in deep, confused thought.

The next few days passed uneventfully, and Tuesday came as usual. The only problem, from my point of view, was that I had become exceptionally sick with the flu. I had to call off my participation in Steve's planned escapade to see Range Four Harry. Nothing would stop Steve, though. As planned, he loaded Matt, Ed, John, Wayne, Doug, Bryan the Air Policeman, lots of food, water, coffee, and punch, into two power wagons and set off for range four just as the sun as setting. I spent the evening in my barracks vomiting my supper into the commode.

The next morning, everything was normal enough. I was quite weak, but feeling better. I was already having breakfast in the chow hall when Steve and the Range Four Harry viewing crew entered. I had expected them all to be laughing together. I was quite wrong. Matt still looked wild eyed and confused. Steve was livid with rage at Ed and John. "Ed, what were you doing screaming in terror in that side room? I told you before we went out there that I didn't want so much as a whisper out of any of you when we were out there. If Bryan hadn't told you to shut up, you'd have gotten us all killed. And you John! You IDIOT! You could have gotten us all killed too!" Steve was shouting. For an initiation rite, Steve seemed to be taking everything a bit far. "You were so mighty lucky they chose to run away. I told you Harry was real! The way you went walking out there to get a closer look was the stupidest thing I've seen lately. The only person I've ever seen who could do that stuff and get away with it, is Charlie. He's the only man who has ever lived who they'll let walk up to them, or in among them. Everyone else that's tried it has gotten his butt burned but good! Remember, none of us is Charlie! We all have to keep our wits about us. When we're out there on the ranges, my word is law - especially if old Harry is around! The first rule is that you never walk towards him. He'll burn you every time. John, do you and Ed understand me?"

I didn't know what to think any more. Steve's initiation rite seemed to have gotten way out of hand. Still, I was dumbfounded as I sat there. I hadn't told anyone about having walked out into the desert any of the times I had done so. How could Steve know? The only person who knew was me - me and the floating white fluorescent patches.

Having finished my breakfast, I hiked back to my pickup truck and headed back out to the ranges for the 8 o'clock run. It was a beautiful summer day. Range three wasn't in use. I had just finished the 8 o'clock run and phoned the results into Desert Center when the chow hall truck pulled up outside my range three weather shack. Matt got out slowly, and looked around in an extremely nervous manner. I stepped to the front door of my weather shack and greeted him. Once he saw me he settled down noticeably, and asked if he could come in. It was obvious to me that he needed to talk to someone. As an experienced soldier, I felt it was my duty to fill the shoes of big brother. Happily I brought him in, showed him my place, and gave him the best seat in the cool breezes by the front door.

He started nervously at first. "In the time you've been out here, have you ever seen anything unusual?" he asked.

"Well, yes, sometimes," I answered defensively, "But the observers before me had many more unusual experiences than I've had." I paused for a minute or so. Matt was so up tight, I decided to try relaxing him a little. I tried to make some humor. I continued, "How did things go out at range four last night? Did you actually see the legendary Range Four Harry?"

"Yes," Matt answered quickly and in total earnestness.

"What does he look like?" I answered, still searching for a point of humor.

"Well, after John went out there, I went out there too. I guess it's not real smart to do so. I guess you're the only one who is able to do that and live. Steve became very angry. I thought he was going to kick both our butts. I stayed out there longer than John. I even used my binoculars, but I still couldn't see much of anything. The fluorescent light hurt my eyes."

"Well, if you couldn't see anything, what were you looking at?" I asked.

"It was a large soft white fluorescent patch of light," Matt answered. "It was floating just a few inches off the desert up to the northwest of the range four lounge. Steve said that if we'd all kept quiet like he ordered, it would have gotten a lot closer. He said that he's even seen it come in around the range four buildings."

"H-mm," I answered thoughtfully.

Matt continued, "Steve said that when it gets up real close, you can see something that looks like people floating inside of it. But he says that when it gets that close, you have to be real careful or the people inside will burn you real bad."

I no longer had the faintest idea what to think. What I thought had began as an initiation rite was now so far out of hand, that I didn't know where to put the pieces any more. Hoping to gain some time to think things over, I continued, "A week ago Sunday, when you were out driving around, did you see anything when you were up in those mountains west of here?"

"Yes," Matt answered in that same intensely earnest voice. "When I was way back up in there, I went out to that beautiful little valley that's up in those mountains over there. The valley is at least fifty miles from here. It's real beautiful. It has a spring. The valley is covered with grass and beautiful flowers and wild strawberries. It even has some fruit and apple trees. It was in that valley, located right up against the base of the other side of those mountains that I saw a flying saucer parked on the ground."

"That's pretty desolate country up in there," I responded, trying to hide my disbelief. "Especially for a young man like yourself, having grown up in New York City. You're telling me that on only the third day you were here on base, that you drove way back up in there, more than 50 miles out into that desolate section of desert, alone? Once you got out there, you saw a parked flying saucer?"

"Yes," Matt answered. "The valley way up there, the one with the spring in it, is so beautiful. I was homesick, and it reminds me of my home back east. Well, for some reason, the people in the flying saucer didn't see me coming. It must be pretty easy to surprise them. When I got close, my truck started running rough. I didn't know what was up ahead, so I stopped my truck, turned it around and faced it down hill. I set the parking brake, turned off the engine, and walked the last mile up the road. I found a secluded spot where I could peer over the valley rim and look inside."

"What did you see?" I asked, stunned.

Matt responded, "Well, down in the valley by the spring sat this large flying saucer, with its door open. It was at least as big as the range three lounge building. It was chalk white and ellipsoidal. Outside there were these three white people. They were chalk white, taller than you are, and they looked almost human. They had strung hammocks between some trees. They were all sleeping, the way people do on a picnic."

After a short pause to control his emotions, he continued, "They're a lot thinner then you and I are. They were so white and thin that at first, I thought I was looking at some humans who were sick, or maybe suffering from some kind of wasting disease. After I studied them for a few minutes, I realized that they had to be people from another planet, and that they were just naturally thinner and whiter than you and I are. When the reality of what I was seeing finally sunk in, and when I realized how alone I was out in the desert, miles from anywhere, terror spread through me. As fast and silently as I could, I ran the mile or so back to my truck. I started the truck by letting it roll a ways down hill and throwing it in gear. Once it started, I came out of there about as fast as that truck could travel. I was miles down the road before I finally started to calm down."

Then he became very agitated. Fear began to overcome him, and tears starting forming in his eyes.

Still struggling to maintain my big brother attitude, I asked, "You had your binoculars with you. If the door was open, what did you see when you looked inside?"

To my shock, Matt continued without hesitation, in that same intensely earnest tone of voice, "Hieroglyphs."

"Hieroglyphs?" I asked, stunned.

"Yes," Matt responded, "Hieroglyphs, just like Egyptian hieroglyphs. Just inside the door was this panel of switches or buttons. On each switch or button was a different hieroglyph."

Stunned beyond description, since I was certain that Matt was completely unaware of the discussion that I had had with Wayne during the poker game, I asked, "Do you remember what any of the hieroglyphs looked like?"

"Yes," Matt responded simply. "Taking a pencil and piece of paper from my work area, he proceeded to draw three of the hieroglyphs. Handing it to me gently, he stated, "These three are from the top row of buttons. The top row

95

had five buttons that were bigger than the other buttons which were below them."

The three hieroglyphs that he drew matched perfectly with the first three hieroglyphs drawn by Wayne. Steve's rite of initiation had now come full circle. Now I was the one becoming initiated - initiated into a new world - a new world of nighttime terror. A world so terrifying that soon, I would no longer be able to deny that it was real.

Is It For Nothing?

...one day, when the sons of God came
to present themselves before the Lord,
Satan also came among them.

And the Lord said to Satan,
"Whence do you come?

Then Satan answered The Lord and said,
"From roaming the earth and patrolling it."

And the Lord said to Satan,
"Have you noticed my servant Job,
and that there is no one on earth
like him ...?

But Satan answered the Lord,
"Is it for nothing
that Job worships God?..."

...Job 1:6,10

The Mojave Wells gunnery ranges were serene and beautiful places. In the summertime I enjoyed sitting quietly alone in my different weather shacks. In between balloon runs, I enjoyed reading history books and listening to the radio for entertainment. Sometimes I brought out paint-by-number sets and spent many afternoons painting pictures of fall mountain scenes. This beautiful summer day down at range one, was no exception. After finishing the 12:30 balloon run, I tuned my radio to some soft music, reached for my favorite history book, and assumed a comfortable, relaxing position in my favorite chair.

My range one weather shack was similar to my range three shack. The side door to the shack opened to the east. Cool afternoon breezes washed gently through its open doors and windows. Through the open door, could be seen the sagebrush covered desert stretching for 35 or 40 miles down the range one valley to the southeast. The sagebrush stood probably four feet tall and was in full bloom. The bright purple sage flowers formed a velvet blanket of beauty. Dust devils were already playing out among the heat waves. The hot afternoon sun continued to desiccate the already dry desert floor. Long and narrow, bisected by a dry arroyo north of my shack, flanked on the far north by mountains, and seldom used by the Air Force for gunnery practice, the range one valley existed in beautiful, quiet, and splendid isolation. After reading a few pages from my history book, I found it unaccountably difficult to concentrate. For some reason that I couldn't explain, I began to feel very uneasy. Still new to the ranges, I wondered if I had been eating properly. I carefully closed my history book and placed it on the shelf next to my nearly full jar of drinking water. I always kept at least two gallon jars of water with me, one in my shack and one in my truck. I realized that the desert, for all of its beauty, could also be unmerciful.

Turning my attention to the open door, I leaned back in my chair and let my mind wander. My eyes naturally wandered out through the open door, and soon my gaze fell on the beautiful purple sagebrush flowers. In the distance, slightly off to the southeast, perhaps two miles away, a group of unseen meadowlarks could be heard singing. I counted as I listened. First one would start the chorus; then a second would join in. Soon I could count perhaps 5 or 6 meadowlarks singing from various places faraway down the valley. It seemed natural enough. I frequently heard meadowlarks singing in chorus when I was out on the ranges, sometimes even at night. Usually the chorus lasted only a handful of minutes.

The problem I had was that, for all of the singing, I had never actually seen a meadowlark out on the ranges, day or night. Today was no exception. Despite the continuing chorus, there simply wasn't a bird in sight.

My mind wandered a little. The gentle breezes rustled the curtains which hung by my windows, and softly jingled the safety chain which hung around my supply of helium cylinders, moving a half empty box of white neoprene balloons which sat precariously at the edge of one of my supply shelves. Instinctively, I reached over and moved the box to a more secure position. The balloons were fragile. Normally I kept the boxes stored securely towards the back of the storage shelves. I had been using red balloons for several days now. I was certain that I had left the half empty box of white balloons sitting at the back of its storage shelf when I had used it last. I spent a few moments wondering how it could possibly have moved to such a precarious position at the front of the shelf.

As I sat semi-daydreaming, I wondered why the Air Force had wanted me to spend all last week and this week making the balloon runs from this isolated valley. Normally I made the runs from the range three valley several miles to the northwest of here. Normally, the Desert Center air base considered the range weather reports to be of the highest importance, eagerly awaited the information, and carefully examined the results. However, these last few days spent at range one had been quite different. My friend Dwight had checked with the Desert Center command post. We both agreed that not a single airplane had used any part of the ranges during all of that time. Dwight informed me that most of my wind reports had ended up in the forecaster's waste paper basket, unused, unneeded, and unread. The officer at the command post had refused to even take the time to be told the results. It seemed to be a waste of good paper just to write them down. Yet the Desert Center command post had been exceptionally explicit, direct, and insistent. This was the valley they wanted me in. The Desert Center base commander had personally given the orders. They specifically wanted all of the weather reports taken. Yesterday, in addition to the usual full schedule of wind measurements, they had even ordered an additional 3:30 p.m. late afternoon run. Yet, when I phoned in the results, the command post said it didn't need to know the results. They only wanted to verify that I had been on duty at range one, and had taken the balloon runs as scheduled. It didn't seem to make any sense, and I naturally wondered why.

Then I began wondering about the meadowlark calls. I had been hearing them all day yesterday, and during the late afternoon of the day before. Today I had been hearing them ever since the first run of the morning, more than seven hours earlier. Something about it didn't feel right.

I felt safe enough being out on this range alone, even though this was the valley that had so terrified Sullivan before me. I remembered the scar on his arm. I wondered if a lost little boy had actually attacked him. When I had first started coming here, I felt certain that I was alone. Sometimes however, despite the valley's isolation, I found it impossible to actually feel alone. Other times I felt certain that I was being watched as I took my weather reports. Yet I hadn't been able to answer the question, "Watched by whom?"

One day, although I was apparently alone, the feeling was so overwhelming that I chose to park my pickup truck less than 10 feet from my theodolite. On that day, I sat in my truck for more than a half hour studying the sagebrush down to the southeast, as Sullivan had done before me, trying to determine what was causing the feeling. On that day, nothing appeared to be unusual. All I could identify was a few half glimpsed white patches. They were way out in the heat waves, moving through the hot sunlit sagebrush. It was a long time before I was able to put my uneasy feelings aside, and go on taking the weather reports.

On this beautiful summer day as I sat wondering and watching the purple sagebrush rippling in the gentle summer winds, I noticed that a section of the sagebrush underneath my gaze was moving somewhat more than expected. The moving section was within easy walking distance from my weather shack. It was bordered on the north by the deep, dry arroyo. That section was more or less a quarter of a mile down the valley and somewhat northeast of my weather shack. That section was healthier, taller, and much thicker than many of the other sections. It was also much closer than the sections where the meadowlark sounds were coming from. Those sections were some two miles distant and down the valley southeast of my weather shack.

I thought about things for a while. I noticed that the sagebrush plants weren't uniformly spaced across the valley floor. Rather, they were arranged in irregular patches with narrow, maze like open lanes in between.

I continued gazing out towards the moving section of sagebrush. Suddenly my gaze fell on something white. It was there and then gone so suddenly that at first I thought it was just my eyes playing tricks on me. After watching the moving section of sagebrush for another ten minutes or so, I started seeing more glimpses of the white patch out in the sagebrush. The few glimpses seemed innocent enough. I guessed that I was probably just catching glimpses of a bird, or a sea gull, or a desert mirage, or something.

Suddenly, I got an unusually good glimpse of the chalk white patch as it dashed across one of the open lanes. It was perhaps a quarter of a mile out in the moving section of sagebrush. I couldn't be certain what it was. At first I thought it was probably a small coyote or maybe a large rabbit, but it also looked as though it might have been a little girl, maybe age four. It's movements seemed unusually erratic, and desperate. I wondered if it was lost out there in the narrow lanes in the hot, thick, sagebrush maze.

Curious now, I decided that I needed to get a closer look at whatever it was that was out there. Rising slowly from my chair, I put on my new fatigue hat and snapped a full canteen of water into position on my belt. I slowly stepped out through the open door of my weather shack onto the small patch of gravel. I put on the thick leather gloves that I frequently kept stuffed into my back pocket. Sagebrush could be hard on a man's hands. Using the doorway as a footrest, I re-tightened the thick laces on my heavy military combat boots. I stood there in the sunshine for a few minutes watching. Nothing happened. I called out in a loud voice, "Is anyone out there?" There was no response. I called again, "Does anyone out there need help?" Still, there was no response. After waiting for a few minutes, I decided to investigate the sagebrush further. Stepping slowly across the steel cable fence that separated my weather shack from the desert beyond, I began walking slowly into the sagebrush. I was in no hurry. I would take a few steps, then stop and watch for a while. Sometimes I would take a sip of water. Then I would call out some more, "Is anyone out there? Does anyone out there need help?" Still, there was no response. I had just started feeling noticeably foolish when I got another glimpse of the small, white thing dashing up a cross lane in the thick sagebrush. It now seemed obvious to me that the little white creature was lost and trapped in the maze of plants, and unable to find its way out. Becoming still more curious, I continued my policy of taking a few slow steps. Then I stopped and watched for a while.

Since I was wearing a good pair of protective military combat boots, a good sturdy set of military fatigues, and thick leather gloves, I wasn't limited to traversing the open lanes in the sagebrush, as the small white creature was. Since I was much taller than the plants, I also had a much better view of the maze. It was a simple matter to open new lanes by breaking and trampling down some of the plants. Using my weight and my heavy military combat boots, I proceeded to carefully cut a series of new lanes through the irregular patches of sagebrush. This made it easy for me to out-maneuver the object of my interest. A slow motion game of cat and mouse followed. I would stand motionless, watching the sagebrush for a while. Then I would call out in a loud voice, "Are you lost? Do you need help? Are your parents here to help you?" Then I would cut a new lane, stand waiting for a few minutes, and call out loudly, "Don't be afraid, I won't hurt you. Do you need help finding your parents?"

After only a few moves in the game, I became convinced that whatever I was pursuing was far more intelligent than any animal. I decided that it probably was a lost little girl. For that reason, I continued to play the cat-and-mouse game in a slow, cautious manner. The game took me further and further into the sagebrush. Soon I found myself at least a quarter of a mile northeast of my weather shack, immersed in the beautiful purple meadows.

I continued calling out in a loud voice, every now and then, "Little girl, don't be afraid. Are you lost? I will not hurt you. I only want to help you find your parents." There was never any response. By now, I was certain that I needed to get a good close look at the white creature that I was slowly pursuing. I began playing this game with still greater intensity.

Keeping track of the little white creature's movements required my utmost attention. I had to carefully study the movements of the clumps of sagebrush as they swayed gently in the summer winds. Sometimes I had to wait patiently for several minutes for a quick glimpse of something white, dashing up some distant side lane. Without thinking much about it, I noticed that the meadowlark sounds, which had previously been some two miles down the valley, had now moved quickly up the valley towards me. One of these unseen meadowlarks, using the maze for concealment, had moved swiftly up the valley and was now positioned behind a large, nearby clump of sagebrush. It was only fifty feet or so, off to my right. Another unseen meadowlark, concealed by both the maze and the near side of the arroyo, fell in behind another clump of sagebrush less than 70 feet to my left. Then I noticed that another three or four used the deep part of the arroyo for cover, redeploying in swift military fashion. They now formed a large arc a couple hundred feet across, and were located on the far side of the thick clump of sagebrush that I was now searching.

Then I noticed that the unseen meadowlark on my right issued a series of sounds noticeably higher pitched and louder than usual. Upon hearing it, the white creature that I was pursuing came to a full stop and stood motionless. She stood waiting for me to break through the unusually thick sagebrush into the lane where she was. Not feeling any fear, I ignored the unseen meadowlarks and continued my cat and mouse game. Having come so far into the desert, in the heat and in the sage, I was determined to close on the little white creature that I now felt certain must be lost.

Closing slowly on the object of my interest, I continued my policy of trampling straight wide aisles through the otherwise beautiful sagebrush. Opening another new lane by cutting easily through the last section in the maze, I trapped the small white creature in the short dead-end sagebrush alley where it stood. It was apparently waiting for me to finish my work. By now I was more than a half a mile out in the hot sunshine and out in the dry, beautiful purple sagebrush. A chorus of sounds from the unseen meadowlarks could suddenly be heard on both sides of me, and in front of me. However, none came from behind me. It had been a pleasant game of cat and mouse. It was with obvious satisfaction that I stepped through my newly created lane in the last irregular patch of sagebrush. My presence blocked the entrance into the small dead-end lane and closed the trap on the small white creature that I had been pursuing. The lane was no more than 15 feet deep. I had the object of my slow pursuit trapped, standing no more than 10 feet in front of me. As I was completing the winning move in this slow game of cat and mouse, I was saying gently, as though I were speaking to a lost little girl, "Don't be afraid. I will not hurt you. I will not even touch you. Are you lost? Are you out here alone? Do you need help finding your parents? Do you need a drink of water? If you're lost, I will help you find your parents." Turning at last towards the little white creature, the shock was too great to fully register on my brain.

Standing barely 10 feet from me, and shaking in absolute terror of me, stood a small little white girl, probably only 3 feet tall. Yet, as I looked at her, my mind numb from shock, I realized that she wasn't an ordinary little girl. Her skin was chalk white. She wore a chalk white jumpsuit with solid white astronaut like boots. The suit appeared to have been constructed from an aluminized canvas like material. Her boots appeared to have been made from a molded nylon like material. She had short blonde hair and bright blue, intelligent looking eyes. She was obviously exhausted. As a wave of shock tried to pound its way into my consciousness, I noticed that she was much thinner than any little girl I had ever previously seen. Then I noticed her eyes. They were much larger than those of any other little girl I'd ever seen. Her intelligent looking eyes molded smoothly around the side of her head, noticeably farther than those of any human. I began to feel dizzy from shock as I noticed that her gloved hands contained only 4 fingers, and appeared to end in short sharp claws instead of fingernails.

Retreating in shock and fear, I stepped back a couple of steps into the cross-lane. This released the trap on the little white creature and opened her escape route. It also took her out of my view, so that I could calm down a little. Slightly behind me and hidden in the thick sage some fifty feet off to my right, I could hear an unusually loud, piercing, and shrill sound. Still another sound, much softer than the first, could be heard once or twice coming from the lane where the little girl was. For the first time, fear began building from deep within me. It seemed like someone else was talking as I slowly recited, "Don't be afraid. I'm not coming any closer. I will not touch you. I thought you were lost. I thought you needed help finding your parents."

Knowing that the little girl was shaking in terror of me, feeling shock and fear myself, it seemed only natural for me to turn back towards the west, towards the direction of my weather shack. I took a few steps in that direction. Speaking now with my back towards her, and trying to block the scene that I had just witnessed from my mind, I continued, "Don't worry. I won't hurt you. I'm the weatherman out here. That's my weather shack over there. I'm going back to my weather shack now." Then I took two or three slow steps back towards my weather shack. I continued speaking loudly and slowly, "If you need help, just come over to my weather shack and ask me. See, I've already opened a wide lane for you. You don't have to come inside. You can just stay out in the desert and throw a rock at my shack to get my attention. I'll help you find your parents if I can. I could phone the Desert Center base commander and tell him you are out here alone. He would know where your parents are. He would tell them for sure."

Taking two or three more steps back towards my shack, I continued, "You're probably thirsty. You probably need some water. I have some water in my shack if you need a drink." There was no response from behind me. I could hear only soft, pleasant meadowlark sounds. I continued walking slowly back towards my weather shack, still speaking loudly and slowly. I was shaking noticeably from shock, "I'll put some water on that post for you. If you need it, you can drink all you want. I have plenty more."

I continued walking slowly back towards my weather shack. My nerves were still shaking. When I had covered about half of the distance back to my weather shack, I stopped for a moment and turned slowly around to see if anything had changed behind me. I expected to see the little lost girl following me from a distance. Instead, I got just a momentary glimpse of a tall thin adult white creature, probably 6 feet tall, running down one of the newly created lanes and turning into the dead-end alley which held the small white creature. Then in one smooth motion, it ducked down behind the sagebrush.

I was in far too much shock at the time for the scene and its implications to fully register on my numbed brain. There are scenes that your mind will allow you to see, and scenes that your mind will not allow you to see. From deep within me, I could tell that this was a scene that my mind would not allow me to fully see. Turning back towards my weather shack, I continued walking slowly back towards its safety. Arriving finally back at my weather shack, I stepped back into the quiet shaded safety of my isolated world. I closed and locked the doors. I sat down in my favorite chair and proceeded to try to forget everything I had just witnessed.

After sitting quietly for a few minutes and taking a few drinks of water, I started feeling guilty for not having set out the water as I had promised the little white girl. After thinking about it for a few minutes, I arose again. I located my jar of water and slowly reopened the side door to the beautiful desert outside. I happily noted that everything outside seemed normal. Nothing seemed out of place. I carried my jar of water outside and located a wide square wooden post with a flat top. The cable fence consisted of a row of such posts connected by a single steel cable. Although all of the posts were similar, finding a post with a flat level top was quite difficult. Consequently the post I selected had unique features. I set the jar of water on top of the post. I carefully positioned it so that any child could find it. I slightly loosened the cap. Then I shouted loudly out into the desert, "See, little girl. I am placing some water here for you. You may drink it anytime you want." I stood there silently for a few minutes watching the sagebrush in the distance. As before, there was no reply. Everything seemed to be beautiful, purple, and normal. The only difference I noticed was that now there were no meadowlark like sounds coming from out in the sagebrush. I was greeted only by the quiet whispering of the desert winds.

After watching the sagebrush for a few more uneventful minutes, I decided to phone the Desert Center air base and ask if any children had been reported missing. Returning to my weather shack and dialing the phone, I was soon speaking to my friend Dwight, the duty weather observer for the day. Dwight checked with the Desert Center command post. As I had requested, he asked to speak personally with the base commander. The base commander insisted that no lost children had been reported. Yet, according to Dwight, the base commander, a two star general, had thanked him profusely for making the phone call.

Like everything else, it didn't seem to make any sense. The conversation with Dwight was a friendly conversation. However, the phone line was heavy with static. Both Dwight and I quickly became convinced that someone else was listening in on our supposedly private line. Still shaking from my experience and feeling very ill at ease, I told Dwight that I wasn't feeling well. We both decided that the best thing for me to do was to cancel the last run for the day and head back into base. For some reason, the Desert Center base commander happily agreed. Without further ado, I hung up the phone, closed up my weather shack and headed for my parked pickup truck. As before, nothing outside in the desert appeared to be out of the ordinary. Yet the feeling that I was being watched by something out in the desert was absolutely overwhelming. I didn't actually feel threatened. I just felt certain that five or six people were watching me intently. I felt certain that these people, for some unexplained reason, approved of whatever it was that I had done. Every time I turned my head to look out into the sagebrush, I would catch momentary glimpses of things, things that my shocked and confused mind refused to let me actually see. My brain kept saying to me, "Just keep walking. Don't listen to anything. Don't look back. Everything will be all right. Just keep walking, and don't look back."

Once I was safely inside my truck, I locked the truck doors, and started the engine. I quickly put the truck in gear and headed back into town. All of the time, as the road carried me across the dry lakebed, through the tall sagebrush and up the mountain slopes beyond, the feeling that I was being watched was simply overwhelming. I understood why Sullivan had deserted. It wasn't until I reached the low pass in the mountains that I was finally able to calm down and start thinking again. Only then did I stop praying. Only then did I stop asking Jesus to protect me from whatever it was that I had encountered.

Coming out of the pass, I could see the Mojave Wells base in the distance. It looked so beautiful and peaceful as it lay exposed in the afternoon sunshine. As I drove towards this image of beauty and peaceful security, I realized that like Sullivan, I too, had a decision to make. I realized that the weather reporting schedule for the coming day was identical to the one I had been ordered to follow on this day. Like Sullivan, I realized that whatever had been watching me from out in the sagebrush today would be watching me from out in the sagebrush tomorrow, and the next day, and the next day. The prospect of driving out to range one alone, at 3:15 a.m. in the morning, was scary enough. Now the prospect of working out there alone in the nighttime, knowing that something unknown was hiding out in the sagebrush watching my every move, was terrifying beyond description. Yet, I realized that I had no other choice. The wind-reporting schedule came as a set of orders from the Desert Center base commander. He was a two star general who had developed the bad habit of expecting his every order to be obeyed to the letter. Failure to obey a general's orders would lead to a simple drumhead court martial. I knew what I had to do. For my own good, I had to force myself to forget what had just happened. For my own good, I had to force all memories of it out of my mind. I had to remember only that whatever had been out there today, had also been out there yesterday, and the day before, and the day before. For my own good I had to remember that it hadn't attacked me on any of the many occasions in the past when it obviously could have. I kept reminding myself that I hadn't done anything today that would cause it to change its mind. I decided at last to rely on God for protection and to close my mind to the entire incident. I set about convincing myself that nothing whatever had been watching me from out in the sagebrush, down at range one. I proceeded to spend the remainder of the day thinking up possible alternate explanations for what had happened. Silly as some of the explanations were, they gave me the courage to continue with my weather observing duties out at range one. I decided to convince myself that what I had really seen was a new and undiscovered type of large white seagull. I gave it a name. I called it, "The Gull of the Distant Sage".

The following morning the drive out to range one was a simple test of courage. My sea gull story had given me very little. There was only a sliver of moonlight. I was terrified of every shadow, every rock, and every rabbit. Yet, emotional vegetable that I was, I was determined to perform my weather observer duties as ordered. I rolled down the window on my truck. I sang my summer sunshine songs loud and slow. As my truck traversed the low mountain pass and began heading down towards the dry lakebed in the distance, my hands were shaking from fear so much that my truck left the gravel road and bounced harmlessly across the desert. After a short distance, I regained control and got my truck back onto the gravel road. I stopped my truck on the road and surveyed the dry lakebed ahead in the distance before continuing on.

Nothing appeared to be out of place, but that did little to calm me down. In order to overcome the terror that I felt, I worked hard trying to convince myself that my sea gull explanation was correct. I decided that since I was the discoverer of this supposed new kind of seagull, I should make up more names for it. Silly as this game was, it did help me get better control of myself. I decided that I would give my seagull a second name. I decided I would also name the new seagull "Charlie's Gull". Playing this silly game let me finally get back to where I could laugh a little at myself. Even so, I approached the range one area with as much fear and caution as Sullivan ever had.

When I finally arrived at range one, nothing appeared out of place. Nothing, that is, except the bottle of water which I had left sitting on the post the day before. During my absence, someone had removed half of the water, replaced the cap snugly, and placed the jar on the ground next to the post. Around the post were two new sets of footprints, in addition to the footprints that I had left in the soft desert soil the day before. One set of footprints had been made by a small child wearing boots. The other set was similar to the first, except they were those of an adult. I estimated that the child didn't weigh more then 30 pounds. The adult appeared to weigh not more then 110 pounds.

Alone in the desert night, once more terror began welling up inside of me. In terror, I realized that I had no choice but to take the morning winds and phone them in using the phone inside my range one weather shack. It was a good hour's drive back into Mojave Wells. If my winds were that late and made up, I would be looking at a court martial and a section eight, for sure. It was with a certain determined military grimness then, that I set about my duties. I climbed into the safety of my truck and started it. I locked the doors and turned the headlights on bright. I carefully inspected every square inch of the graveled area at range one. I positioned my truck so that the open front door of my truck was less then 4 feet from the theodolite stand. I set the parking brake and left the truck engine running. I also left the lights on bright. The truck was positioned so that the bright lights shone out into the sagebrush maze where I had been walking the day before. Then, singing loudly in a high voice to build up my failing, vegetable-like courage, I gingerly got out of my truck and opened my weather shack.

I phoned the Desert Center weather station to make sure they knew I was on the job. Then, in hurried fashion, I took the morning wind measurements. I performed the calculations in record time and phoned them into Desert Center. I closed down and locked up the weather station as fast as humanly possible. With terror and fear building within me, I sprinted back to my waiting truck and climbed in. I locked the doors, put the truck into gear, and began heading out across the graveled area towards the road back to the Mojave Wells base. I had been jumping in fear of every shadow, every trembling leaf, and every gust of wind. Even though nothing had actually happened on the morning run, I was, by now, so terrified, that my brain had switched to tunnel vision. I was in near panic.

Emotionally I had switched into complete denial of the previous day's events. For that reason, I assumed that my mind was playing tricks on me as I brought my truck out onto the gravel road. On the edge of my vision, I got a momentary glimpse of something tall and white, standing only a hundred feet or so, out in the sagebrush northeast of the range one area. In near panic as I was, I hit the gas, shifted into high gear, floored the gas pedal, headed out across the dry lakebed and back towards base.

There was something about the range one area this morning that had felt far different from anything I had ever felt before. When I had gotten the glimpse of the white creature, this time it had felt as though it were a young woman, standing, waiting in the sagebrush to thank me for whatever I had done the day before. It felt as though the little white girl was her daughter and had actually been lost. It felt as though I had actually located her for them. My mind was so locked in terror at the time that I was barely able to drive. For a moment it felt as though a friendly African lion had been waiting to thank me. Then it felt as though someone very important, like Abraham Lincoln, had been waiting there to thank me. With panic spreading rapidly through my brain, I hit the gas some more and sped up until my truck was just barely able to stay on the gravel road. It was in this wretched state that I struggled to keep control of myself as I headed back towards Mojave Wells. It wasn't until I was back through the pass, and the Mojave Wells base area had come into view that I was willing to turn my head from one side to the other. I had been too terrified to even look in my mirrors as I drove.

Halfway from the pass to the base area, the terror of it all finally overwhelmed me. I stopped my truck and fell out of the driver's side door. I landed on my hands and on my knees, on the hard rocks and gravel. I proceeded to vomit my guts onto the desert floor. I was sick from terror. When I stopped, I was so hysterical that I momentarily forgot I'd been driving my truck. Except that I was on my knees vomiting, I would have broken into total hysteria and ran screaming in terror down the road back to base. After I had spent some twenty minutes on my knees, crawling in the dirt and sagebrush, vomiting my guts into the sand and sagebrush and onto the gravel highway, I was finally able to drag myself back into my truck, wild eyed, with tears of fear and terror filling my eyes. Ignoring my scrapes and cuts and scratches, I placed my truck in gear and drove back towards base with the brutal determination of a soldier coming home from a war zone.

I pulled my truck up in front of the chow hall and parked. I sat there for several minutes, my face in my scraped hands, trying to regain control of myself. I was thanking God for the chow hall, and its feeling of closeness and security. I was sick from the morning's experience. Knowing that I still had four more wind measurements to take, just today alone, made the terror even worse. My head was pounding. I was shaking so badly that I wasn't sure I could get out of my truck and walk into the chow hall. I decided to rest for a few minutes and pray for help before making the attempt to go in for breakfast and coffee.

As I sat there with my window rolled down, reciting the Lord's Prayer over and over, trying desperately to regain my courage, my friend Smokey, the head cook, came out of the chow hall. Good friend, confidant, and genius that he was, there was little point in ever trying to hide anything from Smokey. With one glance he could see my terror. He knew exactly how to calm me down. He walked up to my truck, greeted me, and laughing a little, said, "Charlie, I don't know what you have gone and done now, but that base commanding general down at Desert Center has gone and memorized your name. He told me so himself. You're sure in a lot of trouble now. I told you, you'd get yourself in trouble going out there into the desert every morning like you do, didn't I? Didn't I tell you that you should be spending your mornings setting in there in the chow hall drinking coffee, shooting the bull with me, and making up those winds, just like all those other weather observers used to do before you." Then he laughed some more. You're as white as a ghost, Charlie. You wouldn't stand out any more, looking the way you do, if you were to go back out there tonight wearing neon diapers." He laughed some more. Turning more serious, he continued: "You know, if you're going to go out there alone every night like you do, and expect to survive, you're going to have to face up to whatever is out there. You're never going to be able to hide from it, not with all that baby white skin of yours. You're going to have to learn to stand your ground when it walks in on you from out in the sagebrush. Before you go out there again, Charlie, it's my duty before Jesus to get you to brown down like me, so you can blend in with the shadows like I do. That way, that base commanding general down at Desert Center won't ever get onto what you've been doing out there. That way, he'll never learn your name."

My head still aching, and my pulse still pounding from the morning's events, I finally asked, whispering meekly through my veil of tears, "The Desert Center base commander knows me?"

Smokey laughed and responded, "Yes, he knows you, Charlie. Just a few minutes ago, he personally called up the chow hall here with a message for you. He ordered me to fill a couple of large thermos' with coffee the way you like it, collect up six, eight pieces of toast along with some good breakfast things, eggs, bacon, and stuff, and come get you using the chow hall truck. That new cook and I were in there right now getting the stuff together when we saw you drive up. That general said you were stopped out there on the range one road, sick and vomiting, down on your hands and knees, and unable to drive. He even knows you by name, Charlie. You know you got to be in a lot of trouble now - now that the Base Commanding general has gone and learned your name."

Off balance and still in shock, I meekly asked, "What was the message?" Smokey pretended not to notice that I was wiping the tears of fear from my eyes at the time.

Smokey laughed as before, bent over, spit on the ground, and responded, "He said 'Thanks'."

"You mean 'Thanks for the morning winds?'" I asked.

"No," responded Smokey. He straightened up and looked me straight in the eye. "You know he doesn't care anything about those winds. That's why you should be making them up for your own safety, like all of those other weather observers did before you. He said 'Thanks' for whatever it was that you did yesterday. He said, 'don't worry. The butterfly is unharmed and perfectly safe now. He said the butterfly ran off while playing in the flowers and got hopelessly lost. She got trapped out in that thick sage and couldn't get out. He said everyone was looking all over in the wrong places. The sagebrush was so thick that it screwed everything up. Everyone was worried sick, including the general himself. He said you were the one that figured it all out, and showed everyone where the butterfly was. He said you went out there like some big gorilla, cut through the thick sagebrush, and set the butterfly free. He said they wouldn't have found the butterfly in time or

118

gotten through that thick sage in time without you." Then Smokey paused for a minute before continuing. "The general also said the rest of the wind runs for today are canceled. The winds for the rest of the week are also canceled. The cancellation order is irrevocable. He said he's ordering you to take the rest of the week off as free medical leave. He suggested that you calm down by having fun in Los Angeles at Air Force expense. The normal wind schedule will resume from range one next Monday morning at 8:00 a.m. He said they'd skip over next Monday's 4:30 morning run so you could rebuild your courage in the sunshine. He also promised that all of the ranges would be deserted on Monday."

With my mind now in total denial and confusion, I breathed out one more question, "Did the general say anything else?"

"Yes," responded Smokey. "He said he admired your bravery. He said nobody down at Desert Center or back east at the Pentagon, has the slightest idea how you could have gone and done such a good thing. He said that he has never seen any man with the guts that you have. Then he said something really strange, Charlie," stated Smokey matter-of-factly.

"What was it?" I whispered.

Smokey looked serious for a minute or so and responded, "He said he wanted you to know that because of what you did yesterday, there wasn't anything white out on the ranges which you would ever need to be afraid of. He said that he and the Pentagon, and everyone else that's white, has gone and learned all about you by name. You know that you have to be in a lot of trouble now, Charlie. There's no doubt that the base commanding general has got you in his sights 'cause he's gone and memorized your name."

I was too confused, sick, terrified, and shocked, to respond. Smokey, laughing again, gently opened the door to my truck and said, "Come on, Charlie. You've at least gotten a decent 'Deer in the headlights' look, back in your eyes. Whatever is out there, I can see it's put you through one fine piece of living hell. Whatever it is, it can wait 'till Monday. This is one morning when you need your brother Smokey to come look after you. Remember, you and I, we're blood! It's even the general's orders for me to take care of you. Come on in, brother. Let's get us some coffee. We'll give you that nice breakfast we've fixed. You can brown down again and get some color back in those four baby white cheeks of yours. You need to spend some time forgetting about whatever white is waiting for you out there on those distant, sage covered hellish ranges. Remember, you and I are of a kind. Neither one of us is white.

That morning as I walked, shaking, towards the chow hall with Smokey steadying me, and telling me the humorous version of his life's story, I said a little prayer. First I swore that I would religiously forget whatever I had seen out in the sagebrush on range one. Then I thanked God for Smokey.

Olympic Tryouts

So the king ordered Daniel to be brought
and cast into the lion's den.

To Daniel he said,
   "May your God,
      whom you serve so constantly,
        save you."

            ...Daniel 6:17

It was a beautiful evening in Mojave Wells. After the evening chow, I had spent several hours shooting pool in the Mojave Wells Airmen's club. It was unusually late, slightly past midnight, when I finally got back to my barracks. I was still bunking in the huge, empty double barracks by the Mojave Wells flight line, the barracks with the bathrooms in the middle. The barracks were long, had only two doors, were very poorly lit, and had only two windows. With its unusual creaks and shadows, it certainly wasn't a barracks for the faint hearted. It had enough bunks and cubicles for 60 or 70 men. However, I was bunking alone in the barracks because no one but me would agree to spend a night sleeping there.

I had just taken my nightly shower, and I was drying off when I heard something in one of the compartments down by the west door. I would have run out the other door, but I didn't have any clothes on. I couldn't see anything, but I felt certain that I was being watched by something.

121

Whatever it was, it seemed intensely curious about little things…things like how I was drying my shoulders with a towel.

After a few nervous moments, I finally got my civilian clothes on. Getting dressed took some doing because I was too scared to go back into my compartment and turn my back on whatever it was I'd heard. After I got dressed, I left the barracks through the other door and got to my truck. I started my truck and parked it at the east end of the building. I specifically parked outside the barracks door on the north side next to the east end. This let me see the entire Mojave Wells runway and the complete desert valley that ran straight north from the barracks. I could see all the way up the valley, to the mountains on the far north end, perhaps 105 miles away. I locked my truck doors and decided to sit and watch the barracks to see who or what came out. At about 2:00 a.m. my patience was rewarded. Something came out from hiding on the west end of the barracks and went running out into the valley towards the mountains to the northwest. It happened so fast that I could hardly believe my eyes. It appeared to be a tall shockingly white person, approximately 6 feet tall. It appeared to have solid, chalk white skin, shoulder length blonde hair, and it ran at least twice as fast as any Olympic runner would have run. It appeared to be wearing some type of aluminum clothing that gave off a soft white fluorescent light. The way the creature ran was distinctly feminine. It had surprisingly thin arms and legs, and it had three little children, just like itself, running after it. When they got about a mile and a half out where the sagebrush started getting tall, they all bent down, and disappeared by hiding in the sagebrush. I stayed locked in my truck and kept watching the barracks. About ten minutes later, I saw a second tall white creature peek at me from around the opposite end of the barracks. This second adult creature moved in a manner that was distinctly male and also stood approximately 6 feet tall. After a few more minutes, he too, went running out from hiding on the west side of the building. He ran out into the desert to the northwest, as the others had and hid in the sagebrush. I clocked him. As a weatherman, I had long since memorized the location of all of the hills, gullies, and points of interest in the Mojave Wells valley. I was wearing my watch, and it was an easy matter to time the creatures. Computing the speed with which the runners had traveled was also a simple matter. The woman and the children were running between 25 and 30 miles per hour. The man was running a little faster. He was running at about 35 miles per hour.

As the reality of what I had seen sank slowly into my brain, I found myself becoming terrified. For a few minutes, I sat in my truck, shaking in fear, not even able to light a cigarette.

I watched the sagebrush some more, and nothing happened, but after a half hour or so, I could see some fluorescent patches up in one of the mountain passes, some 10-15 miles northwest of the Mojave Wells Base. I decided that the emergency must be over. The whole experience had left me dog-tired. I was afraid to go back into my barracks, so I went to sleep in my truck. I took the morning winds in my civilian clothes that day because my fear of going back into my barracks didn't subside until well after sun up. When I finally did go back in, there wasn't anything unusual to be found except that a few of my clothes had been moved.

When I told Steve about everything over the supper table, he became really angry with me. He criticized me, saying, "I really like you, Charlie. You're the best and closest friend I've ever had. You've been better than any brother to me. I'd die to keep anything from happening to you, but it was so stupid of you to park your truck out there and wait. You've got to learn to get some brains about you, Charlie. You've got to learn to back away from stuff like that. What if they'd decided to come out your end of the barracks, not knowing that you were there? What would you have done then?'

Defensively, I responded, "But what I saw wasn't real, was it? I mean, I was just dreaming, wasn't I, Steve?"

Then Steve, standing up, answered me angrily, "No! You weren't dreaming, Charlie. No man of your intelligence dreams up driving his truck onto the flight line in the middle of the night like you did."

Steve stomped off. As he did so, I noticed that he had tears in his eyes. It appeared that he knew much more than he was telling me.

A few uneventful days passed. Then, late Friday evening, I was hungry for some ice cream. It was going on midnight. I had been playing poker with Steve and my other friends. Before going back to my barracks, I walked into Mojave Wells and continued down along the main highway to the ice cream stand on the southeast end of town. In those days, Mojave Wells was a tiny little town in a very big desert. It didn't have any nightlife. Usually, they rolled up the streets when the sun went down. The ice cream stand was located on the poorly lit east edge of town next to the main highway under some large old oak trees. I arrived at the stand just as it was closing. The attendant filled my order for a cola and an ice cream bar. Then the attendant closed the stand, turned off the lights, locked up, and went home. I wasn't in any hurry. As a weather observer, I was long since used to being outside alone at night. I took my cola and my ice cream bar to one of the outdoor tables that sat hidden back in the shadows under the trees. The few side streets of Mojave Wells were deserted and the traffic through town was very light. I was taking my time, calmly enjoying my ice cream on this warm summer night.

In the distance I noticed something unusual across the main highway on the other end of town. There, on the side of the highway walking slowly towards me and just reaching the western edge of Mojave Wells, were two thin, unusual, forms. They were only two blocks from me, so I could see them clearly and plainly. They stood a little less than six feet tall and had a slightly unusual manner of walking. They had the same appearance as the creatures I had seen by my barracks. They were walking very close together, one slightly behind the other, and were less than Three feet apart. They were looking around a great deal as they walked. They were as similar in appearance as any two identical twins; yet, because of their actions, I thought they might be brother and sister. Despite the fact they were walking along the main highway through Mojave Wells, they appeared to be afraid that someone would see them. Feeling threatened, I sat quietly, hidden by the shadows and the trees and watched them carefully for at least twenty minutes. Several cars passed them during that time. I noticed that the automobile headlights did not illuminate their suits. Rather, the suits appeared to generate a field of some type that absorbed the light from the cars and generated different light of their own. However, the two did cast shadows as the car lights passed them. The drivers of two cars appeared to panic when they saw them. The cars accelerated rapidly through town before disappearing down the highway towards Palm Meadows.

When they were less than a block from me, I decided that for my own safety, I would quietly head back to base. I continued to stay hidden by the shadows and trees. The plan worked well for a short distance. However, when I was directly across the highway from them, they suddenly caught sight of me and reacted with alarm. The highway and streets of Mojave Wells were deserted at the time. Since I was certain they had seen me, and I was concerned for my own safety, I hailed them from across the highway. I was planning to warn them to keep away from me and from my barracks. To my surprise, once I hailed them, they took off running away from me. They immediately left the main highway and went running up the arroyo and up the canyon into Big Bear pass which overlooks Mojave Wells. Dogs could be heard barking at them as they ran past some houses on the distant edge of Mojave Wells. Within a few minutes, they had disappeared into the canyon, the sagebrush, and into the mountains that separated Mojave Wells valley from the next valley to the south. Once again, I instinctively timed them as they ran. They ran uphill for more than two miles as they headed into the pass at speeds greater than 30 miles per hour...far too fast for a human to run.

This time I had gotten a good clear look at both of them. Carefully, I crossed the highway and studied the boot prints that they left in the sand and in the soft dirt along the highway. Comparing the depth of the boot prints with my own, I concluded they each weighed approximately 90 pounds...much less than a typical human of the same height. I walked slowly and warily back to my barracks. Nothing about Mojave Wells seemed to be making any sense at the time.

A few nights later at about midnight, I was walking alone back to my barracks from a late night poker game with Steve and my friends. Once again I saw the same two white creatures cautiously walking along the main highway into town. This time I hid in the shadows of one of the empty barracks on base and watched them from a distance. After walking through town, by way of the main highway, they cautiously inspected the side streets and the houses on the south end of Mojave Wells. They disappeared at last into the sagebrush along the base of the mountains to the south. Once again, after watching them for more than twenty minutes, I still had no idea what to make of it all.

Nothing unusual happened in the barracks for a few more days. Then one afternoon when I returned to my barracks, I noticed that my clean laundry and uniforms were slightly ruffled and had moved noticeably while I had been out on the ranges. At first, I wasn't alarmed because the military has so many inspections. Then I noticed my safety razor lying on the floor. I was certain that I had placed it in my shaving kit and locked it in my duffel bag before leaving for the 4:30 a.m. run. I was also certain that I had the only set of keys.

A couple days later, in the afternoon, I was reading a book in the base library. Curious, my mind turned to the sagebrush incident. I wondered if it was possible that the white creatures which I had seen, could possibly have been very athletic humans? The book I was reading stated that well trained Olympic athletes are able to run twice as fast as ordinary humans. Yet, running a mile in four minutes, an Olympic runner is traveling only 15 miles an hour. This meant that ordinary people could be expected to run out into the sagebrush at only 7 or 8 miles an hour. Then there's the fact that the Olympic record for the hundred yard dash is not more than 22 miles per hour. Yet, I was certain of my calculations. The white male creature had traveled at 35 miles an hour for more than 25 times that distance. Now I really began wondering, 'If the white creatures I'd seen weren't human, what were they?' I recoiled in fear from the implications. I was still trying to happily live a life of denial. I decided that my tour of duty at Mojave Wells would be tolerable only if I could convince myself that the people I had seen were homeless people who had wandered in from the nearby desert, wishing only to spend the night in an empty barracks. The problem, I decided, was the Olympic records.

I reviewed my calculations carefully. There was no way around the mathematics. The white male had run into the sagebrush at least two and a half times faster than the best Olympic runner.

I wondered about those figures for many hours. I decided to resolve the confusion in my mind by performing an experiment. I decided to time myself, and see how fast I could run. The next morning out at range three seemed like a perfect time to test myself. It was a beautiful summer day in the desert. The ranges were deserted. All the flights had been canceled for several days. My Olympic training program began at 10:00 a.m. sharp.

Carefully, I measured out a distance of 100 yards. My Olympic training course started at the front door of my weather shack and stretched in a straight line slightly northwest, past my theodolite stand towards the range three lounge. I took a drink of water and checked the second hand on my watch. Then I took off running as fast as I could toward the finish line 100 yards away. Completing the first heat, I tried a second time, then a third. Too tired for a fourth heat, I accepted the inevitable. My best time was much less than 8 miles an hour. Sure, I had been wearing my military boots, and my timing wasn't up to Olympic standards, but the conclusion couldn't be argued. No human could run 35 miles an hour for a distance of a mile and a half.

After resting for a while in the cool breeze in the shade of my weather shack, my mind refused to accept the reality of this conclusion. I wondered, maybe if I trained as Olympic athletes train, my speed would improve dramatically. Maybe if I practiced running, jumping, and throwing rocks, my running speed would improve to Olympic standards. My intentions were deadly serious. Yet, in almost comical fashion, I carefully marked out a broad jump area and a stone throwing area, northeast of my theodolite stand. Then I began my Olympic training program. I decided to concentrate on the broad jump first. I supposed that if I could dramatically improve my broad jumping figures, then my running speeds would also improve dramatically. I decided that if I could ever run at 15 miles per hour in my heavy military uniform, I would conclude that the white creatures had been ordinary humans who had unintentionally given me a good scare. It was more than a passing consideration for me. I did, after all, fall asleep alone in an unlocked barracks, on the edge of a great big desert, night after night and wake up in the dark, hoping to still be alone, morning after morning.

129

For the next few days, I trained with a will. It soon became apparent that the more I trained, the slower I got. One day I practiced the broad jump more than twenty times. Each time I started by the front door of my weather shack, and took off running as fast as I could. When I reached my broad jump line, I jumped as far as I could. It was seldom that my distances, jumping as I was on the hard gravel surface, measured as much as five feet. Soon my running time for the 100-yard dash was down to a mere 5 miles per hour, and my distance was down to less than 3 feet, little more than my stepping distance.

On Wednesday of the following week, I decided to try another attempt at the broad jump. As usual, it was another beautiful summer morning in the Mojave Wells valley. The blue dome of the sky contained its usual decorative cirrus clouds. Considering the conditions, I was using my usual red balloons. I had just completed the 9:30 a.m. balloon run. The ranges were closed to everyone except me. Therefore, the ranges were otherwise deserted. As usual I had left my truck parked over in front of the generator shack.

Since the range rats had been ordered to stay on base, it seemed like a good time to train. I knew that if I failed or looked silly, there was no one who could possibly see me or make fun of me. As usual I started by the front door of my weather shack. Then I took off running towards my broad jump training area just northeast of my theodolite. My leg muscles were still sore from the previous day's attempts. As I started the jump, I slipped on the hard gravel surface, lost my balance in mid-air, and came down squarely on my left kneecap. The hard graveled surface cut easily through my green fatigues and through my skin underneath.

By the time I had finished sliding to a stop on the hard gravel, my left leg from my knee down was cut, banged, bleeding, and swelling fast. My left hand was cut and damaged. Numbness and swelling was spreading rapidly from my left wrist down through my fingers. I spent the next few minutes vomiting in pain and screaming in agony from it all. Only the knowledge that I was alone, some 22 miles out in the desert, gave me the strength to endure the pain of rolling over onto my back and sitting up in the gravel and thorns. At first I was convinced that my left leg was broken in several places, along with my left knee, my left wrist, and maybe a few bones in my ribs and feet. I sat there for almost a half hour screaming in agony and pain and swearing at my own stupidity. Alone as I was, there was no one to hear me, so I didn't hold back my screams and swearing.

Finally, the feeling began to slowly creep back to my swollen left wrist and hand. Slowly and painfully I picked the thorns and gravel out of my left wrist, my left hand, and my left leg. In extreme pain, I used my handkerchief to stop the bleeding from my flesh wounds. Then I used some dirt, as best I could, to clean my blood and vomit off my torn uniform. Spitting on my fingers and on my wounds, I pressed close the minor cuts on my left wrist, my left hand, my left knee, and my left leg. Then I calmed down as best I could and assessed my desperate situation. I had sat up facing east merely because that was how I had fallen. The pain I felt was far too great to allow me to stand up or to walk. Yet, I knew that I would die where I lay, if I couldn't get myself back to my weather shack and phone for help.

I began by inspecting my left wrist. It was swelling fast. By now it had turned completely black and blue. I carefully

131

inspected each of the bones in my left wrist and hand. I carefully compared them to the corresponding bones in my right wrist and hand. Since they all matched, I decided that none of my wrist or hand bones were broken. So I began slowly exercising my left wrist and hand. I knew that to get out of this situation, I was going to need the use of my left hand, so I ignored the extreme pain and kept exercising it. Sometimes I was swearing in anger and agony as I did so. The exercise helped greatly and soon my left wrist was feeling far better.

Then I turned my attention to my ribs, my left knee, left ankle, and left foot. Gratefully I concluded that all of the bones, muscles and ligaments in my ribs, left ankle, and left foot were badly bruised, but probably not broken. By now they too, were swollen black and blue. My left knee was also, swollen black and blue and was far too painful to inspect. In addition, the pain was rapidly getting worse as the shock of the accident was wearing off.

I knew that I was going to have to get back to my weather shack at any price. Trying hard to ignore the intense pain, I sat up straight and dragged myself backwards the twenty feet or so across the hard gravel until I got back to my theodolite stand. I was exhausted and thirsty by the time I got there, but all of my drinking water was in my weather shack and truck. The hot desert sun and my heavy thirst convinced me that if I didn't get back to my weather shack soon, I wouldn't be much longer for this world. Some of the exposed stones and parts of the steel theodolite stand were already becoming painfully hot to the touch. Still, I needed to rest and let the pain in my left knee subside before making any more moves.

I positioned myself so that I was sitting with my back leaning against the theodolite stand, facing slightly northeast. It was a steel stand set in heavy concrete. It could easily have supported several tons. I was sitting there praying for God's help when I first noticed something out of place out in the desert. It was something white, hiding behind the sagebrush out along the road towards the ammunition bunker.

"Oh, NO!" I exclaimed to myself. It was about a half a mile away at the time. All I could see was the top half of its head from its eyes up. It was peering at me from behind the distant plant that concealed it. It stood up momentarily, reaching a height of at least 6 feet, and ran to the next closer plant. It was humanoid, chalk white, and very slim. It covered the distance by running at almost 30 miles an hour. It was now painfully obvious that I was in very serious trouble.

Still further in the distance I could see a large white object sitting on the desert floor. The white object was at least the size of a large two-car garage. It was sitting at the base of the mountains by the ammunition bunker, northeast of me. Slowly, carefully, deliberately, the white creature began closing the distance between us. It continued to hide behind the plants, and peer at me from over their tops. Within a matter of a few minutes, it had closed from three quarters of a mile to less than 500 feet from me. Only a hand-full of healthy plants separated it from me. Peering at it through the hot summer haze, the desert heat waves, the dirt, the sweat, and the blood running into my eyes, I still couldn't tell exactly what it was, but it's presence terrified me. My silly jumping had turned this pleasant carefree morning into a life or death struggle with the unknown.

Sitting on the ground as I was, I would be totally unable to defend myself if the white creature chose to close the distance between us. I realized that if I made the mistake of panicking, my last slim chance for survival would evaporate. Having no other choice and believing that my swollen left knee was broken; I stuffed several large stones into my pockets, grabbed onto my stand, and desperately pulled myself to a standing position. The pain was so excruciating that I became dizzy for several minutes. However, I used my uninjured right leg to support myself, and clung grimly to the burning hot stand until my mind cleared. Through it all, the pain caused me to scream and shout and to curse the fate that had brought me here. In the distance, I could hear the phone in my weather shack. It rang many times before finally falling silent.

When my mind finally cleared and the pain subsided a little, I could see that once again the white creature had closed the distance between us. It remained stationary now, hiding behind the last clump of sagebrush, some 300 feet away, which separated the two of us. I decided to shout at it. I needed to do something to control the terror that was surging within me.

Taking a deep breath, I shouted angrily out into the desert, "You're not going to surprise me. I see you out there. I'm healthier than I look, you know!" To my surprise, the white creature visibly flinched. Then it suddenly fell back a hundred feet or so along the bunker road. I could hardly believe my eyes.

In the distance down by the ammunition bunker, I could see a second white creature advancing slowly, sagebrush to sagebrush, along the same road as the first creature had done. Through breaks in the sagebrush, I could see that it carried a white object about the size of a doctor's medical bag. As I watched in terror and amazement, I noticed that the large white garage sized object had drifted diagonally closer. Now it stood no more than a mile out in the desert. Slowly it closed the distance between itself and the ammunition bunker, all in perfect silence. I momentarily forgot about my injuries and wondered what could possibly be going on?

As I watched, a third white creature appeared from hiding behind the sagebrush down at the far end of the bunker road. Then it too started slowly advancing. It advanced more slowly than the other two along the road towards the first two. Once again the phone in my weather shack began ringing. Once again after many rings, it fell silent.

I stood transfixed for a few minutes by the scene unfolding down along the bunker road. As I watched, the first white creature quickly fell back along the bunker road to a sagebrush covered ridge a half mile back, watching me all the time. The second white creature waited there to meet him. Then they both waited behind the sagebrush on the ridge while the third white creature slowly advanced to meet them. When the third white creature finally arrived at the ridge, it was handed the small medical-like bag by the second creature. Then the first creature fell back quickly along the road towards the white garage sized object, which now sat on the desert floor near the ammunition bunker.

The second white creature remained stationary, peering at me from behind the brush on the half-mile ridge along the bunker road. He appeared to react now and then to orders given him by the white nurse-like creature, convincing me that she must be of very high rank.

After a few minutes the third white creature, carrying the white bag, began to advance towards me. It was advancing much slower than the other two had. However, it was advancing with such steadiness and such obvious determination that I was now certain it intended to continue advancing, until it had broken out from the sagebrush and confronted me close up. Once again, terror started welling up inside me.

Believing now that I understood how men feel, men who are forced to fight desperate battles and face the unknown alone, I grimly assessed my situation. I had to get back to my weather shack at any price. Unable to crawl or walk, I was going to have to hop the distance on my right leg. There was simply no other way. I took a deep breath, bravely let go of the metal stand, and began hopping on my right leg towards my weather shack some 50 feet distant. It wasn't much of a plan. After only three hops, I lost my balance and began falling towards the concrete hard gravel. Without thinking, I used my left leg to catch my weight and regain my balance. The pain that shot through my left knee as my left leg took the weight of my body can't be described. Instinctively I turned back towards the safety of the stand. I hopped some more and once again was forced to use my left leg to catch myself before finally reaching the safety of the stand. Grimly I hung on to the stand and waited for the dizziness and pain to subside. I could hear the phone in my weather shack ring again another eight or ten times.

After a few minutes my mind cleared and once again I took stock of my situation. The third white creature had paused and was now watching me from some 500 feet distant. I began checking my left knee to see how much damage I had caused by hopping. To my immense surprise, my left knee now felt better than it had before. As I carefully tested the four muscles around my kneecap, the conclusion was inescapable. I had a terrible bruise, especially under the kneecap, but my knee wasn't broken. None of my knee ligaments seemed torn or damaged. My knee easily took the weight of my body and was now beginning to improve rapidly. Carefully I began placing my full weight on my left leg and knee. It hurt, but the more I pressed down on my knee, the better it felt. I could hardly believe my good fortune.

I waited for a few minutes for the pain in my left knee to subside from my last weight test. I decided that I should stay active, to control the terror within me. I grabbed hold of the metal cover for the theodolite that sat on the ground by the base of the stand. Lifting it carefully, I placed it in its normal position over the theodolite. Then I closed the cover and locked it, accidentally pinching my finger when I did so. Once again I found myself shaking my tender left hand in pain. As I did so, I noticed that the third white creature resumed its slow and steady advance towards me. Now it had closed to the last clump of sagebrush only 300 feet distant. Instinctively I stepped out from the theodolite stand and pretended to place my weight equally on both feet. Hoping to scare it off, I shouted angrily, "I'm ready for you. I'm not injured like you think. I'll put up a good battle. Don't come any closer because I'm getting healthier by the minute. I'll defend myself to the death. I'll go to my God like a soldier."

This white creature didn't flinch or react. It just stayed there, carefully watching my every move. It was obvious to me that it was planning to break out of the sagebrush and close on me. I was terrified by the prospect of having to confront it alone and out in the open. The pain had subsided in my left knee. I took a deep breath of air. Once again I took off hopping and limping towards my weather shack. The more I exercised my left knee, the better it got. By the time I reached the front door of my weather shack I was walking with only a heavy limp. I expected the white creature to be right behind me. When I reached the front door to my shack, I immediately swiveled, placed my back to the outer shack wall and turned to meet my expected attacker. I expected to find the white creature out in the open, closing on me fast, but when I turned I was greeted only by the gentle laughter of the desert winds. After several minutes of searching, I finally located the third white creature. It had fallen back more than a quarter mile along the bunker road. Hardly believing my eyes, I stood there for a few minutes catching my breath and studying the situation. I checked my watch. The entire ordeal had taken more than two hours.

Carefully I climbed into my weather shack and closed the side door for safety. Then I got hold of the gallon jar of drinking water that I had brought with me and began drinking. I placed my phone on the floor by me and sat down in the front doorway. I used a little of the water to clean several of the deeper cuts on my left leg and arm. Then I spit on my deeper wounds, and one by one, I carefully pressed them closed so that they would heal properly. I rested for a little while more, rehearsing in my mind the words I would say to Desert Center. It was now clear to me that I could easily make it over to my parked truck and drive myself into Mojave Wells, so I wouldn't need to be rescued. Usually, I enjoyed my duty on the ranges. I was reluctant to give up the extra pay and independence that came with it. All I would really have to tell Desert Center was that I was canceling the winds for the rest of the week. I could just say that I had the flu. Out along the bunker road, the third white creature had fallen back to the half-mile ridge and appeared to be giving orders to the second. Then the second fell back towards the white garage sized object that was parked by the ammunition bunker. The first white creature was nowhere to be seen.

After my knee had rested for a few minutes, I decided that I would call Desert Center and tell them my flu story, and head into Mojave Wells. The flu seemed like a good enough excuse now that my left knee was healing so rapidly. I was drinking some more water and getting ready to dial when the phone rang. "Range three, Charlie," I answered.

"Charlie, You're alive!" exclaimed my friend Dwight, on the other end of the line.

Taken off guard, I responded, "Why wouldn't I be?"

"The Desert Center base commander has called the station here, at least three times in the last couple hours, Charlie. He's been near beside himself with anxiety. He said that some woman up in Mojave Wells reported that you were in serious trouble up there. She said you'd broken your left leg, and couldn't get back to your weather shack to phone us for help. She said you were lying injured in a pile of thorns, screaming in agony. She made it sound like you were out of water and dying or something."

Caught with my guard down, I responded showing surprise, "I don't understand what you're saying, Dwight. Some woman in Mojave Wells phoned the two star general commanding Desert Center just to tell him that I had bruised my knee out in the desert?"

"Well, yes," responded Dwight, obviously giving his answer some thought. "That's what the general said. I spoke to him myself on the phone. He didn't actually say that she'd phoned him though. He made it sound as if she'd phoned the Pentagon, and they'd phoned him. Right now, the entire Desert Center base hospital is on emergency status waiting to rush you in for knee surgery. They're waiting for the base commander to allow the two rescue choppers to take off and come get you. Your friend Payne is packing his things over in the barracks and getting ready to replace you. The first Sergeant is planning on bringing him up to Steve's barracks at Mojave Wells as soon as it's dark. But if you're healthy, I'll call the barracks and tell Payne to forget it. He didn't want to go up there anyway. You know how the ranges frighten him."

"I don't understand," I continued. "Sure, I fell and bruised my knee, but its much better now. Sure I was lying out in a patch of thorns and sagebrush out in the desert for a long time screaming that my knee was broken. But you know I'm more than 22 miles out in the desert. You know that when I'm out here, no one in town could ever possibly see me. I don't know any women up here. What woman could possibly have seen me bruise my knee and phone the Pentagon?" My gaze wandered naturally out into the desert. Out there, along the bunker road at half-mile ridge, the third white creature remained posted behind the sagebrush, watching my every move.

Dwight continued, "As I understand it, she called some four star general in the Pentagon in D.C. He phoned the Desert Center base commander. I guess she got him out of a

National Security meeting and everything. According to the general, you have more friends than you realize, Charlie.

"You know Jackson, that weather observer I told you about who claimed he had spoken in person with Range Four Harry? Well, you know, a few years ago when I was talking to Jackson, he claimed that one time he got a little drunk and stumbled around out at range four for a few hours in the daytime. He claimed that old Range Four Harry came in out of the desert in broad daylight and everything and stood around and talked to him, just to make sure that he was OK. Has anything like that ever happened to you?"

Defensively, I answered, "You know I'm not much of a drinking man. I never drink anything alcoholic when I'm out here or when I'm going to be driving or anything. But one morning when I had the flu real bad and I was too sick to walk, something like that happened to me down by the range three gate. I'll tell you about it the next time we get together."

Dwight laughed, "I'll take you up on that one, Charlie. You know Jackson always claimed that he was the only alcoholic whose hallucinations could rescue him if he ever got in trouble. I'm sure glad that woman was wrong about you breaking your leg."

Out along the bunker road, the white creature continued to watch me from half-mile ridge. I noticed that she appeared to flinch and became very agitated when Dwight said that the woman had been wrong about my broken leg. I wondered what it all meant. I wondered if she could tell what Dwight was saying to me. After all, it was my private telephone line, wasn't it?

"Right, Dwight." I responded. "But whoever she was, she wasn't very wrong. Well, I have to lock up now and get back in to my barracks to nurse this bruised knee."

"You sure you don't need knee surgery or some x-rays or stitches or something?" Dwight continued. "You know the entire Desert Center base hospital is waiting for you! You know the Pentagon has ordered the base hospital to move to emergency status just to get you back into working order! You know the base commander is worried about your medical status. Shouldn't you at least let the rescue chopper come pick you up once you get back into base and bring you down here for x-rays? According to the general, the chopper would even take you back up there once the doctors said you're OK."

"No thanks, Dwight," I replied nonchalantly. "Tell the general none of that is necessary. I'll be good as new by morning. Tell the base commander thanks, but I'm fine. I don't need to be wasting the base hospital's time with these minor bruises."

"Well, if you say so, Charlie," stated Dwight, obviously not convinced that my injuries didn't need a doctor's attention. "I better hang up now and spread the word that you're alive and well. Both Payne and the base commander will be glad to hear it."

I hung up the phone, locked up my shack, limped over to the generator shack, and shut down the diesel. Then I limped to my truck, climbed in and started the engine. The truck was manual shift. Shifting gears with my left knee bruised was quite awkward. So I took my time and drove slowly back into base. I was surprised to find the gate to range three was open when I got there. I was certain that I had closed it in the morning when I last came through it. At the time I was actually quite glad it was open. Getting in and out of my truck to open it, had it been closed, would have been a painful operation because of my knee.

Once I got back to my barracks, I spent the remainder of the day nursing my bruises, taking a warm shower, putting some rubbing alcohol on my cuts, resting my knee, and sleeping in my bunk. The day's events had left me exhausted. It was going on 6.00 p.m. when I finally awoke. I hurried up to the chow hall for the evening meal, still limping noticeably, very hungry from having missed the noon meal. My friend Smokey met me at the door. Teasing, he greeted me, "Charlie, you're so late that we're all out of the regular food. But don't worry. Just for you, we have sugar sandwiches and barbecued squirrel." I was laughing almost too hard to get my coffee. Then turning serious, he continued, "You know, Charlie, even though the ranges are closed, there must be something very special going on out there tomorrow."

"Why do you say that, Smokey?" I asked thoughtfully.

"The Desert Center base commander himself called up the chow hall here. He called three times in the last hour trying to reach you. I guess you were sleeping too soundly to hear your barracks phone. The air policeman is on his day off, so the general made me swear that I would personally deliver his orders to you, under pain of court martial."

Once again, off balance and nervous because of my unnecessary bruises, I asked defensively, "What would he want with me?"

Smokey answered slowly and deliberately, "He wanted to make certain that you received the balloon schedule for tomorrow."

"What is it?" I asked naively.

"The Desert Center command post needs exactly one balloon run tomorrow. Then you'll be given free medical leave for the rest of tomorrow and all day Friday, Saturday, and Sunday. That will allow you plenty of time to spend the weekend having fun and resting up in Los Angeles. The first balloon run of next week won't be until 10:00 a.m. On Monday, you will be able to have a nice breakfast and make a leisurely drive out to the ranges," Smokey responded carefully. "However, the Desert Center base commander made it crystal clear that you are ordered to take the 4:30 a.m. run tomorrow, and only the 4:30 a.m. run, at any price. I'm ordered to phone the Desert Center command post as soon as I have delivered his orders."

Nervous, I responded, "Did it seem like he was angry with me? Or out to discipline me for injuring myself?"

"He's a general," answered Smokey. "Who can tell how generals think. He was emphatic that no one but you is allowed out on the ranges for the rest of the week." Then, after pausing, Smokey continued seriously, "Whatever is out there, Charlie, You're going to have to face it alone."

Trying to regain my composure, I shrugged, "That's no problem. All that's out there are jackrabbits and coyotes. the guy before me must have barbecued up all the squirrels." Then I tried to laugh some.

"I hope so, Charlie. For your sake, I hope so. Just the same, I wish you would let me or one of the range rats like Steve or Doug go out there with you. You'll need someone out there to watch your back while you're working. You'll need someone to protect you. We could hide in the truck or behind the buildings or out in the sagebrush. No one would ever have to know that we disobeyed the general's orders."

"That's nice of you Smokey." I answered sincerely. "But I'm not in any danger when I go out there. There's no reason for you guys to risk court-martial just for me. Don't worry, I'll be perfectly OK by myself, just as I always am."

But Smokey was not to be put off so easily. He continued probing. "Seriously, Charlie, when you're out there, do you ever see any sign of those people that Wayne says live up in those mountains northeast of here?"

"You mean that story Wayne tells of seeing chalk white people with hieroglyphics and writing like the ancient Egyptians? The ones he swears are dug into those mountains way up at the north end of Mojave Wells valley?" I responded.

"Yes," answered Smokey. "I know it's more than 100 miles up there, but you know how Wayne always swears that Range Four Harry is one of those people, and that he speaks perfect English."

"No," I casually responded. "I've never seen much of anything up in those mountains. I've never been able to accept Wayne's story, anyway." Denying reality, even to myself, came so easy.

Smokey could see that I was obviously lying to myself. He persevered. "How about that family of lost pioneers that Doug says lives up in those same mountains?" He asked intently. "You know how he believes that back in the 1800's a pioneer family got lost up in those mountains and could never get out. You know how he believes that incest and in-breeding set in, and their descendants still live up there, today, super intelligent and all chalk white and mutated."

"No," I smoothly responded. The pleasant smile on Smokey's face proved he could see right through my obvious self-deception.

"Well, you'll be in good company if you ever do see anything unusual out there, Charlie," Smokey stated sincerely. "All those other weather observers did. What they saw used to scare the devil out of them. Sooner or later, every one of them showed up here begging for sympathy with their coffee and sandwiches. That's why you're the only one who'll ever go out there anymore."

My knee started to ache again. I said goodnight to Smokey, and returned to my barracks for a warm shower and a good night's sleep.

The next day began simply enough. Nothing unusual had happened in my barracks during the night and I'd slept quite well. I had also gotten exceptionally good at denying the reality of the previous day's events. The desert, this summer night, was wearing its usual cathedral-like beauty. Warm gentle nighttime breezes greeted me as I walked, sang, and limped slowly across the barracks parking lot towards my weather truck. It was 3:05 a.m. on my watch. Since the general had ordered that the 4:30 balloon run be taken, I wanted to be punctual. Generals aren't usually very good at accepting excuses.

It was a beautiful drive out to range three. There was nothing unusual about the drive but I drove cautiously just the same. When I passed through the range three gate, I carefully stopped my truck and closed the gate behind me. I was following the range procedures to the letter because I was afraid of upsetting the general any further.

I visually checked every nook and cranny in the valley before getting back into my truck. As I drove, I continued to carefully check every distant canyon and ridge where I had ever seen lights, other objects, or even jackrabbits. On this morning, there was simply nothing out of the ordinary. Consequently, I soon relaxed, assumed a boyish type attitude about everything and passed the time singing to myself as I drove.

I wondered why the Desert Center base commander had been so insistent about this morning's wind measurements. It certainly wasn't like him. After all, I noted to myself, he wasn't even part of my normal weather service chain of command. After giving the matter some thought, I decided that he was probably upset over my silly "Olympic training accident". I guessed that he had probably decided to come down hard on me for a few days. Privately, I agreed with him. A little more military discipline certainly wouldn't hurt me any. I decided to wait a week or so and let my knee heal up, before taking my truck on another joy ride up the valley or over to the ammunition bunker.

Soon the buildings of range three could be seen sparkling in the moonlight up ahead. I approached the buildings with extra caution, but there was nothing unusual to be seen. The entire Mojave Wells Valley was simply deserted.

I let my truck roll to a stop on the west side of the generator shack. I got out to start the morning's activities, singing as I went. My knee was still tender but I was now walking with only a slight limp. I was quite proud of myself, really, for having 'walked off' such a painful bruise. By the time I got the diesel generator started, I was well on my way to having a wonderful morning.

I left my truck parked parallel to the generator shack facing north, just opposite the second set of double doors that remained closed. The generator shack held two huge diesel engines. This morning, for no particular reason I had started the southern diesel. Therefore, I had opened the southern set of double doors, the set in front of the diesel that I had started. Without the slightest bit of apprehension, I easily walked the remaining distance to my weather shack. I was very early, so I was surprised to find my phone start ringing as I unlocked the front door. "Either Desert Center is awfully impatient for the winds, or that base commanding general is determined to burn me," I said to myself as I answered the phone. "Range three weather shack, Charlie speaking."

The voice on the other end was my friend Payne. "Charlie, I'm glad you're there," He exclaimed. "I just reassured the Desert Center base commander that you were out there, wide awake, and on duty this morning. After I got him off the phone, I thought I'd better make sure. Don't worry, Charlie, if you'd been sleeping in the barracks or something, I'd have covered for you. I'd have even made up the winds," he laughed. "You know I'm good at it."

Laughing, I responded, "Thanks, Payne. I really appreciate it. But it surprises me that the General would be up this early, just to make certain that I'm releasing a balloon in the desert. Makes you wonder what the rest of the officers are doing with their time, doesn't it?"

"It sure does, Charlie," responded Payne. "But this place is so screwed up that it doesn't surprise me. What does surprise me, Charlie, is where you get the guts to drive out there alone every morning as you do. I sure never would. Man when I'm up there, if I don't have a range rat or someone to go out there with me, I just make up those winds and phone them in using the chow hall phone. I would never dream of going out there at night as you do. That stretch of desert is just too scary to suit me."

"Well, you certainly have more common sense than I do Payne," I laughed, "or I'd be sitting down in the Mojave Wells chow hall making up the low level winds right now too." Good friends that we were, we both laughed for a few minutes. Then I continued, "Well, I'd better let you go and get this balloon in the air or that general will have me for sure."

"Right," responded Payne. Then he continued, "That general had something else he was real worried about too, Charlie."

"Really, what was it?" I asked in surprise.

"He wanted to make certain that you shut down the diesels before you leave the ranges this morning," Payne stated in a matter of fact manner.

Flabbergasted, I responded, "But you know I always shut everything down and lock everything up before I leave. You know I've always been very good about that. What's he going on about that for?"

"I don't know, Charlie." Payne answered sympathetically. "But he sure loves that generator this morning, so be sure not to forget it when you go back into base."

"If he calls again, be sure to tell him that I have everything covered," I replied submissively. "And tell him I'll be more careful about my knee in the future."

"Right, Charlie. Good luck," said Payne as he signed off.

Angry and frustrated, I hung up the phone. "That general has no reason to be riding me so hard just because I slipped on the gravel and banged up my knee," I muttered angrily to myself. "If that healthy high-ranking general wasn't so military, this'd be pretty good duty," I exclaimed as I assembled my helium gauges and filled the balloon.

Ready now for the balloon release, I turned on my radio, tuned it to a local Palm Meadows radio station, and verified the time on my watch. I decided to perform one last security check. I stepped outside into the warm moonlit summer night. I visually checked the valley again, the ammunition bunker and its road, the mountains to the north and to the northeast, the entrance to a small side canyon on the west side some forty miles north of me, and the shadows behind the range three lounge. There was simply nothing out of place. The starlit cathedral-like valley could hardly have been more captivating, or more deserted. The desert silence was broken only by the music from my radio.

The balloon run went smoothly and flawlessly, so it happened that by 4:50 a.m. I was phoning Desert Center with the results. Payne reminded me that this was the last run for the day, and that the general had phoned a second time to guarantee that the diesel would be shut down properly. He finished copying the results. Then he informed me that the Desert Center forecaster, master sergeant Adams had just received another phone call from the general. He was relaying the winds to him as we spoke. I thanked my friend Payne and hung up the phone. I noted that it was now 4:55 a.m. Satisfied with my punctuality, I exclaimed to myself, "That should get that base commanding general off me for a while."

I shut down my weather shack, locked the doors, and walked smoothly to my parked weather truck. My left knee was continuing to improve. My left hand, my knee, and my ankle, were still swollen and bruised, with black and blue spots all up and down my left leg. Although my wounds, especially my knee, were still very tender, I now walked easily without a noticeable limp.

I climbed into my weather truck, started the engine, and turned on the headlights. It wasn't unusual for me to start my truck before shutting down the diesel generator. Usually, I did so because the sound of my truck engine made me feel more secure, which I enjoyed, being alone so far out in the desert. This morning was no exception. It was still dark outside. The moon was beautiful and shining. As I sat letting the engine in my truck warm up, my gaze turned naturally towards the northern set of double doors on the generator shack, the closed set. From behind them, a soft white fluorescent light showed out through the various cracks. I knew the inside of the generator shack like the back of my hand. I couldn't think of anything inside which could possibly be a source for the light. It was immediately apparent to me that something was out of place. I hadn't eaten yet, and was hungry for breakfast. One way or another, before I could eat I was going to have to shut down the diesel. I supposed that the light was probably the moonlight, or stray light from my truck's headlights. Without giving the matter so much as a second thought, I set the parking brake on my truck, left the engine running in neutral, left the lights on and opened the truck door. I stepped smoothly out of my truck onto the gravel outside, and humming to myself, I strode quickly across the graveled surface in through the southern set of double doors, the open set. Still humming, I stopped at last, directly in front of the still running generator. With a practiced hand, I threw several switches to the 'off' positions and shut off the fuel flow to the carburetor.

Then as I waited for the diesel to start shutting down, a process which takes several minutes, I began turning my head to check on the fluorescent light coming from the inside corner of the shack, to my left. My head was still only half turned, but already the source of the light was coming into my field of vision. Instinctively, the muscles in my body began to tighten as my eyes began to focus. There was a tall thin man-like creature wearing a white fluorescent suit, probably six feet tall. He had chalk white skin, blonde hair, large blue eyes, a non-protruding nose, and an otherwise human-like mouth. He was standing only 15 feet from me. He had a pencil-like instrument of some type pointed directly at my left temple. "This is not going to hurt Charlie, but your generals really have to inspect that damaged knee," he said in perfect English.

There wasn't time for me to move or respond. There was only time enough for me to realize that I was standing face to face with Range Four Harry.

I felt a slight shudder run through my body, and my vision suddenly went out of focus. Then my muscles seemed to freeze into place and my mind seemed to wander into a daze for just an instant or so. It seemed like only a second or two passed before I was able to regain control over my thoughts and snap out of the daze I was in. It took only another second or two for me to refocus my vision and take a couple of deep breathes. Finally I got control of my muscles and came to my senses. I found myself still standing in nearly the same position in front of the diesel, with my head still half turned, looking at the sidewall of the generator shack. Only now, there wasn't anything in the corner to my left. Now there wasn't any light. There wasn't any plastic. There wasn't any man-like creature. There simply wasn't anything but reflected morning sunlight coming through the cracks in the closed set of double doors. The corner was completely empty. Stunned and confused, I turned my attention back towards the diesel engine. It was totally shut down. Shocked, I checked the manifold, expecting it to be nearly red-hot, but it was stone cold. There was no way to fight the confusion flooding over my mind. I knew from experience that the diesel's manifold took more than an hour to cool off. Still it seemed as if only an instant of time had passed. I checked myself over. I was unhurt. I didn't have a mark on me. Dazed, I stumbled from the generator shack, trying to regain control of myself. As I came through the open door I was almost overwhelmed by the feeling that I had stood there just a short time earlier and watched something land out in the sagebrush to the west of me. I checked my watch. It had stopped at 5:05.

Outside of the generator shack I found the sun was already well above the horizon. My mind fought with the obvious fact that at least two hours had passed since I had first entered the shack. I stood there in the morning sunshine for a few minutes, and took stock of my situation. My handkerchief, which I usually kept in my left rear pocket, was stuffed awkwardly in my right front pocket. My left pants leg was turned up by half a turn. My fatigue hat, which I had worn into the generator shack, was no longer anywhere on me. I stumbled to my truck and grabbed onto the door handle and the open window, more for the feeling of security than anything. Then I noticed that my truck engine was no longer running and my headlights had been turned off. My fatigue hat was sitting on the truck's front seat. The truck itself had moved more than ten feet. I found myself filled with a momentary deep-seated unwillingness to look towards the mountains in the distant northeast, or out into the desert to the west. Yet nothing in sight appeared to be out of place.

Unable or unwilling to comprehend what had happened, I decided that I needed to get back into base immediately and regroup. I was so confused. I hardly knew what to do. I just couldn't accept the obvious fact that at least two hours had gone by since I'd entered the generator shack. Feelings of fear and dread were rapidly welling up inside of me. I quickly closed and latched the doors to the generator shack and climbed into my truck. I breathed a big sigh of relief as the truck engine roared to life. Feeling terrified, confused, alone, in total denial, I wasted no time heading back into town, to the security of Smokey and his chow hall. It was also clear to me that starting tonight, I would be bunking in a barracks with the other men.

In Memory of Me

…As often as you shall do these things

…Luke 22:19

"Bless me Father, for I have sinned," I began slowly. It was Sunday morning at the Mojave Wells base chapel. Confessions for Catholics, like myself, were held just before Sunday Mass.

"Yes, yes, my son, on with it," the old priest hurried me along. He was a wonderful, holy, and dedicated priest, easily pushing 75, and very Irish. He was based in far away San Bernardino. Each Sunday, he and a younger priest drove a circuit that covered half of the Mojave. I loved his sermons and admired his honesty. Frequently, I thanked God for my conversion to Roman Catholicism just because I enjoyed his sermons so much. He was large, tall, and heavy set. How he found the energy to make the long drive from San Bernardino was always a mystery to me.

"I had too much beer to drink last night, Father, and almost got drunk," I humbly continued.

"Yes, Yes," he hurried me along. "Young Irish lads like yourself always get together and enjoy a few good beers. Jesus understands. Now get on with it. There are others waiting."

Off balance, I humbly continued, "And I got into a fight with one of the other Airmen. It was my fault. I should have been more patient with him. I apologized this morning and shook hands with him before coming to Mass."

155

"Yes, Yes," he hurried me along. "Young Irish lads are always up for a good fight. That's how we protected ourselves from the heathen English. A few good bruises never hurt any one of them. Now get on with it. There're English sinners waiting."

"And, and," I stammered, "I overslept last Sunday and missed Mass."

Right there, he stopped me. "Missed Mass?" he exclaimed in raised tones. I could see immediately that I had sinned badly, and I was in big trouble.

"Our Irish Catholic heritage is so precious," he continued angrily. "If we start missing Mass on Sunday, why, we'll be no better than the English. Always remember that God created two chosen people. First there were the Jews. Then Jesus came, the Jews rejected him, and he was crucified. Then God chose the Irish! Every Irishman knows that salvation of the world is coming first through the Jews, and then through the Irish. God wants you to attend the Mass every Sunday, my son, even if you're sick, bruised up, dead drunk, or hung over. Every Sunday, your place is here in the church kneeling before God, celebrating the Mass. God wants you here, not because you are worthy to be here my son, but because he chose you and called you to be here."

I could see that the good father had his own ideas about things.

It was a hot summer Sunday. The blue desert skies were decorated with the usual high wispy cirrus and cooled by the usual gentle desert winds. After Mass, I rested, back in my barracks. Then I went for the noon meal. When it was over, I returned to my barracks, picked up a clean towel, switched into my swim trunks, and headed up to the Mojave

Wells base swimming pool, which was an open swimming pool, and perfectly maintained. There was no lifeguard. I began by opening the pool. Then I unlocked the pool equipment house that sat next to it, and turned on the circulation pumps. The equipment house was constructed entirely out of concrete blocks. Like the pool, it was surrounded by gravel. It had no windows, and was only 6 feet high, with a peaked roof.

As usual, when I arrived I found six or so young children in swim trunks waiting for me. Their parents lived in town. They would let them swim only if an adult were present. I opened the pool, recited the rules, and jumped into the warm water announcing that I was ready to play our favorite water game. It was a game that I had made up myself. I called it "The destroyer Haymman game". The idea was to teach each of the young children how to swim by making it a fun game for them. Those children who already knew how to swim would pretend to be German submarines, lurking out in the deep water, waiting to attack by splashing water in big columns. Those who were still learning would pretend to be British cargo ships trying to make it across the cold dark waters of the North Atlantic from America to England, really the shallow end of the pool, trying to make it across any way they could by swimming or learning to swim. I was the destroyer Haymman, who was trying desperately to protect the convoy by teaching them to swim better, and by splashing big columns of water, supposedly depth charges, to drive off the German submarines, who might attack under water. If the German submarines couldn't be driven off, the destroyer Haymman would be forced to cry 'UNCLE' and all of the British cargo ships would be forced to head for the safety of Iceland, also known as the side of the pool. The game also taught the children some geography. It was a fun game, and the children just loved playing it. Soon I had them all swimming like experts across the deep end. My friend Clark usually came as well, and we all played together.

There was one little girl I especially remember. She was only six years old or so. On this day she was sitting on the steps of the pool, laughing as happy as a little girl can laugh. She had just gotten used to holding her breath and ducking her head under water. I was bent over on the side of the pool next to her, laughing because the destroyer Haymman had just been forced to break off a convoy run in mid ocean. The little German submarines were getting too good. As she sat there laughing, she giggled, "Mr. Charlie Baker, you are so much fun, my other friends want to play with you."

"Well, you can bring your other friends with you when you come," I laughed in return. "Tell them to come in their swim suits, and I'll teach them to swim too. Tell them the destroyer Haymman has lots of cargo ships that have to be convoyed to England."

"But, they aren't able to swim," she responded.

"That's no problem," I laughed. "The destroyer Haymman can teach any human how to swim."

"I know, but their mother told them they can't come because they can never learn to swim," the little girl continued innocently.

Stunned, I stood there, waist deep in pool water for a few minutes, staring at the little girl. Mojave Wells was a very small town. I thought I had met all of the children. I remembered that this little girl lived in an ordinary house on the southeast edge of town. Only an ordinary short wire fence separated her back yard from the sagebrush and the nearby mountains beyond. I had seen a group of four white fluorescent lights float out of those mountains, cross the fence, and continue into the little girl's backyard, as I was walking back to my barracks a few nights before. It took me a few minutes before I could form my next words. Then I continued slowly, "But surely their mother knows that every human can learn to swim."

"Yes," the little girl answered. "Their mother knows that very well. She's a teacher."

"Do you play with your friends often?" I slowly asked.

"Yes," she responded. "On summer nights I leave my bedroom window open. Then after my mother puts me to bed, my friends come down from the mountain, and in through my window. Then they play with me. Their teacher always stays outside. Usually we play in my bedroom, but sometimes they take me outside and we play in my backyard."

"Doesn't your mother ever hear you playing, and come into your room to see if you're asleep?" I asked.

"No," the little girl replied. "My friends always wait until my mother is asleep."

"But your mother stays up quite late, doesn't she?" I continued. "I know your father works late into the night. Doesn't your mother stay up and wait for him?"

"Yes," she replied. "But that doesn't matter. My mother always goes to sleep just before my friends come. Usually my mother goes to sleep in the kitchen. Usually she goes to sleep sitting in one of the chairs at the kitchen table. But one night last week, she was standing in front of the sink, getting ready to do the dishes for almost an hour. When I went out to get a glass of water, she just stood there without moving. My mother wouldn't speak to me, or anything. The teacher told me not to worry. She said my mother was just asleep and that she would wake up and be just fine, as soon as my friends left. The teacher was right. As soon as my friends left, my mother woke up happy, and just went right on humming and washing the dishes."

I was too numb, confused, and cold to answer. I took a lap of the pool around the deep end to collect my thoughts. Then I returned to the side of the pool, and continued, "If your friends want to come to the pool with you, and just play on the other side of the fence, they can. That might be fun."

"OK," she laughed. "But they can't come in the daytime, Mr. Charlie. Could you come out and be the lifeguard tomorrow night after dark so me and my friends could come and play?"

I struggled for a long time before answering. "Ok. Just for you, I'll come out tomorrow evening at 6:30 and be the life guard until 9:00 p.m."

"But that's not late enough, Mr. Charlie," she responded. "My friends never come that early. Could you come out at midnight and be the lifeguard until 3:00 a.m.? We can play then."

Still struggling with my answers, I responded, "I can come out at 6:30 in the evening and stay until after midnight, but I will have to close the pool by 12:30 a.m. If you want me to walk you back to your house, I will, but then I have to go right back to my barracks and get my sleep. That will leave me with only 2 hours of sleep before I have to get up again and take the first weather report. But are you sure that your mother will let you stay up playing at the pool that late?"

"Don't worry. It'll be alright," the little girl replied. "My mother will go to sleep and the teacher will bring us over. She'll take us back, too."

I didn't quite believe that her mother would actually allow her to go out to play until 3:00 a.m., but her story intrigued me nevertheless. I went to the pool at 7:00 p.m. the following evening and swam and loitered until 12:30 a.m. It was a beautiful night with a nearly full moon. The little girl never showed up and neither did her friends. I slept for a time in one of the lounge chairs, and had a very unusual dream. I dreamt that some tall chalk white man walked over from the nearby town, and sat on the roof of the equipment building watching me for a time. After my dream ended, I woke up, closed the pool, and headed back to my barracks.

The next Sunday, a new priest celebrated the Mass. He began by informing us that the elderly priest had died in a car accident the previous Sunday, while commuting his territory. He led us in a prayer for the repose of the soul of the deceased priest.

Tumbleweeds

...But as I told you,
   you have seen me
      and still you do not believe.

...John 6:36

That summer in the '60's, passed quickly at Mojave Wells. The days were captivatingly beautiful, and innocent. I was the range weather observer. My orders instructed me to spend my duty hours out on the ranges, in my range weather shacks, day or night, rain or shine. The duty had been pleasant. The summer weather had been desert hot, with the usual gentle winds. I returned to base at Mojave Wells only for meals or when my duty hours were finished for the day. It was lonely duty, but those were my orders. Sometimes I wondered why no weather observer before me had ever fully obeyed those same orders. Sometimes I wondered what it was about the ranges that they had all found so terrifying. Sometimes I wondered why the weather observer whom I had relieved, had quietly deserted, rather than obey orders. In the end, it all meant nothing to me. Orders were orders.

I purchased a paint by number set from the small Mojave Wells BX and busied myself painting. Soon two paintings of fall mountain scenes adorned the walls of my weather shack. I'd done my best on them. Although I doubt that Van Gogh would have agreed with me, I felt they were quite beautiful. Displaying them for my friends to see, meant a great deal to me. I doubt that Rembrandt was ever prouder than I was as I carefully positioned them on hooks that I'd nailed into the walls of my weather shack. The paintings had been done on wood. They were quite sturdy and hung securely in the places where I positioned them. I never actually saw either of them move when the summer winds whispered through my weather shack. Yet, some mornings when I opened my shack, the two paintings would be hanging somewhat differently than when I had closed the shack the day before. One morning they had even been switched from one nail to the other.

The first few times it happened I thought it was just my mind playing tricks on me. Then for a few times, I supposed it was just the wind that had moved them. On this morning, however, the wind had been calm for the entire day and evening before. So it was with mixed emotions that I carefully re-positioned the paintings after opening up at 3:45 a.m., in preparation for the 4:30 a.m. run.

The two paintings had moved slightly during the night. I wasn't sure if I should blame the desert winds and just ignore the incident, or if I should feel pride because someone cared enough to study my art work, or if I should feel fear because the only reasonable explanation was that something unknown had entered my locked weather shack the night before just to study me and my paintings. That morning I spent more than a few minutes looking out into the darkness, alone with my thoughts and my emotions wondering what it was that had so terrified the weather observers before me. I decided that if something unknown was lurking out there, watching my every move from the pre-dawn darkness, it must appreciate beauty as I did. Why else would it care about my two paintings? I said a quick prayer. I asked God to continue to watch over and protect me from everything that might be hiding out there in the darkness. Then I decided I would live a longer, happier life if I just shrugged off the incident and chalked it up to the desert winds. What I didn't know about, I decided, wasn't going to hurt me.

Other things at Mojave Wells had captured my pride and emotions, too. One of them was a rock. It was a small granite rock colored with unique shades of gray. It fit easily into my right hand. It had several flat spots, and this made it quite useful. On windy days, I used it to hold my clipboard and paper forms in place as I was taking the balloon readings. For this reason, I stored it on the ground at the base of the metal post that held my theodolite. I could get to it easily, and it was always there when I needed it. I frequently left it lying outside, and seldom paid much attention to the exact details of where I'd left it. It was, after all, just a rock. These summer days had been so beautiful and innocent, that I had never felt any alarm when some mornings the rock seemed to have been moved when it was lying out on the ground out of my sight.

I remember well this Friday morning. The ranges weren't being used and everything was unusually peaceful. After re-positioning my two paintings, taking the morning balloon run, driving in for breakfast, and making the long drive back out to Range Three, I found myself sitting quietly in my weather shack, reading another interesting history book, this time on the history of ancient Greece. At the time, I was reading the chapter on the experiences of the ancient Greek warrior, Xenophon, and the 10,000 Greek soldiers in his command. He was an ancient Greek warrior who had saved the lives of the 10,000 men under his command because he could see danger even in the wind.

I had both the front and side doors open, and my weather shack was filled with cool, gentle breezes. It was still another two hours, or so, before I was scheduled to take the noon balloon run. Without warning, my phone began ringing intensely. The ringing surprised me because it was unusually loud and strong. Usually the connections to my phone weren't that good. The timing between the rings was also unusually short. After noticing these facts, I picked up the receiver and answered, "Range Three weather shack. Charlie here."

To my mild surprise, there wasn't anyone on the other end. After realizing that I was listening to an unusually faint dial tone, I hung up the phone.

A few minutes passed. Again my phone rang. This time, though, the rings were not as loud and were spaced further apart so that the ringing phone sounded almost the way it usually did. Again, after noting these facts, I answered the phone, "Range Three weather station. Charlie speaking."

Once again, no one was on the other end. After listening for a minute or so to the faint sound of the dial tone, I decided to just hang up the phone and go on with my history book.

A few more minutes passed. Still again my phone rang. This time, though, the rings were at the perfect level of loudness and were spaced perfectly apart, so that the ringing phone sounded exactly the way it usually did. Again, after noting these facts, I answered the phone, "Range three weather station. Charlie speaking."

Once again, no one was on the other end. After listening for a minute or so to the faint sound of the dial tone, once again I decided to just hang up the phone and go on with my history book.

As I was reading, a curious thought forced its way into my consciousness. I wondered if someone was just testing their electronic equipment by ringing my phone until they had their instruments set correctly. But then, I thought, if that were the case, how would they know when their instruments were set correctly?

I wondered for a few minutes. Then, for some unknown reason, my mind stumbled across a curious question. I no longer felt alone, and I didn't feel comfortable reading anymore. The constant gentle wind made me feel uneasy. I began to feel much like Xenophon. I got up from my chair and stepped out my side door for a quick look around.

Outside, it was a beautiful summer morning and everything seemed perfectly normal. I returned inside and continued reading my history book. After reading on for a few more minutes, though, I found myself still wondering why my phone had rung. Was it really a wrong number, I wondered, or had someone intentionally meant to disturb me from my reading? After all, the differences between the first series of rings, the second, and then the third didn't seem accidental. I put my book down and decided to go outside for a better look around.

Outside, in the desert sunshine, everything still appeared to be normal. I found myself singing some happy songs and taking a short walk around the Range Three buildings. Now and then I would happily shout, "Hello," out over the apparently empty desert. Then I'd listen carefully to see if any echoes came back from the distant mountains. To my surprise, on at least two tries, I was certain that I'd heard echoes, even though the shape and distance of the mountains and the gentle winds made that physically impossible.

The winds that filled the blue dome of the sky supported several large white fleecy clouds. Their shadows danced playfully over the mountains and over the sagebrush covered valleys. Every now and then, the radio would play one of my favorite songs, and the wind would blow some dry sagebrush and tumbleweeds between the buildings. I reached out and caught a couple of them as they bounced gently past me. Then I threw them high into the air so that the wind could blow them on through the open spaces in the buildings and on out into the desert beyond. I decided that I was playing "catch the wind." After I had caught several tumbleweeds and thrown them up over my head to see if they would miss the buildings as they drifted on out into the desert, something curious happened. I noticed that all of the tumbleweeds that were coming toward me, were coming from the same section of the desert down to the southeast. They were drifting with the wind, drifting towards me from the southeast, from the direction of Range Two. At first this seemed perfectly reasonable. The gentle wind was coming from that direction, and the tumbleweeds were obviously drifting with the wind. After watching them for only a few minutes, however, I become mildly alarmed. I felt as though I were seeing a certain danger, hidden in wind. The tumbleweeds were coming from the place where the desert changed elevation. The tumbleweeds would first appear by drifting up over the rise, as though some unseen person was tossing them up into the air, in almost playful fashion as I had been. Then, as the wind blew them, they would gently roll or bounce towards me, sometimes making it to me, sometimes missing me by wide marks.

I began to worry that my mind might be playing tricks on me. It began to seem as though all of the tumbleweeds which the wind was blowing around were coming from the same little stretch of desert, the stretch which lay perfectly downwind of me. I counted for a few minutes and mentally computed the statistics that seemed to confirm my suspicions. When I tried to re-compute the numbers, it suddenly seemed like tumbleweeds were appearing everywhere out along the desert rise except from the place where they had appeared before. I became convinced that a large group of people, or children, were hiding down behind that rise in the desert and playing catch with me by intentionally releasing tumbleweeds into the wind for me to catch.

I studied the drifting tumbleweeds some more. They were coming from too many places for it to be just one person playing with me. I spent a few minutes counting tumbleweeds. I decided that if the tumbleweeds were being released by a group of children, the rise in the desert would have to be hiding at least twelve or thirteen of them. Then, as I watched and studied some more, an even more curious thing happened. Even though the wind continued to blow gently, the same as it had before, the tumbleweeds suddenly and completely stopped coming.

I was stunned. The silence and emptiness that engulfed me that morning, left a permanent imprint on my consciousness.

As I stood there, I wondered if I should get in my truck and drive out to that rise in the desert. It would let me actually see what was hiding below it. Then, as I thought about it for a few minutes, I found myself becoming afraid to do so. I began to feel that it would be dangerous for me to know very much about the wind and the way it blew from down there. I found myself becoming terrified of the distant ridge and of the winds. My fears were becoming too real and were being carried to me on the winds.

I decided that I would be safe enough if I stayed where I was as long as I didn't make the mistake of going down to see close up what lay beyond that distant rise in the desert.

I tried to get an echo from the distant mountains, as I was certain I had done before, but no matter how many times I shouted, "Hello," out to the mountains, absolutely nothing came back. In frustration with the emptiness of the ranges and the gentle desert winds, I paced back and forth several times, wondering what to make of it all. Having nothing else to do, I decided to try throwing rocks out into the empty, sunlit stillness. Choosing five smooth pebbles from the desert floor, I first tried throwing them, one by one, out into the desert. At first nothing happened. Then, on the fifth rock, I scared some birds that were resting out under a distant sage plant. Feeling as though I'd sinned, I decided, instead, to just throw the rocks at the large wooden billboards that stood on the northeast corner of the building area. Pebble after pebble, rock after rock, I bounced off the billboards. Soon I was convinced that I could easily hit any board on any of the billboards, even those highest up and furthest away. Then, without thinking, I picked up my favorite rock. Getting a good grip on it, I threw it as hard as I could, up against the upper right corner of the most distant billboard. It hit the wooden support post straight on, and bounced out into the distant sagebrush. Realizing suddenly that my favorite rock would now be lost out in the desert, I began reproaching myself. I spent the next half hour searching through the sagebrush and the desert sand looking for my favorite rock. It didn't surprise me. The rock was simply lost forever, hidden out in the desert beyond recovery.

Upset with myself and still not sure what to make of the situation, I reluctantly decided to return to my history book.

The time passed slowly until noon approached. Putting my book aside in the middle of a paragraph, I prepared my weather balloon, and began taking the noon run on schedule. Naturally, I wished to hurry through the run, so I could close my shack and make it into base in time to eat the noon meal. I quickly released my weather balloon and began taking the timed readings, as usual. The wind tore at my paper report form, and I was soon very annoyed with myself for having thrown away my favorite rock. It had been so useful. I found myself wishing that some friendly person would find it and return it to me. Then I had to laugh at myself. Since I had never told anyone about my favorite rock, how would anyone know it was 'my' rock, even if they were ever to find it out in the desert? Then my mind stumbled across the simple fact that although it was just a perfectly ordinary rock, unique only to me, someone who had seen me with the rock might know it was mine if they ever found it. Only they would know that I would be happy if they were ever to return it to me. As I stood there cursing the wind and laughing at myself, I decided that it would take a person far more intelligent than I just to identify which rock had been mine in the first place, let alone find it out in the desert and return it to me.

As I was resting my eyes between readings, wishing I still had my favorite rock, I returned to studying the sagebrush down to the southeast, down where the desert changed elevation. To my surprise, one tumbleweed bounced playfully up over the rise and drifted in the wind, bouncing up and down over the desert toward me. It happened that the wind blew the tumbleweed in a predictable fashion until the tumbleweed bounced straight up to me. As my mind struggled with this, I pulled the tumbleweed off my boots and legs, and tossed it aside. In the short time it took for the wind to blow it beyond my reach, another second tumbleweed bounced playfully up and over the rise, obviously coming from the same place. I took another reading as this one, too, was blown directly up to me, scraping up against my boots and fatigues. I tossed this one, too, aside. Then, while my mind still struggled to make sense of these events, still a third tumbleweed bounced playfully up and over the distant rise. Like the first two, the wind gently blew and bounced this one directly towards me. I took my last balloon reading, and as the tumbleweed gently bounced towards me, I closed up my theodolite. This tumbleweed, too, was blown directly up to me. I picked up my clipboard, pencils, and data sheets, and tossed this one too, aside. Then, I stood there for a minute or so, waiting for another tumbleweed, but no more appeared.

With my hungry stomach reminding me of the time, I returned to my shack, completed my calculations, and phoned them in to Desert Center. I checked the time. I had about ten minutes to spare, so I decided I would quickly finish reading the paragraph in my history book. Then I would head to the chow hall. I had just sat down at my desk and opened my book when my phone rang. I let it ring a few times before answering it. The ring was the very same tone, loudness, and timing as it normally was. I was no longer fooled. I picked up the phone and answered, "Range

Three weather station, Charlie speaking." As I looked out through my front and side doors, I could see a single tumbleweed bounce playfully up over that distant rise in the desert. The wind blew it, gently bouncing it over the desert, until it directly struck the metal pole that supported my now locked theodolite. Through the side door I could see another tumbleweed bouncing up over that distant desert rise, coming from the same place as the first one had. In the phone, all I could hear was the faint sound of the dial tone, much fainter than normal. Understanding at last what was happening, I spoke pleasantly into the phone. I said truthfully, "I don't know who you are, but I'm sorry. I can't play with you right now. I am very hungry. I have to drive in to the chow hall and eat the noon meal. But if you wish to play with the tumbleweeds out here while I'm gone, you may. I won't be back until almost two o'clock. This place will be deserted for the next hour and a half." Then I paused and listened for a few seconds. Looking out the side door, I could see first one, then two, then three, and four, then more, tumbleweeds bounce playfully up over the distant rise in the desert. All of them were apparently aimed for the metal post that held my theodolite.

Chuckling to myself, I hung up the phone, closed and locked the doors to my weather shack. I walked directly to my truck and headed in to base. "It must be a bunch of kids," I laughed to myself, "judging by the way they've organized this game of 'catch the wind'."

I took my time eating the noon meal. Then I took a quick nap in the barracks. I felt I could use the rest. I finally arrived back at my Range Three weather shack at 1:50p.m. I needed to take just one more balloon measurement for the day. The tumbleweeds weren't blowing around anymore even though the winds hadn't changed. I decided it must have been a large group of children and that they must have had lots of fun. Before I could unlock my theodolite, I first had to clear more than 13 tumbleweeds, all stuck together, away from the metal pole. Like children everywhere, I guess, they were proud of their aim. Although I had no idea what kind of children would be hiding 22 miles out in the desert on a nice day like today, I could hardly have been angry with them. Under the first tumbleweed, lying in the position where I usually stored it, they had placed my favorite rock, the one I had previously lost by foolishly throwing it out into the desert. It took months for me to get over my amazement.

Unlocking and entering my weather shack that beautiful afternoon, I received another jolt. One of my two paintings was missing from the inside wall of my weather shack. I was so shocked that I could hardly comprehend what had happened. The one that was missing was my least favorite of the two. Several months would pass before I would again, on one cold winter morning, open my weather shack and again see the missing painting, looking just as it had, without a mark on it, hanging there once again on the same hook that had held it on that summer day so many months before. I hardly needed more proof that the children whom I had played with on that beautiful summer day were real. They obviously appreciated a beautiful picture when they saw one.

As I stood there looking out over the desert on that beautiful summer day, I thought I glimpsed something playing in the heat waves off to the east. The heat waves came up off the desert like those off a furnace. The heat waves blended the images of the sagebrush, the sunshine, and the desert sands in with the images of distant children with chalk white skin, wide blue eyes, and blonde hair. The images all blended together in the heat waves and in the hot bright sunlight until all I could see were chalk white patches that seemed to float and play out there in the heat. There were almost 20 such images drifting out along the base of the eastern mountains. One of the images seemed to be proudly carrying my painting. Yes, like Xenophon, I felt that I had gotten glimpses of things out there in the wind.

Millennial Hospitality

Those living far away fear your wonders;
where morning dawns and evening fades…

Psalm 65:8

At night, under a midsummer moon, the desert valley
stretching north from Mojave Wells was a valley of restful
stunning beauty. In the evening, cool musical breezes swept
gently along more than one hundred miles of sagebrush
meadows. Long, thin, and cathedral, the north-south valley
connected smoothly at its southern end with another "L"
shaped valley, which, in turn arced gently towards the
southeast, flowing into a broad "Y" shaped valley, ending at
last in the green meadows of the Palm Meadows golf
courses. Meadows to meadows, a single gentle breeze could
drift over more than 250 miles of desert, and under more
than 250 miles of starlight. I had given these beautiful
meadows a name. I named them, "The Meadows of
Arcturus".

Looking at my clock as I lay quietly in my bunk, I could
see it was going on 2:20 a.m. Sleeping in the barracks at
Mojave Wells had taught me to be very quiet as I got up. It
also taught me to enjoy shaving, brushing my teeth, and
getting dressed in near total darkness. I shared the barracks
with 6 other airmen. My duty hours started at 4:00 a.m., but
theirs didn't start until 8:00 a.m. To wake any one of them
by accident would surely get my day started off on the
wrong foot. Thus, almost without thinking, I quietly arose

from my bunk and put on my uniform. Then, having showered the night before, I shaved, brushed my teeth, collected my flashlight, and quietly slipped out the barracks by the back door.

Outside, I found a quiet, beautifully awakening experience. The desert seemed to shimmer under a full moon and countless stars. The moon was so bright there wasn't any reason for me to use my flashlight. Silent and happy in this cathedral-like world, walking in the shadows under the trees, marching in the darkness next to the barracks, or following along in the gray places along the fences, I quickly traveled the four short blocks to the motor pool, reaching at last, my USAF pickup truck.

I was quite proud of myself, really. I had never once turned on any light, and I had been so quiet through it all, that had anyone inside or outside the barracks been awake and watching, no one could ever have known that I was afoot. But, then really, who would care?

Up above me, stretched the beautiful, quiet, starlit sky. My gaze fell naturally upon the constellation Bootes and its brightest star named Arcturus, *The Watcher* by the ancient Greeks. Fourth brightest star in the nighttime sky, it was so beautiful and, since it is only 36 light years from earth, so near. On this evening, I found its light to be peaceful, silent, and relaxing. I remembered reading, somewhere, that the men of ancient Greece, back before the year 1000 B.C., believed that tall white gods had come to earth from the star Arcturus, and on warm summer nights when the men of Greece were out camping, these tall white gods would come and watch them from a short distance.

I had gotten up an hour early because today was a special day. Today, the major, down at Desert Center AFB, would be deciding if I was ready for promotion to the next enlisted rank, the coveted rank of airman first class. Today, I decided, I would really impress my commanding officer. I intended to file my weather report early. First, I would drive the 25 miles out into the desert to range three, to my weather shack, as I did every weekday morning. But, today, when I released the helium filled weather balloon and measured the winds, as I did every weekday morning, it would be special. Today, I would use the special weather balloon that I had carefully hand picked the day before, inflate it with extra care, and track the balloon for at least an extra 30 minutes. This would allow me to report the wind speed and direction for altitudes far higher than any Mojave Wells weather observer had ever done before me. Surely, I thought, the major would be impressed. He would promote me for sure.

I could hardly have been happier, this beautiful moonlit night, as I strode towards my waiting weather truck. Just yesterday afternoon, the mechanics at the motor pool had given it an oil change, lube job, and a general tune-up. Carrying a small V8 engine that was in near perfect condition, it sat waiting to feel my foot on its gas pedal. It didn't make the slightest bit of difference to me at the time, but the truck, like me, was hidden out of sight, and in the shadows. Facing the open road, as it was, I started it up without so much as touching the brakes - and therefore without ever once lighting the brake lights.

As soon as the engine was running, a curious thought crossed my mind. The night was so beautiful and the moonlight was so bright, was it really necessary to turn on the headlights? The engine was very quiet and the truck had no radio. This meant that so far, I couldn't possibly have awakened anyone. Turning on the headlights might change all that. So, on this beautiful moonlit night, I decided to begin driving out towards the gunnery ranges with all of my lights still off.

It was quite easy, really, driving without headlights. I rolled down the window, thought beautiful thoughts, and brought my speed up to 20 mph as I headed the truck down the narrow paved road that headed out towards range three.

The road was sunken a little, and concealed by sagebrush on both sides. Keeping in the shadows on my side of the road, it was a simple matter to see where I was going. I had fallen in love with the beauty of the desert that evening. It seemed like I would destroy that beauty if I were to turn on my headlights. Since I didn't need the headlights, I decided to leave them off for the entire drive. So it happened that, had anyone been watching, they would have had no way of knowing that I was coming. They couldn't have known that I was coming from so far, so quiet, so unseen, and speeding up to 35 miles per hour, coming up on them so fast.

In the few weeks I had been at Mojave Wells, I had learned the road out to range three by heart. As I drove north, up the straight valley, I noticed how clear the night air was. The mountains at the northern end of the valley, some 100 miles distant, stood out clearly in the night sky. After traveling several miles, the turn off to range one slid by on my right. The intersection with the range one gravel road created a window in the sagebrush wall on my right. Gazing out through that window, down the "L" shaped valley towards the southeast, my eyes focused in on the gate, the control tower, the buildings, and the weather shack for range one, located down in another beautiful meadow of sagebrush some 25 miles distant.

Up ahead on the right, another window opened in the sagebrush wall. Through it I could see the control tower, the weather shack, and the buildings of range two. They were difficult to pick out, located as they were, at the base of the distant mountains, on the far slope of the "L" shaped valley, some 30 miles distant. They were always so beautiful and so peaceful in the distance. I wondered why the weather observer I had replaced, Sullivan, had always refused to go over there.

I let my eyes wander slowly back down along the distant range two road following it as it rose up the far slope of that distant valley. I located the place out in that distant sagebrush meadow where the range two road branched off from the range one road, out where Sullivan had stopped the truck suddenly, and turned around, trembling in fear. It was a place I had frequently wondered about. It seemed so peaceful and deserted. Yet, when I looked down there on this peaceful evening, I noticed there, almost hidden in the sagebrush in the distance, in the empty vastness of the desert, just barely visible, were two small, soft white fluorescent lights.

I ignored the lights and drove on through the aisles of this beautiful desert cathedral. The lights were hidden from my view as soon as I passed beyond the window area. They were far too dim to be actual fluorescent lights, and they were very small. At first, I thought they might be large white plastic bags reflecting the moonlight. Then I thought they might be several white fluorescent tubes piled together, or maybe some white paint or pieces of paper. Since I was a weather observer, I had studied the Mojave Wells desert

179

terrain in great detail. I estimated the distance down the valley to the lights to be about 22 miles. Who would drive so far from base I wondered, just to throw away light bulbs?

The sagebrush continued on my right for the next several miles. Then I passed through the gate to range three. I had intentionally left it open the day before, so I just drove on. Range three was fenced. A deep antitank ditch ran along the outside of the fence. The ditch, the fence, the desert, and the federal government had all combined to guarantee that, except for me, this beautiful valley was totally and completely empty of people.

Up ahead, the road got higher, and the sagebrush wall on my right thinned. Curious, now, I allowed my gaze to return again to my right, down the valley in the distance, back down towards the branch in the range one road. The viewing conditions were even better from this angle. Still, it took a while for the results to work their way into my brain. It took a few minutes, but it finally dawned on me - the soft white fluorescent lights in the distance, had moved! Now they were only 18 miles away. In just a few minutes, they had moved at least four miles to the north of where they had been. They were now four miles north of the branch in the range one road.

As I drove on, I didn't know what to think. Perhaps, I thought, the white lights were sheets of thin plastic and were drifting in the wind. Perhaps, I thought, they had blown up from Palm Meadows. Then, as I drove on, I studied the sagebrush. It took only a glance to see that on this calm evening, there simply wasn't any wind in which to drift.

Up ahead, the buildings of range three appeared in the distance. Arranged to form a large open square, they had been built on a raised open stretch of desert that commanded a good view of the valley. Along with the usual control tower, the range lounge, a couple of supply sheds, the generator shack, and the weather shack, the buildings also included several large wooden billboards. All of the ranges had them. Some 40 feet high and angled slightly, the billboards allowed the range crew to signal the airplanes whenever they were working on the targets and the electrical generators were not running.

The first building located along the incoming paved road was the building that housed the two large diesel electric generators. Out of force of habit, I down shifted my pickup. The truck slowed, without need of the breaks, rolling ever more slowly, until my dark blue truck without headlights, rolled to a stop in the shadows of the generator building. I immediately turned off the motor and set the emergency break. Then I sat quietly in the truck, enjoying the quiet desolate beauty of the moonlit desert in front of me. I really hadn't noticed, but since the building was east of the road, and I was parked in its shadows, if anyone were watching, there really wasn't any way they could have known that I was there.

As I sat there, enjoying the beauty of the desert for a few more minutes, I wondered about starting the generators. The moonlight was so bright I really didn't need the generators. My weather shack had two north-south doors and an extra large door on the east. I didn't need the light bulb turned on. I had my flashlight, if I needed extra light.

In any event, I didn't need to start the diesel generators right now, I decided. I could continue to enjoy the beauty of this desert evening, the diesel motors were so noisy. I could start them later if I needed to.

Quietly, I got out of my truck, and just as quietly I closed the truck door. I liked my truck, and I was always very careful with it, so when I closed my truck door, I was very quiet. I walked quietly and slowly up to the corner of the generator shed. Then I turned right and followed along next to the side the storage buildings, staying generally in the shadows, until I arrived at the building on the end, my weather shack. Across the square several hundred feet distant, was the control tower and the range three lounge. On the right stood the billboards, some garbage cans, and in the center of it all was the altar of my cathedral, a steel post on which was bolted the telescope that I used to track my weather balloons. This telescope, this theodolite, had a clear view of the mountains, the desert, and the sky, in every direction. With its metal cover in place, from a distance, it looked much the same as when the cover was off, and I was taking balloon readings using it.

With a practiced hand, leaving my flashlight off, I unlocked the front door of my weather shack and quietly slipped inside, closing the door behind me. Once inside, I slowly opened the doublewide side door on the east. This allowed enough moonlight into my shack so that inflating the helium weather balloon was a simple matter. Then, tucking my clipboard and reporting form under my arm, I backed outside with my weather balloon, carried it around to the other side of the weather shack to the release point, and released it into the night sky. The balloon carried a small, expendable, battery powered light that I had attached to it. To protect my night vision, I kept the light completely concealed before I launched the balloon. Once launched, this light blended in with the stars so perfectly that on some mornings I lost the balloon in among the star fields. So, as I unlocked the theodolite more than one hour early, and began tracking the balloon, it happened that I still hadn't done anything that would have betrayed my presence to a person watching from a short distance.

The balloon readings had to be taken precisely one minute apart. To do this, I had to periodically read my watch. For this I used my flashlight in a special manner. I now had my night vision, so I needed only a tiny quantity of light from my flashlight. To get this light, I would press the lens of my flashlight up against my left arm. A tiny quantity of light would escape through the red plastic lens holder. This was just enough to allow me to read my watch. At first, I wasn't thinking much about it, but it happened that for the first several minutes, as I was reading my watch, my body was concealing this tiny bit of light from the view of anyone north, east, south, or west of my theodolite. It didn't seem important at the time.

Looking through the theodolite was tiring on my eyes. In between readings I would take my eyes away from the eyepiece, and gaze around at the valley. I loved to watch the stars and dream of home. It was so relaxing. I didn't move around at all. Rather, I was standing, leaning peacefully up against the metal stand that held the theodolite. I suppose, I blended in with the theodolite itself. Something down to the southeast caught my gaze. Ranges one and two were down towards the southeast. A rise in the elevation of the desert partly obstructed my view of the beautiful sagebrush covered meadows that lay between me, and the two distant ranges.

At first, I wasn't sure just what I had seen. It looked like the sagebrush dotted horizon in the distance had moved. At first, I didn't pay much attention and went back to taking my readings. Then, after a couple of minutes, I had some free time and my gaze returned to the southeast desert horizon. Way down there, probably seven miles distant, was a large soft fluorescent white patch of something, drifting slowly and silently towards me. When I looked at it through the theodolite, at 75 power magnification, it appeared to have a tall front part and a shorter part behind it. Its shape was very filmy and indistinct, even more than this great distance would imply, but sometimes it seemed to have the shape of a large horse with a tail, floating gently in the wind.

It took a while for the magnitude of this observation to register. The weather balloon that I had released was still perfectly above me. There simply wasn't any wind.

Memories of Dwight's stories started to filter into my mind. I remembered how serious he had been when he swore to me that he'd seen a large, white, fluorescent horse with extra long, radioactive hair roaming about on range four, north of where I was standing. I remembered how he swore that the light looked like the soft light from the radioactive dial of his watch, which glowed in the dark. I remembered how he swore that he'd seen it drifting, even though there was no wind. I continued to watch the distant white patch as it closed the distance between where it drifted and where I waited. It was drifting straight towards me. Now it was six miles away, closing to five and half. Finally, only five miles of sagebrush separated it from me.

My curiosity was starting to awaken. I took some more balloon readings with my theodolite. In between my readings, I continued to watch the distant white patch with my bare eyes as it slowly and silently continued to drift towards me. The distance kept closing, steadily, relentlessly.

At two and a half miles, I could see that the single, large white patch, was actually two patches. The two patches were drifting one behind the other, silently, slowly, steadily towards me. Now, they looked like a very tall prospector being followed by his burro.

The front patch was maybe six or six and a half feet tall. The second patch was noticeably shorter. I made it out to be maybe four and a half, or five feet tall. The distance continued closing.

There was a little used gravel road that connected range three with ranges one and two. The road meandered down across the desert to the southeast, like another aisle in the cathedral, until it connected up with the range two road. Suddenly, I realized that the two soft white fluorescent patches weren't drifting over the sagebrush. The sagebrush in most places was very thick. The sagebrush stood more than four feet tall, and in effect, formed a wall along both sides of the old gravel road. The white patches were drifting along this old gravel road. Therefore, they were drifting in a lane in between the sagebrush plants.

My mind suddenly realized that this old road formed a lane through the sagebrush that continued unbroken, right up to the open square of buildings where I stood. I realized that these two white fluorescent patches would soon be drifting right up to me, close enough for me to reach out and touch them. Not knowing what they were, I began to feel a little nervous.

I took another balloon reading. The distance to the white patches kept closing. I decided to rotate the theodolite and focus it in on the white patches, now less than a mile distant. Through the theodolite, using a magnification of 75, I could see the tall one in front. Tall and thin and very indistinct, it appeared to have a large round head, two arms, shoulders, a body, two legs, and feet. It seemed to be standing and balancing itself on some type of platform that floated 18 inches above the gravel road. On its otherwise featureless face could be seen two large wide eye slits. It appeared to be wearing a suit of some kind with a large white fluorescent helmet. The suit it wore gave off the soft, white, fluorescent light, and its body blotted out the stars behind it. The light it gave off was so soft and dim, that it illuminated the gravel road and the sagebrush for only a few feet next to the road. The white patch behind it looked the same way, only smaller.

There was a rise out there where the desert changed elevation. The drifting patches continued towards me, turning away momentarily, now, to float up the road through the gate into the skip bomb area that adjoined the building area, then turning back towards me as they continued their slow, silent, relentless approach. I didn't know what to do or what to make of it.

I needed some kind of proof that what I was seeing was real. After thinking about things for a minute, I decided to test my eyesight. I focused my theodolite on a plant next to the road in front of the relentlessly advancing white fluorescent patches. I chose a place that was still in deep darkness, and I was absolutely certain that it was a place I had never looked with my theodolite, or seen in person. I turned my weather sheet over to the clean backside. I quickly recorded the theodolite readings of this dark place under the plants, so that I could locate it again in the daytime. I reasoned that if my mind were playing tricks on me, I wouldn't be able to produce an accurate picture of what was in this dark place. After all, I reasoned that I couldn't accurately draw a picture of a real life scene that I had never actually seen.

Without moving my theodolite, I waited for the white fluorescent creatures to reach that place in the gravel road. As they approached it, the light given off from their suits illuminated the sagebrush in a way that moonlight and sunlight never could. As they passed by that place in the road, I quickly sketched the view through my theodolite on the back of my weather form. It was a sketch of a gnarled sagebrush plant, the plants around it, the dirt and rocks underneath it, and the tracks in the dirt road out in front of it. As the white fluorescent creatures passed by, I used my theodolite to measure that height above the gravel road. No portion of their feet or equipment touched the ground, or raised any dust as they passed. My computations showed that exactly 7 inches separated the bottom of their equipment and the top of the gravel rocks on the road, and also showed that the top of the tallest creature was exactly 6 feet 9 inches above the ground, and the top of the second creature came exactly at the shoulder of the tallest creature, 5 feet 7 inches above the ground.

As I stood there by my theodolite, pondering this startling situation that was rapidly enveloping me, I realized that I needed to check my watch to see if it was time for another balloon reading. As I stood there, I was standing upright, leaning against the steel theodolite stand, facing the oncoming white patches.

I had become afraid to turn my back in that direction, and I didn't know what to do next. My left arm, with my watch on it, was out stretched. I wanted a little light so I could see the dial on my watch as the creatures now closed to less than an eighth of a mile. As usual, I had turned my watch around so that the dial lay against the inside of my left wrist. As usual, I pressed the lens of my flashlight up against the inside of my lower left arm, as the creatures now closed to less than 200 yards. I turned my flashlight on momentarily, and turned away to read my watch. Then I turned my flashlight off. The light had been on for no more than one or two seconds. Only a tiny fraction of light from the flashlight had escaped. Only the tinniest fraction of that tiny fraction could have traveled any distance, out over the sagebrush, down towards the southeast. Yet, when I returned to looking at the soft white fluorescent patches that had spent the last 90 minutes drifting relentlessly towards me, my mind went numb with shock. The two white patches were no longer drifting towards me. In a sudden, jerky, and uncoordinated fashion, the two white fluorescent patches retreated swiftly, a mile back down the gravel road to the place where the desert changed elevation. There, by bending down, they concealed themselves from my view.

I didn't have the faintest idea what to make of it all. The two white patches were now out of sight, apparently hiding in the distance, down in the sagebrush. Since I had my pickup truck, I toyed with the idea of driving down there to see these things close up. I still supposed these patches were large pieces of plastic, reflecting the moonlight. Such pieces of plastic would be dangerous to the low flying planes which use the gunnery ranges, so I supposed that I would drive over there, grab hold of the white patches, and throw them into the back of my pickup truck. Then I would bring them up to the two waiting garbage cans that sat over by the billboards. There, I supposed, I would tear them into pieces, and stuff them into the garbage cans. After thinking these thoughts, my mind seemed to become filled with a terrible fear of the garbage cans. Yet, it was an unusually simple matter for me to wipe this fear from my mind.

Using my theodolite and the 75 power lens, I focused in on the patch of sagebrush where I had last seen the tall white patch disappear. Occasionally, I could see the top of its head, down to just below its eyes. The top of its head would appear momentarily above the sagebrush, and it appeared to be looking at me. Then it would disappear. Sometimes it seemed as though a large white cat was looking at me over the sagebrush. After both patches had done this three or four times, they ducked down permanently and remained totally hidden.

I was numb with shock. I had almost given up believing my eyes. I returned the theodolite to tracking the balloon. In order to rest my eyes and to regain confidence in my vision, I began to look around the rest of the valley. A paved road went from the control tower area, straight east past the billboards, down past the strafing targets, down to an ammunition storage bunker located on the side of the mountain to the east. I knew the bunker was one and a quarter miles distant. As I gazed over there, more to rest my eyes than anything else, suddenly I saw a third patch of soft white fluorescent light drifting slowly northeast up out of the valley and towards the ammunition bunker. As it reached the higher ground, the fluorescent haze surrounding it suddenly cleared, and revealed a tall thin man dressed in a chalk white aluminum jumpsuit, with a simple open helmet. He continued walking, taking unusually high steps, bringing his knees almost up to his waist. He reached the ammunition bunker in only a few steps. He stopped there, and waited behind it.

Then I let my gaze run north from there, up along the foothills of the mountains to a low gently sloping ridge overlooking a small deep, narrow valley another mile or so away. To my total surprise, two more soft white fluorescent patches were drifting south in hurried and intent fashion along the mountains to join up with the third white humanoid man, all in total silence.

I checked the rest of the valley. I became certain that my eyes were working perfectly. Nowhere else in the valley were there any white patches to be seen. My mind now started having thoughts that I wasn't sure were my own. These thoughts were fragmented and indistinct. It reminded me of trying to listen to a radio where the transmitter was almost out of range. I began thinking, "The lights scare you. There is nothing there. Stand calmly. Watch the balloon."

It all seemed like good advice. The sudden appearance of the white patches was making me very nervous, so, I decided to not look around anymore for a while and to go back to tracking my balloon. At least it would help me calm down, I thought. I didn't need any more readings, but for a moment, I suddenly seemed to be afraid of everything, as suddenly as a light switch being flipped. I was afraid to stop tracking my balloon. I was afraid to walk to the generator shed. I was afraid to start the generator. I was afraid to start my truck and drive into town. I was afraid to walk to my weather shack. For a moment, I was really in a quagmire of fear.

Then, after a few moments of fear, I shrugged it off, and was stunned and surprised at how easily the fear disappeared. Real feelings of fear release adrenaline into the blood stream. Real feelings of fear can't possibly go away that fast, I reasoned because it takes several minutes for the blood to clean itself of the adrenaline. I wondered how could I possibly feel that much fear so quickly, and, yet, not have any adrenaline in my blood stream?

I took some more readings and tried to calm down. I thought about my predicament. I decided that, since I didn't need any more balloon data, I would stop tracking the balloon, and concentrate on resolving the problem of the white patches. I returned my gaze to the southeast. There was nothing to be seen. Off to the east, by the distant ammunition bunker, stood the two white fluorescent patches that had drifted down along the foothills. The third white patch couldn't be seen. I stood by my theodolite for several minutes, gazing down towards the southeast. Still nothing could be seen. I became convinced that those two white patches were no longer there. "They must have moved," I thought, "but where to?" They obviously couldn't move over or through the sagebrush. If they could, none of this would be happening. They were obviously trapped by the sagebrush.

Then I remembered that the old gravel road had another branch. This branch formed another aisle through the cathedral. It led from the area where the white patches where apparently hiding, straight over to the ditch along side the paved road that I used when I drove out to this range every morning. Although the two roads didn't converge, the aisles they created in the cathedral did.

As I stood there, it dawned on me that my weather shack and the buildings in front of me blocked my view of this cross lane. I decided to move silently directly east to the cable fence that defined the perimeter of the skip bomb

191

area. This would give me a view of this cross lane through the sagebrush. As I did so, there came into my view, one of the most stunning sights I have ever seen. There, down along the fence, were the two soft white fluorescent patches. Both were standing as tall as possible, floating about 18 inches above the desert, and drifting towards me perhaps as fast as ten miles per hour. The top of the tall one in front, may possibly have reached as much as eight feet off the desert. As soon as I saw them, they both stooped over, and turned towards the paved road, and again disappeared out of sight behind the buildings. They moved so that my weather shack, the storage sheds, and the generator shack, again blocked my view.

I hardly dared to think about what had just happened. My brain just didn't want to accept what was so obviously true. Plastic bags and weather balloons don't think and, therefore, don't hide. Only very intelligent creatures would have realized, as they were drifting towards me, that the weather shack was blocking my view. Only a creature with eyesight as good as a cat's would have been able to react to the tiny amount of light which my flashlight had produced earlier when I read my watch.

Then there was another simple fact. All this time, since the one time I had turned on my flashlight, now, some thirty minutes ago, I had been standing there in total silence, with no lights whatever turned on. All that time, whatever it was had stayed passionately hidden. Ghosts don't need to stay hidden. Whatever it was, no matter how filmy or wispy it looked, it had to be a flesh and blood animal, and it had to be terrified of me. Terrified intelligent animals are dangerous animals. Out here, alone as I was, the conclusion to me, was obvious. I'd better be very careful, or I'd wind up dead.

Therefore, tightly gripping my flashlight, I decided to walk slowly and carefully to my truck. I prayed that it would start. I decided that my best course of action was to drive in to town and get help. I began walking towards the west. I stayed away from the buildings. I didn't want to be taken by surprise. I started walking across the open square.

Reaching the other side of the square, I intended to walk south towards the shadows of the generator shack where my truck was parked. I stopped immediately. There, huddling in the ditch on the east side of the paved road, no more than 100 feet from me were the two white fluorescent patches. They were obviously beings of great intelligence, and obviously beings with an extremely advanced technology. At last I understood what had terrified Sullivan, the weather observer before me, Dwight, the major, and the others. I also understood why the observers before me would never come out into the desert alone.

At first, they didn't see me. They apparently were expecting me to be on the other side of my weather shack. I could have run up to them and touched them, but I realized that they must be absolutely terrified of me. If I did anything unexpected, such as start my truck or start a diesel generator or throw a rock at them, they'd become even more terrified. Given their obviously high level of technology, if they became anymore terrified, I decided, my life might just end right here. I decided that the only safe thing I could do was to stand silently right where I was and not make any stray moves. It was a surprisingly easy thing to do. I was almost frozen stiff with fear.

Their suits generated the soft, white, fluorescent light. The edges of this suit appeared to be made of aluminized plastic, and had an indistinct appearance. Since I had watched them travel by floating several inches above the ground, it was obvious that they, the suit, and the rest of their technology were not of this world.

Now it all made perfect startling sense. Intelligent beings everywhere must have male, female, children, and family groups, just as the same requirements when humans were evolving. In order for intelligent life to survive, the men must be willing to bravely and intelligently fight to protect their children and their pregnant females, and the women must be willing to spend time with their children, teaching them about the world. The women must be able to feel fear for their children and to show them places to hide, so that the weak helpless young children can survive. No matter what planet they came from, they must be more like earth people than I could ever have imagined.

My brain was numb at the revelation. I must be looking at the wife and child of one of the white patches waiting over by the ammunition bunker. The tall and short patches in front of me must be a woman and daughter pair, unarmed, helpless, and terrified of me. I must have accidentally surprised them as they were out hiking and enjoying the beauty of this remote desert valley. Maybe it reminded them of their home planet. Being women and children, they must be unarmed and I must now have them trapped away from their other male family members. The fluorescent lights at the base of the mountains to the east must be the other members of their family.

My mind thought on. Based on the movements of the other three white patches, all of the white creatures must be in constant radio communication with each other, including these two. The logic was inescapable. The other male members of the family must now be rushing over here to kill me, in order to protect the woman and child. This conclusion hammered its way into my brain. I would need to plan my next move carefully or it might be my last.

I decided to continue standing very still, not to make any threatening moves. I remembered when I was a child growing up on a farm in Wisconsin how I used to herd the cows around the barnyard, staying back and never getting too close. I decided to herd the two creatures back to safety as though I were herding cows. The technique required patience. To begin with, I needed to give them time to see me standing still. It took a few minutes. I stood very still and just waited. After several minutes, the little girl rose up and looked around. She obviously saw me standing where I was and immediately communicated this to the woman.

Another minute or so passed. The woman slowly stood up, until she was totally straight up, and apparently waited bravely to be attacked. She appeared to be absolutely terrified of me. As she stood there, her head swayed back and forth. Then the little girl stood up slowly. She, also, stood bravely awaiting for me to attack.

It was obvious to me that they were having some temporary trouble with their suits and floating devices. It took them a couple of minutes of stumbling and fumbling to rise up out of the ditch in which they were hiding. As they did so, a large amount of dirt on the sides of the ditch was knocked into the ditch by the operation of the suit. They also left some footprints. The damage to the ditch remained clearly visible for more than a year. The depth of the footprints showed that the woman weighed about 100 lbs. and the little girl about 60.

I could see they were totally helpless for the several minutes it took them to climb out of the ditch. Yet, I also knew that it would be suicide for me to try to help them, so I just stood patiently still and waited. After a short time, the two of them, never taking their eyes off me, formed up on the paved road and began floating towards me. When they were less than 10 feet in front of me, they came to an open flat area on the south side of the generator shack. With the woman leading the way, they turned and floated behind the buildings, temporarily out of view.

I saw their problem immediately. In order to join up with their remaining family members, they needed to travel across the open square in front of my weather shack. They needed to get to the paved road that ran east towards the ammunition bunker where their remaining family members were waiting for them - and I blocked the way. I tried to solve this problem by slowly walking south towards my truck and slowly following them around the generator shack. I had expected that they would just keep floating towards their destination. I honestly felt the same way I used to feel when I herded cows around a corner of the barn. As I came around the southern corner of the generator shack, I could see them floating ahead of me, next to the corner of my weather shack. They were trapped at a dead end by my shack, the sagebrush, and the fence to the skip bomb area. I decided it was best to turn around and go back and stand by the theodolite. This way, I reasoned, the other male family members could see me, and they could see that the woman and child weren't in any danger. I hoped this would convince them that I didn't need to be killed just yet.

I walked back and stood by the theodolite. I waited for a while. Nothing seemed to be happening. I could see that the woman and child were still hiding behind my weather shack. I was out of ideas as to what I should do next, so I decided to look around and see if I could locate the other three family members. Off to the east, by the ammunition bunker, I could see two soft white fluorescent patches standing and waiting. They had floated down to the other end of the paved road that went over there. This was the same road that ran past the billboards.

I looked around for the third white patch. At first, I couldn't find him. I looked some more. Surely, they must care greatly about each other's safety, I reasoned. He must be coming over to where I am, in order to help the woman and the little girl.

Then I saw him, the third soft white fluorescent patch, the one who almost certainly matched the description of Range Four Harry. He was a young adult male standing approximately six feet tall. He had taken a tremendous risk to rescue the woman and child. While I was distracted, he had floated the mile and a quarter down the paved road from the bunker to the open square. Then, when he arrived at the first billboard, he had held on to the crossbeams and braces in order to balance himself, and had floated up to the top, some forty feet up. Hanging on to the sides and top of the billboard, he was now in a position from which he could coach the woman and child. I also noticed that his position gave him a clear field of fire for any weapon he might be carrying, in case he felt it necessary to kill me.

I had no idea what to do next. I stood there in numbed shock, studying him carefully. After a few minutes, I thought maybe things would be easier for him if I retreated still further away from the two white patches floating behind my weather shack. I stood up and turned so that I was facing north, away from the woman and child. I started walking slowly towards the control tower. As I was turning, the left temple of my brain was momentarily facing directly towards the helmet of the white fluorescent man I believed to be Range Four Harry. It was like turning on a radio station. My mind suddenly began filling with soft pleasant thoughts. Thoughts like, "Stand still, stay still," began slowly and quietly appearing into my brain. I was thinking about walking at the time, so I realized that these couldn't possibly be my thoughts. Startled, I turned around and returned to standing by the theodolite.

As I stood there, I tried to comprehend what was going on. The man must be wearing a radio transmitter and receiver in his helmet. The human brain is a very low power electrical device that transmits tiny weak pulses of microwaves when a person thinks. These microwaves are transmitted mainly from the temple part of the human brain. The man must be wearing a microwave receiver in his helmet. He must be receiving the microwaves that are naturally transmitted by the nerve cells of my brain. The electronics in his high tech suit must be able to decode these waves, thereby allowing him to read my thoughts. Now I understood why he hadn't killed me just yet. He knew my thoughts and understood that I meant no harm to the woman and child. Now, I also understood, the electronics in the helmets of his wife and daughter must not be tuned properly. Otherwise, the woman and child would have spoken to me.

It was a heavy dose of reality for me to accept in such a short time. I waited there by the theodolite more in shock than anything else. Still, I understood exactly what it meant. The nerve endings in the human brain receive microwaves as well as transmit them. The man's electronics must work both ways. I understood, at last, that if I turned the temples of my brain towards the man's helmet, full of electronics as it obviously was, that he and I could communicate just by thinking.

Standing straight up and turning the left temple of my brain towards him, I thought slowly, calmly, and distinctly, "I will not harm the woman. I will not harm the little girl. I will not harm you."

Then I waited calmly and patiently, clearing my brain of all other thoughts.

Then it happened, after perhaps thirty seconds, a thought appeared in my brain. It was calm, clear, and it appeared slowly, at about half the rate that I normally think. There was no mistaking it. It certainly came from the man. It said, "I know. You have not been harmed."

Elated, terrified, surprised, shocked, and struggling to overcome my fear, I continued, thinking slowly and distinctly, "How can I help you?"

A long pause followed. Then I received the response, "Calm down. My equipment will work better."

I could see that he was right, but staying calm was a lot easier said than done. After a few minutes, I realized that I had no choice. If he couldn't communicate with me, he might still have to kill me in order to extricate the woman and the girl from this predicament. Therefore, after nearly heroic efforts, I calmed myself enough to continue.

"Where are you from?" I thought.

After a short pause, I received, "There is no time to talk. We must help the woman. Stand still by the metal stand. I must talk to the woman. The woman must come over to the wooden towers."

I stood still by the theodolite, with my left temple turned towards the man, waiting. Now that I was becoming calmer, it became apparent that the man's brain must contain electronic nerves just as mine does. Although the aliens must certainly be communicating between themselves using longer-range radios, the man's electronics were re-transmitting the messages between him and the woman as he was thinking them. This meant that I was able to listen in on his thoughts, the same way he was able to listen in on mine. My brain now became full of thoughts, as though I were listening in on a CB radio channel.

First, there was a thought that sounded like it came from a grown woman. "The man was going to kill us," it said in panic. The man wanted to tear us both into pieces. The man wanted to stuff us into those terrible garbage cans."

"The man thought you were plastic bags. The man will not hurt you. The man knows what we are. Come to where I am," came back the answer.

"We cannot come. The man will see us. I did not want the man to see us. You said never let the man see us. The man is too intelligent. The man will know what we are like," responded the woman.

"The man has already seen you. Your life is in danger. Your equipment will stop soon. You must come across now," implored the man.

"We cannot," was the answer. "You must come to get us."

There was a short pause. Then the man responded, "I cannot. I would not be able to communicate back to the

Captain. The Captain does not allow it. The Captain says I have come as far as the Captain permits."

"Where is the man now?" asked the woman.

"The man is standing by the metal post," was the man's answer. "Do not worry. I can talk to the man. The man will not harm you."

"The man is too close," responded the woman. "Tell the man to stand on the other side of the shed where the man cannot see us. Then we will cross the open area."

"If the man stands behind the shed, I will not be able to talk with the man. The shed will be in the way. I will ask the man to stand by the side of the shed where I can see the man," he replied.

"Tell the man to hide in the sagebrush. Then we can come across," said the woman.

"If the man hides in the sagebrush, I cannot talk to him. We are safer if we talk to the man," he said.

Then a clear, distinct thought appeared in my brain. "Stand by the edge of the building and face me," he said.

"Yes," I responded.

Walking over to the edge of the generator shed, I stood quiet and still facing east. This meant that my left temple was still exposed to his electronics. "I am standing here," I thought.

"He is not standing still," said the woman.

"Don't move your feet," he said. "Stand quietly."

Doing as requested, I calmly stood very still, and waited. As I did so, I thought, "I am standing still."

As I waited, the man repeatedly tried to coax the woman to cross the open area in front of me. She was hiding behind the weather shack. She was terrified at the prospect of my seeing her cross over to the billboards where he was. Then, after more than ten minutes of coaxing, the woman agreed to try. There followed one of the great dramas I have ever witnessed. As I stood quietly, not moving my feet or arms, the woman at last agreed to make the crossing. She began by apparently turning her equipment up to full power. This caused her suit to shine noticeably brighter. While remaining on her floating device, she stooped down as far as possible. This apparently helped her balance the device. Then, activating the equipment, she floated high enough to clear the cable fence and high enough to clear the sagebrush. With the equipment apparently turned up to its maximum power, she began floating diagonally upwards and towards the middle of the billboard that the man was using to balance himself. Obviously afraid of losing her balance and terrified by my gaze, she continued to guide her path upwards and forwards across the open space in front of me. She was shouting in terror sometimes, for him to help her. As she neared the billboard, she raised her right arm slowly. He reached out and grabbed her hand. Now, at last, he was able to help the woman to a safe place behind the billboard. As she floated, with his help, around the east side of the billboard, some 35 feet above the desert, there could be no doubt that she had been entirely overcome with fear of me.

He kept reassuring her, "Calm down. You will feel better. The man cannot harm you now." Then, behind the billboard, she held on to the cross beams to steady herself, and slowly floated back down towards the ground, until she floated only 18 inches above the pavement which was behind the billboard. Through it all, I stood quiet, still, and quite dumbfounded.

Now he began coaxing the girl to come across the open area. This was obviously a much easier task.

"He is standing still," he said to the girl. "The man will not harm you. The man did not harm the woman. Come as soon as you are ready."

"Is it all right if the man sees me?" asked the girl.

"Yes," he said. "The man has already seen you."

"Can I make it?" asked the girl.

"Yes," he said. "The Captain says if you fall, I can come to get you. The woman can maintain the communication link."

"I am coming now," said the girl.

Now, the girl, like the woman before her, turned her suit up to full power. Stooped over like the woman before her. With her suit shining brightly, she floated over the cable fence. Then, floating a few feet above the sagebrush, she began crossing the open area in front of me. She was obviously less afraid of me than the woman had been. Therefore, she stayed much lower down than the woman had. Her thoughts, by way of the man's electronics, kept appearing in my brain. She seemed to be reassuring herself by telling him, "I know the man will not harm me. The man didn't harm the woman. The man has no reason to harm me."

Reaching the west side of the row of billboards, she floated around behind them, and floated down the paved area behind them until she was safely floating next to the woman.

I remained standing quietly, still trying to grasp the drama that had just unfolded.

After several minutes of calming down the woman and the girl, the man said to me, "You may move now. Thank you for standing still."

"Is there anything else I can do to help you?" I asked.

"No," he said. "You have been very helpful. The woman needs to rest here for a short time. Then we will go back to the mountain. I must repair the equipment now."

"I will go to my building and compute the winds which I have measured," I said.

"Yes," he replied. "Thank you for understanding us. Thank you for your hospitality."

With that, I walked slowly to the theodolite stand, and picked up my clipboard, my papers, and my wind measurements. Then I walked slowly over to my weather shack, opened the door, and went inside. I left the side door open so that the light of the stars could enter, and I closed the front door. The man's electronics apparently didn't work when I was inside the building. Once inside I could no longer tell what he was thinking. Afraid to turn on my flashlight and still shaky from my experience, I sat down quietly for a while and just rested.

Every few minutes I would take a quick look out the side door to see how things were coming behind the billboards. The man, apparently trusting me, had floated down from the top of the billboard to where the woman and the girl were. There, behind the billboard, he appeared to be adjusting the woman's suit and her electronics. At the time, she had apparently turned her suit off and appeared to have taken all or part of it off. I could see her surprisingly thin form, chalky white skin, long blonde hair, and what appeared to be deep blue eyes. At the time, she was actually standing on the pavement.

Later, the man appeared to be doing the same for the little girl. Standing on the pavement, out of her suit, she looked like a small, near perfect duplicate of the woman. After another 30 minutes or so had passed, the man had them suited up and formed up like two school children. The three of them seemed so happy to be together as they prepared to float out from behind the billboards. Realizing that they wanted to be alone, I went back to my chair and sat down for a few minutes. After some time had passed, I could see the three of them in the distance, floating happily down the paved road. It felt as if they were almost singing as they headed towards the other two white patches that waited for them at the end of the pavement.

When the three of them were just over a quarter mile distant, I decided that it would be all right if I went out and started the diesel electric generator. As I left the weather shack, once again I could receive the man's thoughts. Now, however, I could receive the thoughts of the woman and the girl too. The woman was saying, "The man saw us. The man surprised us. We were so lucky the man understood us. The other men would have killed us."

He was responding, "Yes. We were very lucky. This man is much more intelligent than the other men. This man knew I was there before he saw me. Before I could communicate with this man, he knew that I planned to kill him if he touched you. I have never seen a man that intelligent."

"My equipment would not communicate with the man. I could not put great fear in his mind like I did the others," said the woman.

"He is too intelligent," he said. "Your equipment was not adjusted for that much intelligence."

"I did not see his lights. Why did he drive out here with his lights off?" asked the woman.

"He thinks the desert is beautiful," he said. "He enjoys seeing the light from our star. He is like us in that way."

Then my thoughts cleared as I turned the corner to the generator shack. Entering the generator shack, I turned on my flashlight and started the diesel generators.

When I came back out, in the distance at the end of the paved road I could see the three of them. They were just reaching their two waiting friends. My mind again, began filling with fragmented thoughts. It was obvious that the man's electronics were almost out of range. One of the white patches was the Captain, and the other was the man's brother, and also the girl's uncle. As the uncle greeted the girl, he was saying, "Your trip around these beautiful meadows was very exciting. Your father and I feared for your safety. When you met the man, were you afraid of the man?"

"The man surprised us," said the girl. "The man frightened us. The man is very ugly. The woman was terrified of the man." Then, as if giggling, she continued, "But now we like the man. The man was kind to us."

Unable to receive their thoughts any longer, I entered my weather shack, closed the doors, and turned on the lights. Sitting down, I took a few minutes to calm myself, trying to comprehend what had happened. Then I quietly decided that the best thing for me would be to return to my normal duties. I tuned my radio to some nice relaxing music and quietly completed my wind calculations.

When my calculations were finished, I phoned the Desert Center weather station. The lines were full of static, but after several tries I finally got through. It was Dwight who answered. "You're awfully late with the winds, Charlie," he chided me. "You should have phoned them in more than an hour ago. Don't worry, though. I covered for you with the Major. Is everything all right?"

"Yes," I answered slowly, still struggling for words to describe what had happened. "Everything is fine, Dwight," I said. "I'm late because this morning I finally saw Range Four Harry."

"You did, Charlie? You really did?" exclaimed Dwight.

"Yes," I answered. "I got a really good look at him. I made friends with him. I was able to study him for at least an hour and a half. I'm quite certain that I know what he is."

"What is he, Charlie? What is he?" asked Dwight, excitedly.

"If I told you on the phone, Dwight," I said, "I'm afraid that you'd never believe me. I was shocked when I discovered it myself. But you can tell the Major that it's just as you said. On warm summer evenings, Harry likes to come down into the starlit meadows here at Mojave Wells. Only, it's not because he's a horse. He's not a horse. He only looks like a horse when he's far away. He has feelings and emotions, just like you and I. He just has a special reason for hiking out here. On warm summer evenings, he likes to hike here, out in the sagebrush meadows, when they are receiving the light from the stars."

"Why?" asked Dwight.

"I think," I answered, stammering a little, "I think it's because he calls one of them home."

In the months that followed, I marked that place in the sagebrush that I had sketched. I marked it with a wooden stake, and took more than twenty friends out to it. In every case the conclusion was the same. My sketch was accurate. That meant the light from their suits that illuminated the sagebrush was real. The conclusion was inescapable. The white floating creatures were perfectly real. Still, for months afterward, my mind, my psyche, simply refused to allow me to accept the inevitable ironclad conclusion. Sometimes I would go out and stand on the gravel road, visually inspecting the footprints that the white creatures had left in the ditch. I would leave shaking my head, saying, "I can't allow myself to believe it. I just can't allow myself to believe it."

I wasn't lying to myself. Even with a harsh dose of reality staring me in the face, my body, my sanity, my very inner being couldn't accept the truth. My orders were to take the morning run every weekday morning. It took a special kind of courage to make the long nighttime drive, alone, night after night, knowing that something waited out there in the darkness, watching my every move. I decided that as long as the white creatures were willing to stay hidden in the distant mountains, or run away while I was still several miles away, that I had no choice. For my own good, for my own physical survival, I had no choice but to forget the entire experience. I knew that I had to force myself to forget the entire experience in order to survive even a week, alone, out on the ranges. In order to help myself forget, in order to overcome my nighttime fears, in order to find the courage so I could continue to perform my military duties, I told myself that it had just been a dream. I found myself exclaiming over and over, "just a dream." I kept repeating it as long as they let me, as long as they ran away, as long as they wanted only to hike by themselves, far away, under the beautiful distant starlit Meadows of Arcturus.

Doxology

Then I heard one of the four living creatures say
in a voice like thunder, "Come."
I looked, and there before me was a white horse!

...Revelation 6:1

"Well, Charlie," said Steve, "It's been five weeks, now. I guess you'll be going back to Desert Center next week. We're sure going to miss you. I hope you've enjoyed this TDY up here."

"I sure have, Steve," I responded honestly. "I'll ask the Major to send me up here again, as soon as possible. McIntyre will be coming up here Monday to relieve me. He's never been up here before, so I'll spend next week training him. He's a really likable person. He'll fit right in."

It was another beautiful late summer day at Mojave Wells. Steve, the other range rats, and I were sitting around in our trucks watching a new flight of planes making practice runs on the skip bomb targets. Then Steve turned to me and using his north Georgia drawl said, "You know, Charlie, I really worry about you spending so much time out here alone. It really isn't that safe, especially coming out here before the sun comes up, as you always do. Really, I think you should fake more of those early morning runs and phone them in from the barracks, like all those other guys used to do. You know, of course, you're the only weather observer they've ever had up here that actually took all of those wind measurements that Desert Center requests. I think you should spend more time thinking about your personal safety, and less time thinking about those winds that Desert Center always pretends it needs."

"Oh, don't worry, Steve," I responded. "When I come out here at 4:00 a.m., there's never anything out here. I've never seen so much as a coyote or a rattle snake." Living a life of denial came so easy.

"Well, you can thank your lucky stars for that," said Steve. "Those other guys would have given their eye teeth, to be able to say that. But are you sure that nothing unusual has ever happened when you were out here alone?"

"Well," I said, "There have been a couple of unusual things. For one thing, the diesels haven't been very dependable. Usually, they start up immediately. The mechanics down at the motor pool say that both diesels are almost new and in perfect condition. Only one diesel actually needs to be started. After all, I only turn on a one hundred watt light bulb and a radio. During the last five weeks, however, their performance has been pretty puzzling. Twice last week, when I had turned on the starting motor for diesel one, the batteries were totally dead. It was the same way for diesel two. Both diesels are connected to all 20 batteries out there in the shed and each battery is huge. The mechanic told me that only one battery is actually needed, to start the diesel. He said the idea of all 20 batteries going suddenly dead in the summer time was inconceivable. Yet, on those two mornings, when I punched the start button at 4:00 A.M., absolutely nothing happened. Even the engine on my truck had quit running. It quit on me for no reason, as I was approaching the buildings. I had to walk that last quarter mile in darkness, just to get to the generator shack. Even my flashlight wouldn't work. I had to perform the entire wind analysis in darkness. I had to struggle with my telephone. It just wouldn't work. Then, suddenly, everything cleared up. My phone worked. My flashlight worked. When I went out to the generator shed and tried the diesels, they started immediately. The batteries were charged and everything. My truck also started perfectly. I really can't explain it.

"Then there's the matter of my plastic tools. As you know, my shack has a front door and a side door on it. In the mornings, before I inflate the balloon, I always arrange the plastic rulers on my work table in the shack. As you know, they're used to perform the wind computations. It's just a habit, but it helps me wake up in the morning and get things moving. Well, when I'm tracking the balloon, I have the front door closed, and the side door open. Usually, the morning winds are coming from the south. This means that when I'm tracking my balloon using the theodolite out front, I'm standing with my back to my shack with the door closed. This doesn't let me keep track of what's going on behind me in the shack. But, you know, who cares. I mean I'm out here alone. It's more than 20 miles back to base. Well, on at least three different mornings, when I finished tracking the balloon and went back into my weather shack, I could have sworn that those plastic rulers had moved. Not much, you understand. Most people would have missed it. For example, the last time it happened, my big ruler had moved to the left a full quarter of an inch. I'm certain it had been moved while I was out front tracking the balloon, but I really can't explain how that could happen. I mean, I'd noticed its position before hand and everything."

Steve sat there quietly, as though knowing the answer. Then he spoke, "I know you're telling the truth, Charlie."

Then, turning to the range rat, sitting next to him, Doug, he said, "Tell him about those ghosts you saw out at Range Two, Doug. It isn't that far from here."

"I won't go out to Range Two anymore, unless we're all together," said Doug sincerely. "And I won't go out there at all at night. A year ago last summer, we were all out there helping out on some night missions. It was going on midnight. I had laid down on the sofa in the range lounge and gone to sleep.

In between missions, the rest of the range rats had gone out on the range to score the targets and had left me there alone. Since I was sleeping, they didn't want to wake me up. While I was sleeping, something suddenly woke me up. I was so surprised. I almost died of fright. There were four ghosts standing in the darkness just inside the door of the lounge, looking at me. A fifth one was keeping watch outside. Then one of them stayed by the door while the other three floated over to where I was, and looked at me up close. I tell you, I just about had a bird I was so terrified."

"What did they look like?" I asked.

"Just like ghosts," said Doug simply. "They had faces and they were all white and filmy, just like ghosts. When they moved, everything was totally silent. They just floated silently into the room. I was so terrified that I laid there screaming."

"He sure did!" exclaimed Steve. We could hear him way out on the range and it's almost three quarters of a mile out there."

"After I began screaming," said Doug, "The ghosts floated out, just as silently as they had floated in."

"Where did the ghosts go then, Doug?" I asked. "They floated out around the corner of the range lounge. After that

I couldn't see them anymore. There's no way I was going to follow them. After that, they could have floated up into those mountains east of here without anyone being able to see them."

"I don't understand, Doug," I said, "You said one of them was keeping watch."

"Yes. You see, Charlie," said Doug, "The three that floated over and checked me out, were small. They must have only been three or four feet tall. The one that stayed by the door was taller. That one was probably five and a half or six feet tall. The one keeping watch outside was real tall. That one might have been six and half or seven feet tall."

"But I don't understand why a group of ghosts would need a lookout," I said. "I mean, I didn't think ghosts cared if someone saw them."

"I agree with you, Charlie," said Doug laughing. "But I sure as hell am not going out there again to ask them."

"Charlie, you really ought to give it some thought." said Steve as we all sat there laughing. "Tell me, Charlie," said Steve, "Have you ever seen any ghosts like Doug, here?"

"No. I haven't," I answered, "But, a couple of times I did see a parachute floating around down by the gate."

"A parachute?" asked Steve. "I thought we picked all of them up. You better tell me about it."

"Sure," I said. "You remember that time two, maybe three, weeks ago when I was not feeling well?"

"Yes. I remember that, Charlie," said Steve. "I remember you were up vomiting until midnight. I don't know how you were able to get up and drive out here for the morning run."

"Something happened that morning that I still wonder about. It was a real cold and windy morning. When I went out the front door of the barracks, I was so sick and dizzy that I dropped my keys out in the gravel parking lot. My vision was blurred because I was so tired and had been vomiting, so I had to get down on my hands and knees to find my keys. At the time, I was so sick that I was afraid I was going to die. As I was crawling around, I looked out across the runway, out into the valley. I was looking out at the desert that's straight north of the barracks. Out there, I could see some pale white fluorescent lights. They were a mile or so out in the sagebrush. I only got a glimpse of them because my vision was really blurry, and my head was pounding. I found my keys, so I got up and got in my truck.

"I got my truck started. I turned on the lights and heater, and I began driving slowly out toward Range Three. Well, when I got out there by that little rocky hill where the Range Three gate is, I discovered that the gate had been closed. Now I'm certain that I left that gate open the afternoon before. That was the day you guys were mowing lawns here on base, so I know that none of you could have closed the gate. Well, I stopped my truck just in front of the gate, with that rocky hill right beside me on my left. I set the brake. I left my headlights on, and I left the engine idling. I opened the door and I got out real slow because I was so sick, I was afraid of falling on my face.

"Once I was out of the truck, I looked over by that rocky hill. My head hurt so badly, I thought it was going to explode. My vision was so blurry that I didn't pay much attention to what I saw. There was a tall pale fluorescent white piece of filmy plastic or something floating about 30 feet from me. It was maybe five and a half or six feet tall. It seemed to be floating a foot or so above ground. Next to it was a much smaller piece of plastic just like it. It was only three or four feet tall. At first I thought they might be pieces of some old parachute because I couldn't see anything through them as you can through plastic.

"The two of them were off to my left. They were floating in the lee of that little rocky hill. They were right up next to it on the north side. My head hurt so much that I didn't give them a second look. I didn't look at their tops. I didn't look to see if there were more of them. I didn't look at anything. At the time I was really annoyed that the gate was down because it was so painful for me to get out of my truck and walk around. Well, every step I took made me sicker. The gate wasn't locked. I got over to the right side of the road and got the gate raised, you know how easy it is to swing it up and down. I was so sick that I couldn't help myself. I started vomiting into the sagebrush. I stood there, bent over, and just vomited my guts into the sand. At the time, I was afraid I wasn't going to be able to walk back to my truck. As I was trying to get hold of myself, I noticed that the tall white parachute was floating slowly toward me. I suddenly noticed that it wasn't lying against the rocky hill, the way I thought a parachute should be. Instead, I noticed that it was free standing. It floated toward me, the way a helium-filled balloon might float. It slowly closed the distance between us to less than 15 feet. I didn't know what to make of it because it had to float against the wind to do it. I was so sick that I couldn't raise my head to see all of it. I was only looking at its mid section."

"That must have really terrified you, didn't it, Charlie?" asked Steve in an understanding tone. "You were out there all alone, vomiting your guts out, too sick to walk, and trapped away from your truck. What did you do?"

"That's the funny part," I continued. "I was so deathly sick, I really didn't feel the slightest bit afraid. I know it sounds silly, and I was probably hallucinating, but the large white floating parachute felt like it had come to help me. I remember thinking that the gate had been closed on purpose so that the white parachute could get a close look at me. I remember thinking the white parachute wanted to see if I needed help to stay alive. It's really hard to explain how confused my feelings were. I stood there, bent over by the side of the road, vomiting my guts into the sagebrush. Then I fell down on my hands and knees and continued vomiting some more. At the time, fear was the last thing on my mind."

"What happened then?" asked Steve.

"Well, as I was vomiting, I had to look away from whatever-it-was. I remember thinking that I was going to be all right. I needed to get lots of rest, and to be more careful when I was driving. Out of the corner of my eye, I could see the white parachute had stopped floating toward me. Instead, it and the other little parachute slowly floated back around the north end of that little rocky hill. I finished vomiting, and very slowly forced myself to get back up. Then I hobbled back across the road, in front of my headlights. Finally, I was able to get back in my truck on the driver's side. Once I got the door closed, I sat there for a few minutes, letting the engine idle. My head was pounding, and I needed to rest. I was hoping my blurry vision would go away. The window on my side was rolled down because I needed the fresh air. It really hurt whenever I turned my head, but I forced myself to turn my head to the left and take a closer look at the top of the rocky hill. The white parachutes were floating on the other side, and only their tops could be seen above the top of the hill. My vision was really blurry and I couldn't tell how many there were. My mind kind of recoiled in disbelief at what I was able to see. The parachutes must have been something like helium filled plastic weather balloons or maybe cloth sheets, I don't know. Anyway, the top of the large white fluorescent one was round just like a large balloon. My vision was still blurry at the time, but it sure looked like it had eyes and that it was watching me. Well, anyway, I put my truck in gear and started driving toward Range Three. I was worried because I was sure that my flu was causing my mind to play tricks on me. When I got out here, as soon as I got out of the truck, I started up the generator. Well, you know how much noise those things make. The racket just about killed me. My head was pounding so badly, I thought I was going to break a blood vessel. I stumbled out of the generator shack and fell up against my truck, waiting for the pain to go away. My vision was still blurred. When I looked back down the Range Three road toward the gate, I could see those white parachutes were still there by that little rocky hill. Even though it's several miles down there, I could have sworn they were still looking at me. I took my wind measurements and called them into Desert Center. Actually, I was so sick that I wasn't able to track the balloon for more than a couple of minutes, so I had to make up the last seven readings. I was really mad at myself, but my vision was so blurry and my head was pounding so badly, I couldn't see the balloon in the theodolite.

"When I made up the winds, I was careful to show high winds at all of the altitudes. It really was windy so I guess what I made up wasn't too far from what the winds actually were. Then I told Desert Center to cancel all of the flights for that day because the high winds made flight operations dangerous. That way, I figured if I were too sick to take any more wind measurements, I could make up the rest of the day's runs and none of the pilots would be in danger. I locked up my weather shack and began walking slowly back to my truck. I was getting sicker by the minute, and I decided that I should just drive back into base and spend the rest of the morning resting in my barracks. Well, I was thinking these things just as I was reaching my truck. It was still parked out by the generator shack. Looking down the Range Three road, I could still see those white parachutes floating by the little rocky hill. I remember how comforted I felt.

"I shut down the diesels and staggered back to my truck. Then, starting my truck, I drove slowly and carefully back to base. When I passed through the Range Three gate, those white parachutes where still floating on the other side of that rocky hill. I could still see their white fluorescent tops, just above the top of the hill. I didn't have the faintest idea what to make of it, but I was so sick I just kept driving. In order to make it back into base and into my barracks, I had to do something to take my mind off my terrible headache. The only thing that helped any was to silently sing religious songs. As I was pulling up in front of the barracks, I was silently singing. When I got out of my truck and started up the steps back into my barracks, I can't explain it, but it felt like the large white parachute was actually happy that I was safe. I mean it felt like the parachute was happier than I was. I don't know what to make of it all, Steve, I really don't. One afternoon during the next week, when I was feeling better, I stopped my truck at the gate and climbed that little rocky hill, so I could see what was on the other side. I was so surprised. There wasn't a thing on the other side. There wasn't anything over there but sand and sagebrush. I haven't the faintest idea what became of those white parachutes. I guess I just must have been so sick that my eyes were playing tricks on me. I really don't know what to make of it."

Steve listened to it all. Then he said quietly and carefully, "Oh, there's nothing the matter with your eyes, Charlie. In fact, I'd say that you had good eyes, indeed."

Then he added, "Now I see why Desert Center sent you up here, Charlie. Any man who can keep his wits about him the way you did, is definitely the man I'd send up to this place. Any of the others that Desert Center sent up here, would have killed themselves just turning the truck around at the gate. By now, the rest of them would be up there singing with God, instead of down here praising him."

Missteps

How, then, can they call on the one
they have not believed in?
And how can they believe in the one
of whom they have not heard?

Romans 10:14

The ringing barracks phone finally woke me. Still half asleep, "Charlie," I mumbled. It was Master Sergeant Walters.

"Charlie, I'm sorry to wake you so early. I know it's only 6 a.m., and you worked until midnight, last night, but a problem has developed up at the gunnery ranges. The major and I would like to meet with you in the major's office at 7:00 a.m."

"Yes, sergeant." I answered respectfully, "I'll be there at 7:00 sharp. Is the problem serious?"

"Yes." answered the sergeant. "We'll fill you in on the details when you get here."

7:00 a.m. found me taking a chair in the major's office, directly in front of his desk. Dwight, Sergeant Walters, The major, and the Irish weather forecaster, O'Keefe were present. Sergeant Walters handed me the clipboard holding the last three weeks of wind measurements taken at Mojave Wells, and began seriously. "Yesterday, Sergeant O'Keefe brought these winds to the major's attention. This is Thursday. McIntyre has been up at Mojave Wells alone now, for almost three weeks. You're the ranking Mojave

Wells observer. Look at these winds. What do you make of them?"

Quickly I flipped through the 14 days worth of wind measurements, and answered the sergeant, "Well, he started out OK. His first three days on his own, he certainly had no problems. I see he missed several balloon runs on the next day, the first Thursday he was there. The next day, Friday, I wonder about his last run from range three. The winds look OK, and his report says he took them at 1:30 in the afternoon. The problem is that I was working day shift that day. I'm certain he didn't phone them in until 3:40 in the afternoon. I was almost off shift by that time. I remember it very well because I gave him a hard time about it. He got angry with me when I suggested that he had been sleeping in the afternoon. I pointed out to him that the last flight that day was off the ranges at 10:30 a.m. I told him how I'd tried to reach him on the phone at least six times between 2:30 and 3:30 in the afternoon. He never once answered his phone. He swore he'd been out there on range three, wide awake every minute of the time. I had quite a time calming him down, and convincing him that it was 3:40 in the afternoon. No matter how he explained it there was a block of time between 1:45 and 3:30 that he simply couldn't account for. He swore that he'd taken the 1:30 afternoon winds on schedule. He swore that he had just walked back to the weather shack and performed the calculations in a normal manner. He said his mind had wandered a little bit, and his watch had stopped while he was walking back to the shack. But, even so, that shouldn't have taken him more than 15 minutes.

Then, last week, something really serious must have happened down at range one, on Tuesday afternoon, after he finished taking his readings for the day. As you can see his actual Tuesday readings from range one look fine, but his readings from range three, taken on the next day, Wednesday, can't possibly be right. The rest of his wind measurements since a week ago Wednesday don't look like they're worth the paper they're written on. Last Wednesday, for example, he was reporting the 10:00 a.m. winds for every level from the surface on up to 14,000 feet to be 25 miles per hour from the north. That can't possibly be correct. We've had perfect summer weather there for the last three weeks. Those 10:00 a.m. winds must certainly have been light and variable, no more than 5 miles per hour, from the south west."

Sergeant Walters, smiling, responded, "Dwight, here, says that last Wednesday morning something terrified McIntyre out on the ranges. Dwight thinks it has something to do with Range Four Harry."

"That's what Bryan, one of the range rats, said, when I phoned the barracks last Wednesday morning," stated Dwight, in a matter of fact manner. "I remember the other weather observers we used to send up there a couple years ago reported having blocks of missing time whenever Range Four Harry started coming in close. One time that black guy, Bob Montgomery, was missing from range three for most of an afternoon. The range Rats swore that his truck was parked out there and everything, but that he was nowhere around. Then, just as suddenly, he came walking back in to range three on the road from the ammunition bunker. Bob was in perfect health, but he couldn't remember a single detail of where he'd been or what he'd been doing. He didn't even know that any time had passed. A couple mornings later he came in to breakfast really late.

He was absolutely terrified of the ranges, and had to be replaced."

The sergeant continued, "Sergeant O'Keefe, here, says that these winds were actually phoned in by one of the cooks, and he thinks McIntyre has been somehow incapacitated, and isn't telling us the details. Sergeant O'Keefe says it doesn't seem like McIntyre. We all know that he's very intelligent, hard working, and I know he was well trained when you left him up there. Even if he were afraid to go out to range three for some screwy reason, like seeing a bunch of white shadows, or maybe Range Four Harry, it still doesn't make sense. If he were making up all of these winds, he's so intelligent, he'd sure have made up better winds than the ones recorded here."

"I don't mean any disrespect, Sergeant Walters," interjected Dwight, "and I know you don't believe in Range Four Harry because you have never been out there at night and seen him, but Range Four Harry isn't a screwy reason. He's quite real. Both the Major and I have seen him out on range four."

Then the Major stated simply, "Dwight is right. Just the same, if we don't figure this one out, Charlie, I'm going to have to give McIntyre six weeks in the brig, and a section eight discharge."

Sergeant Walters continued, "We would like you to go up there this morning, and figure out what the problem is. Our problem is that detachment policy, which was given us by our commander at Tinker AFB, Oklahoma, says that because the ranges are considered to be isolated duty, we can't order you to another TDY at the ranges, until you've been back here at Desert Center for at least 6 months unless, of course, you volunteer. We know this is only the third week that you've been back here at Desert Center. We all appreciate the excellent job you've been doing, and we know how difficult the isolation at Mojave Wells can be, but we were hoping that you would volunteer to return to Mojave Wells for the rest of the week, and determine what the problem is up there."

"No problem, Sergeant," I responded. "I'll take the Desert Center detachment truck up this morning, with my TDY clothes, and I'll send McIntyre back with the Desert Center detachment truck, tomorrow afternoon. That'll give me time to figure out what the problem is, and to make up the best estimate of what the winds actually were. Cut me up a new set of TDY orders for the Wells. I'll be down Monday evening, after completing the afternoon runs, to sign them and pick up my TDY pay. Then I'll stay up there for six weeks, unless you decide to relieve me earlier. I'll take along some extra supplies, forms, balloons, and things, as long as I'm going.

"I have no idea what the problem could be, but it's probably something simple. Maybe he's afraid of the desert, and losing his sense of direction, or maybe his equipment needs calibration. Don't worry, major, I'm sure he's trying his best, and I don't think he'll have to be given a section eight discharge, or anything.

"You know McIntyre is not one to frighten easily. He's used to looking after himself in a fight. He grew up in the slums of New York City. He always carries those two throwing knives of his. He keeps them razor sharp, and if he felt seriously threatened, he wouldn't hesitate to use them. He is supporting his mother, back in New York City. She's his only living relative. I know he takes his Air Force duties very seriously, and I've always been impressed with how

225

hard he works. I'm certain we can get this straightened out, just as soon as I can get up to the gunnery ranges to look things over."

Then the major laughed, "You really don't want me to have the fun of convening a court martial board for anyone, do you Charlie?"

"Well, major, if you decide they need it, I always respect the decisions of my commanders and ranking sergeants," I answered respectfully.

The major continued laughing. Then, he asked seriously, "When you were up there on your last TDY, Charlie, did you ever see any evidence of Range Four Harry?"

After mulling things over in my mind for a few minutes, I answered slowly and truthfully, "When I was up at Mojave Wells on my last TDY, I never saw any signs of a radioactive horse, Major, but driving out to range three at 3:30 a.m. on a dark, warm, and windy morning can be a mighty scary experience. I mean, I really enjoy being stationed up at the Wells. I'm really looking forward to another tour of duty up there, Major, but the things that are out there on those ranges at night can sure make a man's blood run cold."

"Like that one summer morning when you were up at the Wells, and there wasn't a cloud in the sky. You reported that a small patch of what appeared to be a rainstorm without water, following you? You reported that it floated down the road from range four, until it was only 150 feet away from you," questioned the major.

"Yes, Major," I answered, truthfully.

"Did it ever take on the appearance of a horse?" asked Dwight, seriously, "You know, did it ever look like a giant Trojan horse, standing out in the sagebrush?"

"Well, yes," I answered, still truthfully. "You see, when I first arrived out at range three that morning, it was a beautiful clear night. The moon was full, and the sagebrush just glistened in the moonlight. After I started the diesel, and had some electricity, I noticed a large patch of white misty, almost fluorescent light way up the valley. It must have been almost forty miles up there. It was way up the valley by the mountains to the northwest, and it was coming down towards the range four buildings. It must have covered the distance from the mountains, down to the range four buildings in less than 15 minutes. Since it was so far away from me, I didn't think much of it. I had no idea what it was, but I felt that I needed to mention it in the weather report. So even though it was a dry hot summer night, I guessed it was probably a little rainstorm, or maybe a small patch of fog.

"Anyway, I watched it for a little while. It drifted in around the range four buildings, as though it was looking into all of them. Then it started drifting down the range four road. Still I didn't think much of it. After all, who's afraid of a little rain? I ignored it and went on about my business. I filled a balloon with helium, attached the light for night viewing. I took the balloon outside and released it. I lost track of the rainstorm for a while. There is that rise in the desert, and I couldn't see the full length of the range four road. Suddenly, after my third minute reading, I was startled to see the rainstorm come up over the rise in the range four road. I was really surprised because there wasn't a breath of wind, yet it had to have drifted down at least 10 miles of road in less than 20 minutes. I mean that's traveling at least 30 miles an hour, and I started feeling a little anxious about my exposed position.

"I looked at it through my theodolite. It was about a mile and a half away at the time. When it topped the rise in the range four road, it looked like a giant floating horse. At the time, I was standing there, saying to myself, over and over, 'that can't be right. It can't possibly be a horse.'

"It floated down the range four road until it had almost reached the edge of the graveled area at range three. Then it drifted sideways, to the west, until it was out in the sagebrush, just behind the control tower, no more than 150 feet from me, and then it just stayed there. It did all of this in total silence.

"I was really confused as to what to do next. I finished my balloon readings, finished my weather report, and phoned the station here at Desert Center. By then, I had been watching it for more than an hour.

"Well, Sergeant Adams was working the forecaster shift. He didn't believe me when I told him about this white foggy patch of rain. He didn't believe that it could possibly be raining for more than an hour out of a clear blue sky, and he wanted me to walk over to it, and get a better look at it.

"When I went over to get a good close look at it, the way the forecaster asked me to, it would just parallel my movements. When I walked in its direction, to the north, it would retreat from me. When I turned around in a circle, it would drift around in a circle. When I returned to my theodolite, it followed me, keeping its distance. It seemed to almost be playing with me. When I looked at it through my theodolite, it would hide behind the range three lounge buildings. Leaving my theodolite open, I walked quickly over to where it was. I got to within 50 feet of it before it drifted away from me. It was capable of moving very fast. It must have been traveling 20 miles an hour when it retreated from me, out into the sagebrush. For a few minutes, there, I could see into the mist. It actually hurt my eyes to look at it when I was up close. When I looked directly into the mist, it looked like there were at least two adult people and three children, all standing or floating inside this rainstorm like patch of mist. The adults looked very tall, maybe six feet, and they were very thin and white. I only got to look at it for a minute or so, before it retreated out into the sagebrush and just drifted back and forth there.

"I started walking back to my weather shack, and I became alarmed when it started following me. Then I became frightened, and I ran the rest of the way back to my shack. I got inside my weather shack, and locked all of the doors from the inside. I tell you, Major, I had become absolutely terrified of that thing. It didn't seem as though it intended to attack me, but it just felt as though it was intensely curious about everything I had and everything I did.

"This patch of mist came all the way up to the theodolite, and seemed to float all around it - as though whatever was hiding in the mist was looking through the theodolite. Then it floated all around the range three buildings, retreated at a leisurely pace back towards the northwest. It split into two patches, and the biggest patch floated up the valley to the northwest. The narrower patch drifted back up the range four road. It would stop and wait, every now and then, as though it were guarding or protecting the white patch floating up the valley. After about a half hour, both patches had reached the range four buildings. Then, both patches drifted back up the valley, towards those mountains to the northwest, where they had come from.

"I don't know what it was, but whatever it was, it couldn't possibly have been an actual rainstorm."

Dwight looked at the major for a few minutes, and the major looked back. Then Dwight spoke, "You say that when you were up close to it, it looked as if there were a family of people inside of the mist?"

"Yes, when I was real close," I answered truthfully. "But it hurt my eyes to look into the mist when I was that close, so I can't be sure. They appeared to look a lot like we do, but there were some differences. They wore chalk white suits that looked like aluminum canvas. They had white skin, just as white as a piece of paper. Their eyes were larger than ours and spread more around the side of their heads. Their noses were flat and they were much thinner then we are."

Dwight continued in big brotherly tones, "Charlie, you got a closer and better look at range four Harry than any weather observer ever has. You be careful, Charlie. Be very careful."

"But I thought you said that Range Four Harry was a large radioactive horse?" I asked Dwight.

"That's how he appeared to The Major and I, because he was over a mile away at the time. He looked to us the way he looked to you when that patch of mist topped the rise in the range four road. Steve, though, head of the range rats, has always maintained that when you get up close to him, he looks more like a person or a group of people than a horse."

Then Sergeant Walters said, "Charlie, even though I've never seen Range Four Harry, all of us here have learned not to disbelieve you when you turn in an observation. I remember a few months back, on that hot summer morning when it was clear as a bell down here at Desert Center, and you reported that the ranges were totally fogged in, with absolutely no visibility. None of us believed you when you ordered the ranges closed to all aircraft flying below 20,000 feet."

"Yes. On the 4:30 run, I couldn't even see the weather shack when I was 15 feet away from it," I answered respectfully, "My barometer was changing so rapidly that I didn't believe my altimeter setting was of any use, so I didn't want any planes coming below the mountains into the Mojave Wells valley until the sun had a chance to burn the fog off."

Sergeant Walters continued, "Well, I remember how we all thought that you had been drinking, and maybe weren't sober enough to be reporting the weather. I remember how all of us were in agreement, and sent those six F105 airplanes up for low level strafing and skip bombing lessons anyway. I remember even talking with the Desert Center tower, and giving them the OK to launch the planes, after you had phoned the tower and ordered all of the flights canceled."

Then Sergeant O'Keefe spoke up, "That bird colonel that was leading the flight, burned us when he got back. I remember him showing up here with the Desert Center base commander, and chewing us up one side and down the other. The tower operator who OK'ed the flight was given an article 15 disciplinary hearing, and demoted one grade. They played back the recording of you ordering the ranges closed and stating why, and the operator didn't have a leg to stand on for OK'ing the flight."

Then the major interjected, "Remember that surprise inspection which the Inspector General from Tinker pulled on us, after that Colonel complained all the way up the line. He claimed that the fog obscured the top of Mount Baldy and one of his men missed the peak by less than 50 feet. I got sick of answering questions from that Inspector General."

Then Sergeant Walters said in fatherly tones, "When you're up there, remember, Charlie, you can call anyone of us here at the station, or at home, anytime. If you should ever decide that you want a second observer up there with you, just phone Dwight, or the major, or me. We'll send someone like Dwight or Payne right up on the same day."

"Thanks, Sergeant," I replied. "Thanks, all of you. I'll remember that, but don't worry about me. I'll be just fine. There's nothing up there that's going to hurt me."

Then Dwight said, seriously, "I hope so, Charlie. I sure hope so."

The meeting ended as abruptly as it had begun. I checked out the Desert Center detachment truck, stopped by the supply warehouse for six months of weather forms, a couple of boxes of batteries, and several boxes of extra balloons. Then, I stopped off at my barracks for my clothes, my shaving kit, and my uniforms. My roommate, Payne, was just getting up. "What's up? Charlie," he asked. Payne stood 6'2", weighed 260 lb., all muscle. He was built like a tank. When he was in a pleasant mood, most men wanted to keep him that way. I was no exception.

"It's McIntyre," I answered in even tones. "He's in some kind of trouble up at Mojave Wells. Something must have scared him, out on the ranges, and now the winds he's sending in are useless. If I don't do something fast, the major will court martial him. He'll get brig time and a section eight discharge for sure."

"Yeah, I agree with you," answered Payne. "I could hear Walters and O'Keefe in the major's office, yesterday when I worked day shift. If Dwight hadn't talked them into giving you a chance to go up there, and check things out, the major would already have him in the brig, and his mother would be starving. What I can't figure out, Charlie, is how anything could frighten McIntyre. He grew up in the slums of New York City, and he always carries those knives with him. Last month I had to stop a fight between him and two white guys in that bar just off base. The fact that there were two of them didn't bother him in the slightest. Then, on the way back to base, he was angry with me for stepping in, but I had to. He'd have knifed those two before either one of them knew what was happening."

"I sure agree with you. I'd better hurry. Maybe I can catch him over the noon meal," I answered as I loaded my duffel bag into the waiting truck, and headed off base.

It was another beautiful late summer day, in the Palm Meadows valley. One beautiful desert scene merged into another as I headed across the valley and northwest towards Mojave Wells. The mountains on both sides of the pass were absolutely stunning as they rested in their late summer foliage.

It was going on 11 o'clock when I pulled my truck off the highway and through the entrance into the Mojave Wells field. I knew that McIntyre was scheduled for an 11:15 balloon run, and there were no planes using range three today. I decided to head directly out to the range three weather shack. I hoped I could get there before McIntyre phoned the winds into Desert Center. That way, I could make sure the winds he phoned in were accurate. I could pretend I hadn't arrived yet so he would get all of the credit.

He needed all the help he could get in staving off a section eight.

As I was driving out the range three road, nostalgia flooded over me. I noticed that 11:20 had arrived. Still no balloon had been released. When I finally arrived out at range three and pulled up in front of the weather shack, there could no longer be any doubt. Not only was the range deserted but judging by the lack of truck tracks, the weather shack hadn't been used for many days.

Using my spare set of keys, I unlocked the front door and peered inside. Everything looked normal, but unused. I stepped gingerly inside and looked around. According to the records, no balloon runs had been taken at range three for almost two full weeks. A quick check of the balloon inventory showed 45 more balloons than it should have. The shelves inside held his personal radio, one of his favorite cigarette lighters, two of his magazines, a letter home dated a week ago Tuesday, and almost $5 dollars in cash.

I decided not to phone Desert Center just yet, until I had a chance to talk with McIntyre. I closed the weather shack and locked it, and started walking back to the detachment truck. It was a beautiful day on the ranges. I lingered a few minutes, just to enjoy the sagebrush, the birds, and the soft gentle winds. Out on the skip bomb area, out in the sagebrush to the southeast, the wind, or something hidden on the ground, was making a path of smooth ripples as it headed down towards range two at the base of the mountains to the southeast. Off in the distance I could hear a gentle barking. I concluded there must be a stray dog or something down that way. As I was climbing into my truck, I was certain I heard a short, sudden whinny, much like that of a horse, coming from the northeast. In any event, it was going on noon. I knew I was going to have to drive fast in order to make the noon meal at the chow hall. I started the truck. As I wheeled the truck around, I noticed one of McIntyre's throwing knives lying in the middle of the graveled area. I stopped, picked, it up, placed it on the truck seat next to me, and headed into base.

It took me a while to make it to the chow hall. There was a lot on my mind, and I had a lot of thinking to do. As I pulled up into the parking area on the west side of the chow hall, I noticed the Mojave Wells weather truck sitting there, parked in the back. Except for the cooks, the chow hall was deserted when I strode in.

"Charlie!" yelled Smokey as I walked in. "It's good to see you. What brings you up here?"

The cooks surrounded me before I knew it. They were all shaking my hand and telling me how good it was to see me again.

"Desert Center wants me to relieve McIntyre," I stated. Then, realizing that criticizing him wouldn't help my purpose, I continued with a fast paced white lie, "We have some new guys arriving down at Desert Center. The Major wants McIntyre to train them. McIntyre remembers what's in all of those manuals better than I do."

Smokey laughed and replied, "You know Charlie, you are so honest that some days you can't lie worth a darn. You're up here because Desert Center has noticed how screwed up those winds are that the new cook has been calling in, aren't you?"

There was hardly any point in denying it to a good friend like Smokey, so I responded truthfully, "Yes, but don't tell anybody. If I don't do something fast, Mic will get six weeks in the brig and a section eight."

"That bad." replied Smokey.

"Yah, they're mad," I answered. "Tell me, what's been going on up here, anyway?"

"Well, I tell you, Charlie, ever since you left, old Mic has been having one hell of a time of it. First there was that barracks down by the runway that you always stayed in. You know, of course that nobody but you has ever stayed in that barracks since white things started showing up in that barracks, way back in 1954. Well, Mic, you know, bunked in there with you. Then, a couple of days after he was in there by himself, he became afraid of the place. That first Wednesday night, he parked his truck over behind the airman's club. He locked the truck doors and laid way down in the front seat. Then he'd look out by using a hand mirror, like he'd learned in New York City. He sat there until way into the morning, watching the barracks to see if anything went inside or not. Sure enough, about one in the morning he saw these two adults and three children come out of the sagebrush northwest of here, sneak up to the barracks and go inside. He was mighty scared. He said they were white all over and something about them didn't look normal."

"You say he saw a white family go into the barracks where he was sleeping?" I asked.

"Yup." replied Smokey. "But they weren't white like the people in town. These guys were really white."

"They were whiter than I am?" I asked.

"Ah, man," laughed Smokey. "You aren't white. You just think you're white on account of all your grand daddies came from England. You'll see. One day both you and I will be standing up in front of Jesus without our skins on

236

and you'll see. Underneath we're both the same color. Remember, Charlie, you and I are brothers – we're blood - blood brothers before Jesus. But these guys, man, I got a glimpse of them later that night when they were out hiding in the sagebrush. They were white - I mean they were REAL white.

Well, Mic came over to our barracks and got a bunch of us together while these guys were still in that barracks. There were 8 or 10 of us. We were going over there to trap them. We all wanted to give them a good beating, but Steve, Bryan, and your friend Doug all got in front of us and told us that it would be the dumbest thing we ever did if we went over there. They swore that those white guys would kill all of us for sure. Since Steve out ranked us, he ordered us back into our barracks, Mic included. That's where we spent the night. There's no extra space in our barracks so we got a bed out of storage. We set it up in the aisle, right by the bathroom. That's where Mic is sleeping now."

"So why is the cook making up the winds now?" I asked.

"We just don't know," responded Smokey, shaking his head from side to side. "That's something he and Steve worked out a couple of weeks ago. Old Mic was out there at range three, one morning. He came back into base scared out of his skin. Steve has been having us cover for him ever since."

"So where is McIntyre, now?" I asked.

"He's out on the ranges with Steve and a bunch of range rats, right now. You'll have to wait until they come for evening chow to talk with him. I'll tell you one thing, he's going to be happy that you're up here to send him back to Desert Center."

My empty stomach reminded me that I hadn't eaten yet. The time for the next balloon run was rapidly approaching. Turning to the new cook, I stated simply, "Starting now, I'll be responsible for all of the weather measurements for as long as I'm up here. So I don't want you to phone in any more weather information to Desert Center. I'll eat, here, real fast, and I'll take the rest of the weather measurements for today and for the rest of my TDY."

The new cook seemed only too happy to hand me the forms he'd been using, the keys to the weather shacks, and the keys to the Mojave Wells weather truck. I grabbed a quick meal, climbed into the Desert Center weather detachment truck, and headed on out to range three. I had to hurry if I intended to get the balloon off on time.

The drive out was uneventful, and soon I was parking my weather truck in front of the range three weather shack. It was a beautiful day. As I climbed out of my truck at range three, I could still hear that distant barking out in the sagebrush.

I opened the weather shack and noted that the time was 1:30 exactly. Since the run was scheduled for 1:30, I decided I'd better phone Desert Center and let them know that the run would be late. First, I jerked a white balloon from its box, for use against clear blue skies. I attached it to the helium-filling nozzle and turned on the helium. The gauges showed immediately that the cylinder was empty. "More delays!" I exclaimed, as I opened the side door to the east. I picked up the phone, and dialed Desert Center. Dwight answered.

"Dwight!" I exclaimed, "It's me, Charlie. I'm up here at range three. I'm running late on the 1:30 run. I'm going to have to change helium cylinders, and adjust the theodolite, so the run will be 20 minutes late."

Dwight laughed, "So, you didn't stop to tease any women in the bars downtown, like Sergeant Walters and I bet you would."

"No." I laughed in return, "But I sure wanted to. Phone me when you finish the 2:00 p.m. weather report. I should be just finishing the winds."

"Right," answered Dwight. "Where's McIntyre?"

I didn't feel it would help McIntyre's case if I said very much, so I answered with a white lie, "I needed a couple of new screws for the base of the theodolite. He's off at the motor pool getting them. The theodolite was moving all over on him because a couple of the screws were broken. He was confused as to which direction is north, so he didn't catch it."

Dwight laughed, "That'll keep him from losing a stripe and getting a section eight, Charlie, but it'll never convince me. I'll phone you at 2:00."

I switched to a new helium cylinder and rushed the balloon run. Of course, there was nothing really wrong with the screws on the theodolite. I was short on time so I didn't pay much attention to the sounds that I occasionally heard coming from way out in the sagebrush. I was just finishing the computations when Dwight phoned back. He never doubted me, but he did sound noticeably relieved when I answered the phone. Now he could be absolutely certain that these winds were dependable.

After I had hung up the phone, I tidied up the place. I didn't disturb any of McIntyre's personal belongings or his money. I was quite tired. I decided that I would wait until the morning to correct the errors in the weather forms. I

239

locked up the shack. Then I spent some time standing by my truck, studying the sagebrush meadows east of the range three buildings. As I stood there watching the beautiful desert scene in front of me, I began to wonder if there wasn't something hiding, or playing, way out in the sagebrush, to the southeast and to the northeast of me. As I watched, I felt certain that I had gotten a glimpse of something white, moving through gaps in the sagebrush. I thought about it for a few minutes. I began to wonder if I was really as alone as I thought I was.

"Oh, well." I said to myself, "I'm certainly not going to make the mistake of going out there to check. I'm too tired for that." I shrugged it off, climbed into my truck, and headed on into base. When I arrived, I naturally parked the detachment truck next to the west end of the empty double barracks. However, I wasn't sure which barracks I would actually sleep in. Then I walked up to the chow hall. I drove the Mojave Wells weather truck over to the motor pool for gas, down to my barracks, and parked the two trucks side by side.

All of this had taken some time. It was good to be back. I naturally spent a lot of time talking with my friends. When I got back to my barracks, it was already time for the evening meal. I spent some time watching the large 4-wheel-drive power wagons of Steve and the range rats as they came in off the ranges. They had been working up the valley way out to the west. The dry dust from the desert formed large and artistic clouds in the late afternoon sun as they came in toward base. Like hungry soldiers everywhere, they headed directly for the chow hall. I could see McIntyre sitting in the seat behind Steve. Even in the distance, it was obvious that he was terrified of something.

I decided to unpack my belongings before going up to the chow hall. I felt that things would go easier on McIntyre if I first let him have a good meal. It shocked me, then, when McIntyre, chose to come running down to my barracks before even going for chow. I still remember how frantically he ran the two blocks or so to my barracks, calling out my name as he ran. I guess I hadn't realized that we'd become such good friends.

"Charlie! Charlie!" he shouted frantically, "You can't sleep there. You can't be in there when night comes."

"Why, McIntyre?" I asked calmly, stepping outside to meet him.

"They'll come, Charlie. They always do!" he carried on frantically. "You're taking your life in your hands. They'll come! I tell you, they always come! Come over to my barracks. You can even use my bunk. I'll sleep on the floor."

"Not even if I lock both doors?" I asked.

"That doesn't mean anything!" exclaimed McIntyre. "The locks on these doors don't mean anything to them. They'll open them right up and walk right in."

"Who's them?" I asked. "Who will open the doors and walk right in?"

"Those white creatures!" replied McIntyre, nearly screaming out his response. "We've seen them, me and Steve and the range rats, way out in the desert north of here. You can't stay here in this barracks, Charlie! You just can't."

I could see that there was no reasoning with McIntyre. The state he was in was just too emotional. I tried to calm him down. I said to him, "Tell you what. After we eat, let's you and I get cleaned up and go out for a couple of beers.

Then you can tell me all about it. We'll take the Desert Center detachment truck up the highway to that bar at Willow flats. It's quiet there. I'll buy the beer. You and I can have a good time talking things over."

McIntyre thought about it for a minute. Then he agreed. Two meals, some warm showers, and fresh clothes later, Mic and I laughed our way up to the bar at Willow flats. I hid the detachment truck behind the large willow trees out back. Mic and I went in for some beer and a nice long talk.

"Don't worry about Desert Center," I said, as we began our second beer. "I told them that some of the screws on the theodolite had worked loose. You, being from the eastern cities, had probably gotten your directions turned around. They don't really believe me, but it'll keep you out of the brig. Just between you and I, though, I need to know why you're not taking the winds every day."

"Yes, old man, you do need to know that," responded McIntyre slowly.

"You know me, Mic," I continued. "You can tell me anything, anything at all. I'd never tell anyone. Especially, I'd never breathe a word of what we talk about to the sergeants and the officers. I've always figured that one of the privileges we have being enlisted men, is being able to speak freely to one another without worrying about officers finding out what was said."

"I agree with you, Charlie," answered McIntyre. "You promise that you'll believe me, no matter what I say?"

"My word and honor, Mic," I answered truthfully. "Why are you spending your time picking up practice bombs with the range rats? That's a lot harder job than being a weather man."

McIntyre thought for a few minutes. Then he answered, "Because it's the only way I can stay alive while I'm up here. If I were ever to go back out to the weather shack alone, one of those white creatures would kill me."

"What white creatures?" I asked in surprise. "Why would they kill you?"

McIntyre, the second beer loosening his tongue as I had expected, leaned back in his chair, and began describing the events of the last three weeks.

"Don't play dumb with me, Charlie." exclaimed McIntyre angrily. "You know they're out there. You have to know they're out there. The way you like to drive alone, way out into the desert north of here. You had to have seen them, the way you always got up at three in the morning and drove alone way out onto the ranges at night. They had to have been out there around those buildings, waiting for you. You had to have known they were out there when you left me up here alone. You had to have known they're out there," he exclaimed in angry and bitter tones.

"Who? McIntyre?" I exclaimed in surprise. "Who's out there? I swear Mic. I give you my word. I've never seen anything real out there. All I've ever seen is some mirages … some tricks that my eyes played on me … some sea gulls through the heat waves … some coyotes … some day dreams when I was tired and half asleep … some lights out in the distance at night. I've never seen anything that I believed was real. Who's out there?"

Calming somewhat, McIntyre continued, obviously not believing me, "Yah, sure. Like you never saw them out there in the desert, up close. Go on, lie to me just I'm not white like you. Say what you want. Where you get the guts to go back out there alone, I'll never know. But you just remember when you're out there, alone, those white creatures will come for you just like they came for me. Just 'cause your skin is white doesn't mean anything to them because they aren't human like we are. You and I should have stuck closer together because we're human! We're the same kind! The first week I was here, I saw them way out in the distance, way up to the north. Like you, at first, I didn't believe my own eyes. Then, the next morning, when I woke up in the barracks, I knew I wasn't alone so I got out of there. I didn't even get dressed until after sunup. Then, after that night when I saw them going into my barracks, I switched barracks and I started feeling safe again. Then there was that Tuesday when I was down at range one."

"Yes. I remember when you were phoning in the weather reports from range one," I interrupted. "That was a week ago Tuesday."

"I had just finished taking the last run of the day, and I had already locked up the weather shack," explained McIntyre. "I was walking to my truck when, as usual, I heard these sounds out in the sagebrush."

"Sounds?" I asked.

"Yes, sounds," responded McIntyre, "Don't play dumb with me! You heard them too when you were out there alone. Sounds! When I say sounds, I mean real sounds! There isn't anything the matter with me. I'm just as smart as you are. I even got a better score than you on the level 5 observer's exam. When I say sounds, I mean sounds! One of them sounded like a dog barking. Another sounded like a horse whinnying. I picked up a good-sized rock and started looking around. Out in the sagebrush, I saw something move. It was white all over. It was hiding behind one of the sagebrush plants. I took aim and threw my rock at it. It jumped back into the brush, but still, I hit it pretty good. I thought it was a dog or something because as soon as I hit it, it let out a loud barking like sound. Then from way out in the sagebrush, I could hear barking and whinnying from all over the place. All the barking scared me so I ran to my truck and got out of there."

"Good thinking," I stated thoughtfully - tacitly admitting that I had heard the sounds too.

"The next morning it happened," continued McIntyre, now becoming visibly afraid. "I got up at 3:15 a.m. same as always, and drove out to range three for the morning run. When I got there, one of those white creatures was waiting for me."

"Waiting for you out at range three?" I asked in surprise.

"Yes! Yes!" responded McIntyre, now showing visible fear. "Don't look at me as if I'm some kind of idiot. I'm just as smart as you! When I have my knives, I'm even better than you in a fight."

"Oh, I didn't mean anything by my look, Mic," I answered quickly. "I was just surprised that anyone would dare call you out in a fight. I thought everyone knew what a great fighter you are."

"I thought so too," answered McIntyre, mellowing somewhat. "You see, when I got out to range three that morning, I put my headlights on bright and started driving around like I always do. I wanted to make sure that there weren't any coyotes or snakes or white shadows around there. Well, I no sooner brought the truck to the edge of the range three buildings when I saw her."

"Her?" I asked.

"Yes, Charlie – HER!" answered McIntyre. "They have male and female like we do. This one was a woman. She was standing at the base of the control tower in plain view, waiting for me."

"What did she look like, Mic?" I asked.

"She was one of the female white creatures," answered McIntyre, now becoming visibly emotional with fear. "She was just standing there waiting for me. She stood maybe 6 feet 3 inches tall. She was real thin. She was white all over. She had a real chalky white skin with blue eyes, and real transparent blonde shoulder length hair. She seemed to be surrounded by some type of white fluorescent mist or veil. It looked as though she were standing there in a large patch of white shadows. She was holding some kind of weapon in her hands. It was long and thin, like a pencil.

At first I wasn't afraid because she was a woman. I thought she probably just wanted to talk. I stopped the truck on this side of the buildings. I arranged it so that the bright headlights shone directly into her eyes. She was only about 100 feet in front of the truck, a little too far for me to use my throwing knives. So I took one of my throwing knives in my hand and stepped out of the truck. I stood right by my open truck door. I figured I'd taunt her and draw her in closer to the truck, so she'd be in knife throwing range. I figured the headlights would keep her blinded, so all of the advantages would be on my side. It's a trick I learned in New York City."

"Pretty clever." I responded.

"But I tell you, old man," continued McIntyre, "She wasn't frightened in the least bit. The bright headlights didn't bother her in the slightest. She never once put up her arm to shield her eyes or blinked or anything. She could look right over at me, through the glare of the high beams, and focus right in on the knife I was holding in my hand. I called over to her, 'Who are you? What do you want?'

She started floating slowly towards me."

"Floating Mic?" I asked.

"Yes, old man!" answered McIntyre. "Those White creatures don't walk if they don't have to. Those suits they wear give them the power to float."

I sat quietly in stunned disbelief.

"Well anyway," continued McIntyre, "She spoke back to me in English. She was angry with me. She said I had broken her little boy's arm. She said they were going to have to take him to a hospital where the air was thicker and warmer or else it wouldn't heal. She said the hospital was a long way away. She said it was going to take about two months just to get there, and it was going to be a very painful trip for her little boy.

I tried to reason with her. I told her that I hadn't broken any little boy's arm and that I liked to play with kids. She wouldn't hear any of it. She told me that I was too stupid to know what I'd done. Then she told me that the American generals had asked that I be given one warning before she and her friends killed me. She said that this was the warning. She said that if I ever came back out to the ranges alone, their Captain would kill me. As she was threatening me, she kept coming in closer. By now, she was only 50 feet or so in front of the truck. I decided to try one of my knives. I stepped to my left, a little, and I let her have it with the throwing knife I was holding in my right hand."

"What happened then, Mic?" I asked.

"That's when I knew I was in deep trouble," responded McIntyre, now shaking with fear. "I aimed the knife straight

247

at her, but when it got close to that suit she was wearing, it just slowed down and fell harmlessly to the ground.

Then she became totally out-raged with me. She said that if I didn't leave the ranges immediately, she'd kill me right where I stood. Old man, I was more terrified than I ever thought I could get. I panicked. I jumped in my truck and laid rubber getting out of there. But I have to tell, you, old man, she couldn't have been human."

"Why do you say that?" I asked.

"Because when I was leaving, she ran up alongside the truck, looked me right in the eyes through the open window and shouted at me, 'Don't ever come back to this place or we'll kill you! Do you hear me? We'll kill you! Do you hear me? Don't ever come back or we'll kill you!!'"

"But why does that prove that she wasn't human?" I asked.

"Because, old man," responded McIntyre, on the verge of breaking down from the terror of it all. "Because I had the truck floored in second gear. She ran along side my truck, screaming at me through the open window for more than two miles. I was traveling more than 30 miles an hour at the time."

I could see that Mic was having a hard time controlling his fears and his tears. I gave him a few minutes rest while I got him another beer. When he was ready to talk again, I continued, "I don't understand why you are helping the range rats pick up practice bombs out in the desert? I mean, if you're afraid to go out to range three alone, why didn't you just stay in the barracks and make up the winds like so many other weather observers have done?"

Downing some more beer, Mic responded, "These barracks aren't a safe place for me to stay alone. If those

white creatures feel like killing me, they'll just come right
into the barracks and get me, day or night. I talked it over
with Steve. The only way I can be safe when I'm up here, is
to stay with the range rats day and night."

McIntyre paused for a minute, as the extra beer found its
way into his consciousness. Then he continued, "You see,
Steve, Doug, and Bryan think they know of a place out in
the desert where they might be able to talk to the white
things. Steve and the range rats believe that if they take me
out there with them, maybe the white creatures and I could
talk things over. Then maybe I could go back to being the
weather observer."

"But, McIntyre," I interjected, trying to hide my
disbelief, "Nobody lives out in Mojave Wells valley. The
valley and the surrounding mountains are totally desolate.
Where would such a meeting take place?"

"Steve says its up in those mountains to the northwest,"
replied McIntyre simply.

I sat quietly for a few minutes, remembering the
mornings when I watched the white rainstorm patches
floating out of those mountains to the northwest.

"Has Steve actually talked to these white things?" I
asked.

McIntyre took a few minutes before responding. "I don't
know for sure. Last Thursday, he left me with the other
range rats and two of the power wagons. Then he, Bryan,
and Doug drove up into those mountains alone in the third
power wagon. Three or four hours later they came back
looking kind of frightened, especially Bryan. Steve said that
the mother and the son had already left for the hospital, and
that nothing could be done until they get back. Nobody
knows when that will be, but Steve, Doug, and Bryan are

certain that I'll be killed if I go back out to any of the weather shacks, with or without them. When you go back out there, Charlie, they'll come around. They always do. They're real curious. When they come, please explain to them that I didn't mean to break any little boy's arm! Make sure they understand that I'm never coming back out to these ranges – NEVER! – even if the Air Force were to court martial me! NEVER! I'm NEVER coming back!"

I could see that the beer was finally getting to McIntyre. Since he'd already told me everything he knew, I decided it was time to take him back to his barracks. I helped him to the waiting truck. Soon I was helping him into his barracks, and then into his bunk. I had just finished doing so when Steve approached me. Old friend that he was, he began, "It's sure a good thing for old Mic that you came up here, Charlie. What do you want us to do with him tomorrow?"

"Keep him with you like you have been, until the noon meal," I responded. "That'll give me time to make up two sets of corrected weather reports for the time he's been up here. I'll bring in his things from the range three shack after tomorrow's 12:30 run. I'll send one set of correct reports down to Desert Center with him. He'll need it to cover his butt in the Major's office. I'll leave the Desert Center detachment truck parked out in front of this barracks. He can drive it back to Desert Center tomorrow afternoon. I'll switch over to driving the Mojave Wells weather truck."

"Right," answered Steve.

I continued, "I really appreciate you saving Mic's life like you did, Steve. I'm certain that Mic appreciates it too. I was just wondering, Mic was saying something about you talking to some white people way up in the mountains?"

Steve thought for a minute before he responded. Then he answered pleasantly, "You really don't want me to answer that question, Charlie, not the way you like to drive around by yourself, alone, way out in the desert. All I'm going to say is that you don't have to worry because no white person would ever mistake you for McIntyre."

I was too surprised to respond. I stood there wondering what to say next. Steve continued in a friendly tone, "Oh, I meant to tell you Charlie, while you were out with Old Mic, the boys and I rearranged this barracks and the barracks next door. We moved some of the boys next door. Then we brought over your things from that barracks down on the flight line where you were going to stay. The bed and locker down there at the end are yours."

Then Steve, standing in front of me, thought for a minute, and stated in brotherly tones, "I know you, Charlie. You aren't afraid of anything, even the things you should be afraid of. Just remember, anytime you want me to go with you, out to the ranges on that morning run, or maybe make up some winds for you here in the barracks like I did for all those other Desert Center guys, you just wake me up. I'm good at making up those morning winds. You and I, we're closer than any brothers, and that's what brothers are for."

I finished McIntyre's remaining four weeks of TDY and returned to Desert Center.

Paperback Hero

…He has told us
that you always have pleasant memories of us,
and that you long to see us,
just as we, also, long to see you.

1 Thessalonians 3:6

It seemed out of place, but suddenly the phone rang. Working in the Desert Center weather station at night was always lonely, but this was a rainy Christmas Eve. I had returned from TDY at Mojave Wells. Loneliness had long since taken over my thoughts. It seemed that no one cared about me and that only Santa would have questions about the weather.

At first I wasn't sure the phone was actually ringing for me, so I wasn't going to answer it. Being single and a long way from home, I had also agreed to work a double shift. This allowed everyone else to spend this Christmas Eve with their families. Extra work was hardly a problem for a man as lonely as I was on that rainy, stormy winter evening.

The hours had seemed to drag on, but something unusual had already happened to me earlier this lonely evening. Along about sundown, I had been standing in quiet silence, looking out the weather station window into the rain, the cold winds, the drizzle, and the darkening fog as the dreariness of this stormy night time settled over the world in which I lived. Slowly, I had begun to feel as though my two guardian angels were standing near me, in sympathy with my loneliness. It felt as though one was standing next to the doorway behind me, and one was standing just behind me, out of sight on my left. It felt as though they wanted to know what I planned to do to celebrate Christmas as I worked these two night shifts. I thought about it for a minute or so, and I decided that for my Christmas celebration, along about 2:30 A.M., I would walk down to the other end of this deserted building. I planned to walk down to where the vending machines and the rest rooms were located. That section of the building was the Base Operations section. It was completely shut down, the doors were locked, and lights were turned off on this Christmas Eve. There, in the dark emptiness of this silent Sunday night, I planned to have my Christmas celebration alone, by buying from the vending machines, a cup of coffee and a candy bar. I had it all planned quite well. There, as I held the coffee and the candy bar in my hands, I planned to say a short prayer of thanks, and to ask God to be with me in the future as he had so mercifully been with me in the past. As soon as I had made this decision, it felt like my two guardian angels were happy. Then it felt as though the two of them left me alone, while they themselves had gone somewhere, out into the storm.

Then, earlier that evening, it felt as though one of my angels had returned for a few minutes. It felt as though he wanted something very simple from me. Following where my feelings lead me, it felt as though he was leading me as I walked outside into the cold rain. For almost a half hour, feeling as though he were standing beside me, pointing towards the base of the clouds northeast of me, I stood in the cold dark storm. Afraid to offend God or my guardian angels on this Christmas evening, I obliged my unseen, unheard friend by very carefully studying the base of the clouds northeast of me. After I had observed one storm pass and another storm begin, the angel seemed to be happy.

The half hour over, and me dripping wet, I had returned inside to warm up and dry off. I felt as though my guardian angel, however, had gone off, once again out into the storm.

Now, hours later, much as I tried to ignore it, the phone kept on ringing. It was already fifteen minutes to midnight, almost time for another weather report and still more than two hours to my planned Christmas celebration. I put down the paperback history book I was reading. It was captivating. It brought to life the first crusade and the exciting hero Bohemond, who had struggled against all odds to get his followers into the city of Jerusalem.

After many rings, however, I decided that, whoever it was, I probably needed to talk to them more than they needed to talk to me, so, putting down my paperback, I picked up the phone.

The night would be long, I decided. I had signed in at 4:00 p.m. and my double shift as the duty weather observer would last until 8:00 in the morning. Maybe, I thought, my guardian angels had sent someone to cheer me up.

"Desert Center weather station," I said. "Charlie speaking."

"Desert Center, Desert Center, are you there?" screamed the voice on the other end of the line.

I recognized the caller as one of my civilian friends. It was one of the duty weather observers from Palm Meadows Field, the civilian airport for the city of Palm Meadows. The city was 20 miles or so, down the valley. I responded, happily, "Dan, how nice of you to call."

"Charlie, thank God it's you," he screamed.

"Gee, I wish more beautiful young women would think like you do." I laughed.

Without responding to my humor he continued screaming, "Charlie, we're in big trouble down here."

"How can that be?" I asked. "According to your weather reports Palm Meadows Field has been closed since before 6:00 this evening. I was surprised that you were open at all because I've seen big thunderstorms down where you are since early this morning. I myself, closed Desert Center for the night when I came on duty at four."

"The idiot before me made the mistake of opening the airport for a half hour before I came on. Two 707 jetliners fully loaded with passengers took off from Los Angeles International and headed here. Then the thunderstorms got worse and when they got here, he closed the airport so they couldn't land."

"Why didn't they just go on to Phoenix?" I asked.

"Those places are all closed due to bad weather, too. Then all the airports in California and all over the west closed. Then the idiot kept telling the tower that the storms would go away and kept the planes circling. Now they're both down to less that 30 minutes of fuel. They're going to have to crash up where you are."

"Crash them up where I am?" I dead-panned, not really sure I had heard him right.

"Yes," he screamed, "There's no other choice. We're getting hail the size of oranges down here and driving rain and lightning and the clouds are laying right down on the runway. They can't do it here. They'll all be killed. My weather radar shows nothing but constant thunderstorms located right over all of your runways, too. I called up your tower. They tell me the storms are so bad up where you are that the tower operators can't even see the ground. There's no choice! There's absolutely no other choice! Your last weather report said that any safe landing at Desert Center would be impossible! They have to crash on the highway, up where you are!

"Now let me tell you what my plan is," he continued. "I've asked the state police to block off that section of highway that goes right past the entrance to Desert Center. They're doing it right now. The highway has two sets of two lanes. They're both real straight. There's room in there to crash two airplanes. To do it, I need your help.

The base has two entrances. I've already told all of your fire engines, all of your ambulances, and all of my emergency vehicles to go to those two gates. The television camera crews are already out there. If you can get those planes to crash real close to those two base gates, it will be easy for the ambulances to get the survivors into the base hospital. It's our only hope."

"I must not have heard you right," I responded slowly. "I thought you said that two planes with lots of people on board, are going to crash out on the highway."

"Yes! Yes!" he screamed. "Yes! Right out in front of where you are! They're ready to crash wherever you tell them to! The stewardesses have already drilled the passengers on the crash procedures. Everyone on board is already belted in and practiced bending over in crash position. All we need is your help to pick out the best place to crash, and to time the impacts properly!"

"Oh, there must be a better way." I responded. Crashing airplanes seemed like such a waste of a good Christmas Eve. "The pavement out there is only thin asphalt. It'll never hold the weight of a 707. The landing gear will collapse and all of the people will be killed. There are telephone poles and high voltage electrical wires out there. Such a landing attempt would be a terrible disaster. How much fuel do they have left?"

"One has 35 minutes and the other is down to 20." he said in a panic. "They have to crash! There isn't time for anything else! They've both been up there circling for six or seven hours!"

"Where are the airplanes now?" I asked.

"They're circling twenty miles up the valley, just west of Desert Center, at 10,000 feet. They're waiting for you to tell them where to crash."

"That won't be necessary," I replied. "Have Palm Meadows tower pass them off to Desert Center tower. Tell Desert Center tower to give me exactly one minute to transmit my aircraft emergency message so the weather center at Tinker, Oklahoma, knows I won't be sending any weather reports for a while. Then have Desert Center tower call me on the emergency telephone. I'll need the tower to relay instructions to the pilots. Tell the pilots I can bring them in here."

"Right!" he shouted. "I'll do it!" As he abruptly hung up the phone, I suddenly realized that the Palm Meadows observer still thought my plan was to crash the planes on the highway. Consequently, the highway remained blocked and all of the emergency vehicles stayed parked at the two gates.

I stepped into my teletype room, and typed up a simple procedure message for the weather center at Tinker AFB, Oklahoma. It read, "DESERT CENTER AFB. GOING OFF LINE FOR NEXT TWO HOURS. BASE CLOSED DUE TO CONSTANT HEAVY THUNDERSTORMS.

VISIBILITY ZERO. CEILING ZERO. CLOUDS ON RUNWAY. RAIN HEAVY. SOME HAIL. WIND 210 DEGREES, GUSTS TO 65 MPH. AIRCRAFT EMERGENCY IN PROGRESS. TWO 707S TRAPPED ALOFT, FUEL SHORT, MUST LAND AT DESERT CENTER. WILL RETURN ON LINE WHEN EMERGENCY IS OVER."

One minute later, my emergency procedure message was just coming out of the teletype transmitter when the emergency phone from the tower began ringing off the hook. I answered the phone. I turned off the lights in the weather station, and opened one of the windows to the outside. I needed my night vision, and I needed to see my instruments from outdoors.

Months ago I had insisted that the phone be located next to the outside door and that it have a very long cord. This made it possible to take the phone with me as I walked outside onto the tarmac.

As I answered the phone, I noticed that the connection was crystal clear. The equipment maintenance men had done an excellent job. "What do I do with these two 707's?" asked the tower operator nervously.

Heavy rain was still falling. I positioned myself under the roof's overhang. From here, if the night were clear, I would have had a clear view of the airfield and the mountains to the north. The position also let me look through the open window at the dimly lit dials on my weather instruments. It also let me look at the clouds from almost the same position that I felt the angel had asked me to earlier this evening.

"Tell the plane with the least fuel to head up the valley to the northeast. Tell him to stay on the navigation beam so he knows where he is." I answered calmly. Then I recomputed the altimeter setting, informed the operator, and waited while Desert Center tower relayed the instructions to the 707.

"You know the mountain straight north of the runway?" I continued. "As you know it is northeast of me. It has a red beacon light on top of it and a radar transponder so he can see it on his radar screen. Tell him when he is three minutes north of the beacon light to turn east and then to come back south, heading straight towards the field. I want him to come back exactly over that beacon light. Tell him to come back at an altitude not more than 50 feet higher than the beacon. Tell him, when he's over the beacon he should have his flaps fully down, his cabin lights off, his landing gear down, and his landing lights turned on. That way I'll be able to see him, and I'll talk him in from there."

I waited as the instructions were told to the pilot.

"He's heading up the valley," responded the tower. "He wants to know where on the highway you want him to crash."

"Oh, no! No!" I shouted into the telephone. "Tell him he's not going to crash! Tell him I intend to have him land at Desert Center. Tell them that I intend to have both of them land safely at Desert Center!"

I waited for a few seconds as the operator spoke to both pilots. After an agonizingly long wait, the tower operator came back on the line.

"None of us think that's possible. They're both terrified at the prospect of crashing out in the desert at night in the rain. Since they have to crash, they're asking to crash out on the highway where they can at least get some help. The pilots need a thousand feet of altitude and one mile of visibility in order to land. I can't even see the ground from the tower windows. They can't possibly find the runway, let alone land safely", returned the tower operator in matter of fact tones.

"I know all that." I replied calmly. "But I can talk them in. The winds have been keeping the thunderstorms away from the mountains to the north. It's storming in the valleys but it's only cloudy and rainy in the mountains.

You're three miles down at the other end of the runway. The thunderstorms have been passing over your end and over the middle, but they haven't been passing directly over my end. It's just raining hard up here.

Up on this end, the thunderstorms have been lasting about 45 minutes as they pass across the field. Then we've had breaks of 15 to 20 minutes. The storm we're having now is just finishing. I'm expecting to have smooth steady winds coming up the valley right towards that beacon light for the next 20 minutes. It was that way between the last two storms. Well, when that happens, it opens holes in the clouds around the mountain and lifts the low clouds off the desert up here at my end of the field. Last time it happened, I could see the red beacon light on the mountain. Then a clear field of view opened between the base of the mountain and my end of the runway. Palm Meadows puts out so much light that the pilots should be able to see those holes in the clouds and follow the light right down to my end of the runway."

"Roger." responded the tower.

I waited while the tower and the pilots talked it over.

"They're both willing to try because you say it's possible." responded the tower. "I told them who you were and how you saved those six F105 pilots last spring."

Then after a short pause, the operator continued, "Remember, I don't have anyone to help you. I'm alone here in the tower and I can't see anything whatever out the windows."

Then after another short pause, he continued, "Remember too, that both 707s are fully loaded with passengers - and both pilots said they would forgive you if you're wrong."

I waited quietly for a few seconds, as the enormity of what he had said sunk in. Then, shrugging off the operator's words, I continued with my instructions. "Tell the first pilot that when he has completed his turn to the south, to have his copilot and all of the passengers looking out the windows, straight down, in case the holes open to the left or right of him.

Tell him the base of the mountain is 100 feet higher than the field, and the desert slopes gradually to the end of the runway. Tell him that as soon as he passes over the red beacon, even if he doesn't see the lights of Palm Meadows, to descend smoothly and quickly to an altitude of 150 feet, and I'll be out here looking for him."

"Roger," responded the tower. "I will as soon as I am able. The head stewardess is leading the passengers in the Lord's Prayer and the pilot didn't want to be disturbed. I guess things are pretty tense on board."

After a significant pause, the operator continued, "The first pilot is proceeding up the valley now. The second is waiting and circling. The first pilot is encountering heavy turbulence, heavy rain and soft hail. He'll be at the turning point in 3 minutes."

The minutes seemed to pass like hours. As I waited, I carefully studied the clouds to the north, just as I had done during the previous break between the storms. Quietly, I prayed that the holes would reopen. Then, in the distance, a great sense of relief came over me as the red beacon marking the top of the mountain became visible in the distance.

"Tell him the storm has just ended where I am." I spoke carefully into the emergency phone. "Tell him that the approach path has opened and that I can see the red beacon light."

A short pause ensued. "He has made it to the turning point. One minute after he turned east, he broke out of the storm." Then a short pause followed. "He's turning south now. His gear is down and his landing lights are on". Another pause. "He's approaching the red beacon."

I listened while standing in the light rain. I studied the clouds in the distance, trying to catch some glimpse of the plane's landing lights. Suddenly, just over the peak of the mountain and its red beacon, a speck of white light momentarily appeared.

"I see him." I spoke into the mouthpiece.

"He sees the lights!" returned the operator. "He sees the lights! When he went over the beacon his copilot got a glimpse of the lights of Palm Meadows! He is back in the clouds and beginning his descent! Do you see him?"

"I see him!" I said, even though he had gone back into the clouds. "Tell him to continue his descent."

Looking down by the base of the clouds, I tried to estimate where he would break out of the clouds. Minutes passed. There was no break out. The clouds were obviously lower than I had expected, but the clearance existed if the pilot could find it in time.

"What's his altitude?" I asked.

A short pause. "He's leveled off at 150 feet."

"Tell him to come fifty feet lower." I said, scanning the clouds for any sign of his landing lights.

Another short pause. "He's down to 100 feet. He can't see anything and he's panicky. Do you see him?" responded the tower.

Suddenly, in the distance, through a ragged group of clouds, I got another momentary glimpse of another white flash.

"Tell him I see him." I responded. He's still at least five minutes from the runway. Tell him the desert is falling away from him and to continue the descent to 70 feet."

Another long pause. In the distance, I could see the clouds were lifting slowly out over the desert.

"He's at 70 feet and he's still in the clouds. Are you sure you see him?" asked the tower.

"Yes," I responded, lying a bit. I had been timing his approach. I calculated that by now the desert underneath him would be no more than 20 feet above the runway.

"Tell him to come down another 10 feet." I spoke carefully into the phone.

A short pause. "He's now at 60 feet." responded the tower.

Still no lights could be seen. "Bring it down another 10 feet." I said.

Another short pause. Then, suddenly in the distance I could see his landing lights just inside the base of the cloud.

"He's at 50 feet. His copilot thinks he got a glimpse of the runway lights," stated the operator.

"I see him clearly." I shouted into the phone. "He's no more than three minutes off the end of the runway. Bring him down slowly another 20 feet."

A short pause followed. Then, in the distance, appeared before my eyes, one of the most unforgettable visions of my life. The 707 began slowly appearing out of the base of the clouds. Without warning, the operator began shouting into the telephone, "He sees the field! He sees the field!"

Then the pilot immediately and intentionally dropped the plane until the landing gear was no more than three feet above the sagebrush. He brought the 707 across that last minute of desert, flaps fully extended, landing gear down, landing lights on, vectoring straight for the end of the runway. The plane raised a little bit to clear the runway lights. I was struck by how much the plane resembled a bride coming down the aisle for a wedding. The plane seemed almost to be floating in the gentle wind. The storm, itself, seemed to retreat before the pilot's obvious determination to bring his plane to the end of the runway.

"Tell him he's going to make it!" I spoke into the telephone.

"I don't think I have to," responded the operator. "That's all He's been screaming into his microphone for the last minute."

"As soon as he lands, start the next plane up the valley." I said.

"Roger," responded the tower.

There was nothing left for me to do but stand quietly in the rain and watch, as the 707 floated slowly over the end of the runway and touched down. The plane was lined up perfectly with the runway. I could hear the pilot break the engines immediately as he touched down.

After the plane had rolled only a thousand feet down the runway, it rolled into the heavy rain that obscured the remainder of the runway and was lost from my field of view. I waited a couple of minutes and I asked the tower operator, "Was the pilot able to stop O.K.?"

"I think so," responded the operator. "I could hear the passengers yelling and shouting a minute ago. They were all pretty happy. The plane has cleared the runway. It is parked down at the end of the field on the taxiway by a hanger. His engines shut down suddenly while the plane was still on the taxiway. The pilot reported that he was out of fuel. He said he needed the help of the ground crew to move the airplane any further. I told him I'd get them there as soon as I could, but it would be a while. I finally found one instrument technician on duty down in one of the hangers. I've sent him out in the pickup truck to check things out, and he reports that everything looks O.K.

The rest of the ground crew is still parked out by the Desert Center front gate waiting for him to crash. They don't know that he's already landed. Right at the minute he's not answering his radio anymore. He seemed awfully shook up, so I guess he's helping the stewardess lead the passengers in a prayer of thanks." concluded the operator.

"Yes", I responded, "I suppose he has a lot to be thankful for." Then, looking down the valley towards the next storm which was approaching sooner than I had expected, I continued, "We better get that second plane in. We probably don't have 10 minutes before the next storm hits. Ask him where he is and how much fuel he has left."

A short pause ensued. Then the operator responded, "He's heading up the valley. He says his fuel is down to less than 15 minutes. He's not sure how much fuel he has because he's never seen his gauges this low."

Privately, I began worrying about the next thunderstorm. I could see that the plane could still make it in safely.

However, between the onrushing thunderstorm and the second 707's short fuel supply, I could also see there was little time to waste.

"Make sure he knows the first 707 made it," I spoke into the phone. "And make sure he knows the holes are still there over the mountain."

"Roger," responded the tower.

Thinking for a minute and performing some mental calculations, I spoke into the telephone, "Tell him to travel only one minute north of the beacon light before turning." I could hear my other phone ringing, but this was certainly no time to answer it.

A short pause followed.

"Roger." returned the operator. Then he continued, "The pilot is terrified. He's more than halfway up the valley. He reports that he is encountering the worst turbulence he's ever seen. The plane is being buffeted at least 50 feet up and down by the storm. He reports that the plane has encountered heavy large hail the size of golf balls. He believes his engines have been damaged and he reports that his plane can't make it in to Desert Center. He's requesting permission to return down the valley and crash land on the highway while he can still get there."

I thought for a few seconds. Then I responded.

"Tell him 'no' on the return. Tell him to continue northeast up the valley. Tell him to adjust his course as far to the east as the navigational beam allows. There'll be less hail over there. Tell him that hail at night always looks twice as large as it really is. Tell him his engines have to be OK because if the hail he's encountering were large enough to damage his engines, his windshield would already have been shattered. Tell him he knows his 707 can take the turbulence. Tell him anything you have to, but keep him coming towards the turning point."

"Roger," responded the operator after a long pause. "He's continuing up the valley. He reports the hail has lightened up, but the turbulence is continuing. He's become absolutely panicky. It's all he and his copilot can do to hold the plane on course. He's certain that he can't make it. He's begging for permission to return down the valley to crash on the highway. He says it's the only chance we have to get anyone off the airplane alive."

"Tell him no on the return," I responded, again. "Tell him he knows well that his 707 can take the turbulence. Tell him to keep his mind on the red beacon. The holes over the mountain are still there and all he needs to do is to get his plane over that red beacon. I can talk him down to the Desert Center runways from there."

After a long pause, the tower operator got back online. "Roger. He's staying on course up the valley. He's certain that they're all going to die I guess, because he's doing an awful lot of praying into the microphone."

"Tell him to leave his landing gear up until he's left the storm. I don't want his landing lights getting iced over." I continued. "Tell him he can think what he wants but I'm certain that he can make it safely into Desert Center."

"Roger." Then after a very long pause, "His copilot reports the hail has ended. The turbulence ended suddenly. He's starting his turn. He's putting the gear down now and turning on the landing lights. They'll be over the red beacon in one minute."

"I'm watching," I responded. "I can still see the beacon."

With a light rain falling, I strained my eyes to see the red beacon in the distance. The beacon was already fuzzy red and it was obvious that the clouds were closing back in. Suddenly the red beacon appeared to blink from red to white, then back to red.

"Tell him I see him." I said into the phone. "Make sure he has begun his descent."

"Roger. He reports that he has passed over the beacon and is descending to 150 feet. "Then a pause ensued. "He has leveled off at 150 feet."

"Tell him to descend to 90 feet." I continued, refusing to admit that I had lost sight of him in the clouds.

"Roger."

Then in the distance, a white light started blinking along the base of a set of ragged clouds. "Tell him I see him." I said. "Tell him to come down another 10 feet. Tell him that when he sees the runway lights, he's to stay as high as possible and not to come lower than 50 feet above the desert."

"Roger," responded the tower. Then a short pause ensued. In the distance the white light became clearer and was now blinking at a slower rate. Then the operator continued, "He seems to be panicky. He's in heavy rain and he can't see anything out the windows. He is certain that the plane is damaged and that pieces of metal are falling off the starboard side of the plane."

"Tell him I can see his plane clearly." I responded, hoping the operator wouldn't notice that I was lying. "Tell him his plane is in perfect condition. Tell him the only thing falling off his plane is ice."

Another short pause ensued. "Roger," responded the tower.

"Tell him there's only one more rain cloud in front of him. He'll be through it in another minute. Then he'll be able to bring his plane down and land." I said.

"Roger." There was another short pause. "He seems to have calmed down some."

In the distance, I watched as the blinking white light continued its gradual descent towards a small rain cloud. The distant light seemed so fragile. I could see that the clouds had lowered. The approach corridor was rapidly closing. The red beacon light was already completely obscured by clouds. I also watched as the next thunderstorm rushed towards the field from the southwest. I could see that it was going to be very close so I started paying careful attention to my wind recorder. It showed a history of the winds for the last 6 hours. I could see that the period of steady winds was almost over and that the air was becoming increasingly unstable. In the distance, the white blinking light entered the cloud. I started counting the seconds. I located a hole in the base of the clouds and began studying it intently, waiting for the plane to pass by it. After a long agonizing wait, a white light momentarily appeared in the hole.

"I see him." I spoke into the telephone. "Tell him to come down another 20 feet. Then descend gradually until the runway lights appear, and then hold that altitude."

"Roger," responded the tower. Then a short pause followed. "He sees the runway!" shouted the operator. "He says it's the first thing he's seen since he passed over the beacon! His navigator says he's just three minutes north of the end of the runway!"

Towards the southwest, I could see the thunderstorm already drifting onto the airbase. Studying the wind

269

recorder I continued, "Tell him he's going to make it safely. There's a wind gust coming in about one minute. Tell him to be ready for it. I expect the gust to be from 210 degrees at 65 mph."

"Roger." Then, there was another short pause.

"Tell him to have his navigator time it," I continued. "I expect it to last no more than 30 seconds. When it finishes, the winds will return to their present heading of 180 degrees at 7 mph. As soon as the wind gust finishes, I expect his plane to drop suddenly about 30 feet. Tell him to be ready for it."

"Roger." There was another short pause.

"Tell him that as soon as the gust ends, to land as quickly as possible. Have him drop onto the runway as soon as he is over it." I stated slowly.

The operator, with dry humor, responded, "I think that's what he's trying to do."

I couldn't help but laugh at myself. The operator's statement certainly seemed to be correct. Watching the wind meter carefully, I continued, "Tell him to get ready - the gust is starting - now."

In the distance, the plane wobbled suddenly, and jumped several feet higher. Then it slowly started returning back down to 50 feet. I watched the wind recorder carefully. "Tell him the gust is starting to end - get ready - now!" I stated.

The plane by now was within one minute of the end of the runway. As I watched, the wind gust ended. As it did so, the plane suddenly fell more than 30 feet toward the ground. When the pilot regained control, the landing gear was less than five feet above the sagebrush.

"Beautiful!" I exclaimed. "Tell him the winds will remain steady long enough for him to land!"

"Roger."

I watched as the plane strained to reach the end of the runway. With the flaps down and the landing gear down, I could see the pilot was straining to pull the plane up the few extra feet needed to clear the landing lights at the end of the runway. With the next thunderstorm now rushing onto the far end of the field, the 707 drifted slowly over the runway lights, lined up perfectly over the centerline, and dropped onto the near end of the runway. The nose gear had hardly touched down when the full fury of the next thunderstorm struck. I could see the plane roll into the rain and disappear from view.

I waited several minutes. I knew the tower operator would be busy while the plane landed. Then I asked into the phone, "Did he make it safely?"

At first there was no response. After an unusually long time, the operator responded, "Yes. He's parked somewhere down by the barrier at the end of the runway. Everything seems to be O.K. I was talking to the head stewardess. She said the engines quit just as the nose wheel touched down and the pilot had to be extra careful when he applied the brakes. She said the plane rolled to a normal stop.

She and the copilot then opened the main cabin exit door so they could get some fresh air and see where they were. She said it was hard to get it open because all the people were cheering and shouting, and everyone was trying to help them.

She says that she doesn't know where the plane is on the runway. She says all of the wheels are on the pavement and that the plane has not suffered any damage. She also told me that none of the passengers were injured.

She said that when she looks out of the cockpit windows, all she can see is a big red and white thing that can't be more than 10 feet away. That must be the barrier at the end of the runway."

"I'm surprised that you were talking to the stewardess," I said. "Where is the pilot?"

According to the stewardess, as soon as they got the plane stopped, she and the copilot went to check the passengers. They saw that everyone was O.K. Then they opened the door and looked out, and saw that the plane was completely safe and O.K. Then the copilot got real shaky. The pilot, she said, came back into the cabin and quieted everyone down. Then he led them all in reciting the Lord's Prayer and in reciting a prayer of thanks. He prayed that God always helped you the way that you had helped them."

"That's nice to know," I said, not quite sure how to react. "Why is the stewardess handling the radio?"

"I understood her to say that the pilot is back in one of the lavatories. She thinks he's crying so she doesn't want to disturb him. She says the navigator is outside, down on the ground walking around in the rain. I guess he needed some fresh air. When the instrument technician arrived in the pickup truck, the navigator was on his hands and knees in the sagebrush, vomiting from the stress. I guess he's going to be O.K. The copilot is just standing back in the galley. She thinks he wants to be alone too. She said that someone needed to handle the radio, so she's doing it."

"Well," I said, "This thunderstorm looks like a big one. It'll probably be another 45 minutes before it's over. Then you'll probably have 20 minutes of gentle winds and light rain. I guess that you have everything under control so I'll go back to my work now.

Incidentally, I see that the two tall passenger-unloading ramps are sitting up here by the base operations building. Everything is shutdown for the night, but you might want the ground crew to tow the airplanes up here, anyway, instead of towing them down to the hangers. It'll be much easier to unload the passengers. It'll make it easy for the buses from Palm Meadows Field to find them. The buses can just pull into the parking lot of the weather station. I'll get the key from the base ops office, unlock the doors, and turn on all the lights. Everything is nice and warm up here. The passengers will be able to get in out of the rain. If any of the passengers need to use the restroom, they're available, too."

"That sounds like a good idea," responded the tower operator. "I still can't raise anyone down at the front gate. I asked the instrument technician to take the pickup truck down and get the ground crew."

"Sounds like a good idea," I responded. "I'll hang up the phone now, and get the lights turned on in the base ops building. Be sure to call me if you need anything."

"Roger," responded the operator. Then, after a long pause, he continued, "None of us know what to say or how to thank you, Charlie. None of us know how, but thanks."

"Oh, think nothing of it," I answered. "I just did what the Air Force trained me to do."

I went back inside, hung up the phone, closed the window, and turned on the lights in the weather station. I unlocked the doors in base ops, turned up the thermostat, and turned on all of the base ops lights. Then I transmitted my missing weather reports to Tinker AFB, Oklahoma, sent another procedure message to Tinker. I informed them that the emergency was over and the planes were safely on the runway. It was a simple procedure message. It read,

"DESERT CENTER AFB COMING BACK ON LINE. AIRCRAFT EMERGENCY HAS ENDED. TWO 707 JETLINERS LANDED SAFELY IN HEAVY RAIN. DESERT CENTER AFB REMAINS CLOSED. CEILING ZERO. VISIBILITY ZERO. CLOUDS ON RUNWAY. RAIN HEAVY. SOME HAIL. HEAVY THUNDERSTORMS IN PROGRESS. RETURNING TO NORMAL REPORTING SCHEDULE."

Then, I went back to reading my book. I still had another seven lonely hours to work.

Several minutes passed. Once again the regular weather station phone rang.

"Desert Center weather station," I responded. "Charlie speaking."

"Charlie, finally you're there. I've been trying to reach you for the last half hour." The voice on the other end shouted urgently. I immediately recognized the voice of one of the other Desert Center USAF weather observers, Dwight. He and I were the closest of friends. "About 40 minutes ago, my wife was changing channels on the TV and saw a TV news break. The TV news is saying that two 707 jetliners are going to crash on the highway right out in front of you! I could hardly believe it! The three local stations are out there covering the preparations live! They've got more than 10 miles of highway blocked off. They've already got a big section out in front of the base covered with foam!

You're going to need some help, guy! You got a great big emergency on your hands! I'll be right out to help you but you know I live way across the valley. It'll take me at least an hour to get out there! I called Sergeant Walters and told him I was coming, but he said that when he tried to get out there to help you, the State Police turned him back. They're not letting anyone through except ambulances and fire trucks! You'll have to tell them I'm coming or they'll never let me through!"

"Oh, that's really nice of you Dwight," I replied, "but there's no emergency going on out here. The two 707s landed and they're out here parked on the runway waiting for the ground crew. You have a merry Christmas with your family."

"But you can't be right!" responded Dwight. "Are you calling the State police, the fire department, and all of the television stations wrong? The television stations are carrying the emergency live! I'm looking at the TV right now. It's right in front of me! They just finished talking to the Palm Meadows Field weather observer. They're waiting for two fully loaded 707 airliners to crash right out in front of the Desert Center gates! The State Police have evacuated those three big apartment houses just down the street in case the airplanes hit them. They have more than 500 people standing out here in the rain! They're telling the people that there can't be any other choice, Charlie! The whole valley has had nothing but constant thunderstorms all day! I tell you, Charlie, what you have on your hands is the biggest emergency I've ever seen! You're going to need my help, Charlie!"

"I'm telling you the truth, Dwight," I responded, "I was just talking to the Desert Center tower. There are no jetliners preparing to crash out on the highway. There were two jetliners up there a little while ago, but they had good pilots. They both landed here at Desert Center. You can call the Desert Center tower if you don't believe me."

"Wait a minute," Dwight interrupted. "The TV news has just reported that the Desert Center ground crew is pulling out to go somewhere, but nobody seems to know where. One of the camera crews has left to follow them. They think maybe one of the planes crashed up the valley. What's going on, Charlie?"

"Well, as I've been saying Dwight, there aren't any jetliners flying in the sky or crashing on the highway which goes by the base. The only airplanes anywhere around are two 707s fully loaded with passengers, parked out on the Desert Center runway. The ground crew is probably coming back to tow the planes up here to base ops. The passengers are still on board and we need to let them get off and bus them downtown. Everyone else can go home and enjoy Christmas.

I tell you what, Dwight, why don't I just give you the phone number of the Desert Center tower. You can call them up and you'll see that I'm telling you the truth." I stated. "There really isn't any emergency going on out here."

"Well, OK," responded Dwight. "Give me the number and I'll phone Desert Center tower. But I'm telling you, Charlie, there's a big emergency going on out there. You're going to need all of us to help you."

"I really appreciate your offer, Dwight." I responded. "It's really nice of you but don't worry. Just phone the tower and put your mind at ease. Then you and your family have a really nice Christmas together. Your wife and your two sons must be looking forward to spending Christmas with you. Here, the number to the tower is 255-2525. I'll talk to you later, Dwight."

"Thanks for the number, Charlie." said Dwight. "But if you're wrong, I'll come right out and help you."

"I know you would, Dwight. But, really, there's no need. There's really nothing going on out here."

With that, I said good-bye and hung up the phone. I filed my teletype reports, transmitted my next weather report, and went back to reading my book.

Time passed, and as the clock continued to tick away, the thunderstorm abated. The winds died down and the visibility improved as another interlude between storms began passing through. Out through the weather station windows I could see the ground crews towing the first 707 along the taxiway in the distance. As it reached the end of the taxiway and the beginning of the long parking ramp, the towing tractor made a wide gentle turn, and continued towing it up along the ramp towards the weather station area. It seemed like such an easy task. Soon the plane was parked on the ramp just outside the base ops building. It seemed as if the passengers on board the 707 had finally reached the Jerusalem that they had been seeking for so long.

Having parked the first 707, the tractor unhooked and went for the second 707. It was still sitting out on the runway. As the unloading ramp was pushed up to the 707's forward doorway, the camera truck and crew from the TV news rushed up out front. Skidding to a stop, the camera crew went running out in the rain towards the parking ramp. The camera lights were on and the cameras had just begun rolling when the door to the 707 was opened. I watched as the first passengers began unloading. One of the first passengers to come down the ramp was an elderly woman heavily clad in a fur coat. It was still raining lightly. It took the lady a long time to make it down the ramp. The camera crew asked her what the landing had been like. She seemed to be having a hard time speaking coherently. She was saying, "The flight was terrible. The flight was terrible. Who was he? Who was the one who saved us? Jesus must have spoken to him. He couldn't possibly have seen our plane in the storm. You have to find him. The captain said we had to thank him."

I turned to my phone. It was ringing again. "Desert Center AFB," I said. It was Master Sergeant Walters, the next step up in my chain of command. He interrupted me. "Charlie, thank God you were there. I called the tower. They told me what you did. Charlie, you saved the lives of several hundred people. I want you to know that I've already called the Major and we're both in agreement. The Major will be awarding you a medal for heroic service as soon as he can push the paperwork through Tinker AFB in the morning. How did you ever see both of those planes at night in these storms?"

"Oh, it wasn't that hard." I said respectfully. "I just had to get used to looking at the clouds."

"Charlie, we can't thank you enough," responded the Master Sergeant. "You know, Charlie, all of the people and all of the ambulances and fire trucks were still waiting down by the Desert Center gate. The State Police had the highway blocked off until Dwight drove down and convinced them the emergency was over."

"Really?" I responded in surprise. "Didn't the Desert Center tower tell them?"

"Yes," said the Master Sergeant. "The tower operator told them, all right, but no one would believe him. The weather observer at Palm Meadows field kept telling them that it was impossible for the planes to land anywhere in this storm. The weather radar down at the Field kept picking up constant thunderstorms and heavy rain over all of the Desert Center runways. None of us can figure out how you did it. Even the radar records prove that any landing was impossible.

When the Desert Center tower operator told the State Police that the emergency was over, they just thought that he'd been drinking because it's Christmas Eve. They thought he was playing a prank on them. At first, they were going to have the Military Police arrest him as soon as the emergency was over. Dwight had to go down there and convince them to check with the Palmdale Air traffic controllers and see that there weren't any airplanes in the sky over Palm Meadows before they would believe him. You can see them right now, live, on the TV. They're still down there shaking their heads wondering how you could ever have seen the planes in this storm. You should see all of the foam they spread on the highway. They must have foamed ten miles of highway. They foamed all of the lanes.

Charlie, I better let you go in case they need you outside. But before I go, let me make sure that I say thanks. Thanks for the Major. Thanks for myself. Thanks from all of us. No one could have done it but you, no one. I tell you Charlie, you are one fine paperback hero."

"Thanks, Sergeant." I responded, still totally unprepared to meet all of these people on this previously lonely Christmas Eve. "I better go now. I see they're unloading the planes. They may need me to show them the rest rooms."

With that I hung up the phone, just as passengers and crewmen from the first 707, followed by the television cameras, started filing into my room. Within minutes, my little weather station was down to standing room only, holding more people than I could ever have guessed. They were all struggling to get in to see me. I was really taken off guard. Out the window I could see the tractor towing the second 707 up towards the parking ramp, with still more people on board. The plane didn't need to be steered and the head stewardess was still sitting in the pilot's seat.

The first pilot, his copilot behind him, grabbed my hand and almost shook it off my body. With the cameras rolling, the pilot broke out into tears, saying, "You did it! Thank God, you did it! I didn't think you could ever have done it! I can't tell you how it feels to still be alive! God knows we'd have all been dead without you! We planned to crash on that highway out there. All of us, we'd all have been killed. We all owe you our lives!"

Then the TV news reporter, a young lady, quietly interrupted him, "Please let the observer say something."

I could hardly have been less prepared. I stammered a little, saying something incoherent about the winds. Then, not having the faintest idea what to say, I shook the pilot's hand and said, "I'm really glad to see you all. It's past midnight, so now it's Christmas. I guess God wants us all to be alive on Christmas." Pausing while my mind went racing in silent confused circles, I continued, "I've turned on the lights and turned up the heat in the rest of the building. There are restrooms and some vending machines and a lounge down at the other end. You're all free to wait inside, anywhere in the building, until the buses come to take you down town."

With the pilot and copilot still shaking my hand, the copilot said to me, "You'll never know how hard we prayed that God would let us all live to see you."

Then, with no one having the faintest idea what to do next, the pilot and copilot, still shaking visibly, led the passengers down through the building to the vending machines, the rest rooms, and lounge on the other end. One by one, with the cameras rolling, the passengers from the first 707 filed through. Each one shook my hand. Most hugged and thanked me.

The passengers from the first 707 had hardly finished coming through the weather station when the passengers from the second plane, led by the head stewardess, began filing in. With the cameras still rolling, once again the room filled wall to wall with people. One of the lady passengers was saying to the TV news reporter, "You should have seen how the pilot brought the plane over that red beacon up on the mountain. It looked like he was going to hit it with the tip of his wing. He couldn't have missed it by more than five feet."

"The head stewardess responded, "He was afraid that the weather observer wasn't going to be able to see us, so he wanted to make the light blink, even if he had to break it with his wing tip. He knew he would only get one chance."

The TV news reporter said to the stewardess, "I guess things were pretty bad up there."

"You'll never know how bad it was," responded the stewardess. "I've been flying for 12 years and I've never seen a flight this bad." Turning towards me, she continued, "If it hadn't been for this man, none of us would be alive anymore. We all owe him our lives. Even the tower operator said we all owe this man our lives. I don't know how he did it. Everyone else had given up on us. They didn't know what it would have been like. They were going to have us crash on the highway. The pilot had already told us he was going to crash on the highway and many of us would be killed. He expected that he and the flight crew would all be killed. He told us all to save ourselves as best we could, and not to try to save the flight crew. If this man hadn't talked him out of it, he would have crashed out there in all of those houses and wires. He could never have found the highway.

Our pilot had panicked. The tower operator was shouting at our pilot. We were all bent over and we were all buckled in. The pilot came on the intercom and told us that the hail and the turbulence had damaged the plane. He said that it was impossible to go on, and that he was still going to have to crash out there in the cold nighttime, rain soaked desert. All of the old people were praying and all of the little kids were crying. The pilot had already started to turn back.

I could hear the tower operator shouting back at our pilot. He was shouting, 'He's already brought the first plane in. Now what are you going to do? Are you going to ruin this man's Christmas just because you don't have the guts to follow his instructions the way the first pilot did? Keep heading northeast. Do like the weatherman says! There's more turbulence behind you than there is in front of you! And if he's wrong, what do you care where you die? The first pilot says the weatherman knows what he's talking about! Now, get back on that northeast beacon!'"

Turning to the passengers, she continued, "Now I want each one of you to thank this man for your lives before you leave, just like the Captain said. The busses will be here in a little while. I'll be waiting to help you down at the other end of this building where the rest rooms are."

Turning back to me, she said, "We all thanked God that you saw us. We were all so afraid that we wouldn't get to see you and to thank you." Then, kissing me on the cheek, she said, "Thanks, from all of us."

I still was at a total loss for words. There was nothing for me to do but stand numbly there, shaking hands, thanking people, and wishing them all a Merry Christmas. At the very end, with the cameras still rolling, the pilot, copilot, and navigator from the second 707, exhausted, came through. It was obvious at first glance that they were having trouble regaining their composure. I understood completely. After landing, they'd all been crying and vomiting from the terrible stress they'd been under.

The three of them, all at a total loss for words, just walked up to me and hugged me like a bear. The pilot, struggling to keep from going totally to pieces in tears, said quietly, "Have we wanted to see you. We were so afraid that you wouldn't be here for us to see."

The copilot, seeing the pilot breaking down again, came to his aid, saying, "What he means to say is that we all owe you our lives. None of us know how to say it, but we all thank God you were here. We all thank God that you could see us."

Then the entire crew hugged me until I was dizzy. They thanked me, and continued down to the lounge. There the passengers and crew from both 707s, many standing outdoors in the rain, many drinking coffee and holding candy bars purchased from the vending machines, all joined together, like crusaders, in a simple ceremony. It was a prayer of thanks. They all thanked God they were alive, and, at the end, they all asked God to be with me in the future the way he'd been with me in the past.

Watching from a distance, I was totally dumb founded. They were all performing the same ceremony for me, which I had planned to perform for myself. I could hardly believe it. It was as though God had stepped out from behind the mist and decided to show himself to me, once and for all. The view from where I stood was simply stunning and humbling.

As the prayer was just finishing, the busses began coming. The parking lot rapidly filled with cars and trucks. Now the friends and loved ones of the passengers and crew began streaming into the already crowded building. For the next several hours a new group of people, families, and friends of the passengers streamed through my weather station. Missing weather reports, it was necessary for me to go off line and send Tinker AFB another procedure message. Then the TV news reporter came. She wanted me to show her the view of the red beacon and the mountains that I had used as an aid. With the thunderstorms back in full progress, all I could show her was the lightening, the wind, and the cold rain.

Hours later, the last of the passengers and friends had filed out. I sadly waved the TV news team good bye. I realized that the weather station was once again, deserted except for me. It was so lonely now. I turned out the lights and relocked the doors in base ops. The vending machines that I had planned to use, to buy some coffee and a candy bar, had been stripped clean by the crowd. Expecting to nurse my empty stomach until morning, I transmitted another procedure message to Tinker. It informed Tinker that Desert Center was still closed and I was back on line.

I went back to my chair and sat down. I picked up my history book and went back to reading about the Great Crusade. It was such an exciting period in history. I loved reading about its great heroes.

I had just started reading when the door to the weather station opened suddenly. In walked the Chief Master Sergeant in charge of the chow hall. He had with him in cardboard containers, the largest breakfast the chow hall could prepare. Three trips to the truck later, setting the last of them carefully on the table in front of me, he said simply, "On that second 707, that old couple in the front row were my father and mother. If it hadn't been for you, they would have died tonight, for sure, out there on that highway. They would never have been able to get out of that airplane alive."

Then he shook my hand and said simply, "Thanks. I brought this over for you. I don't expect you to believe me but I swear that tonight, one of your guardian angels appeared before me in the chow hall. He was kind of tall and he said, 'Even a paperback hero needs to eat.' I knew right away that he meant you. He said your guardian angels want you to remember tonight whenever you have another lonely Christmas Eve. He said they want you to remember that they're always with you."

With that, the sergeant exited back into the night, wishing me a Merry Christmas as he left.

The Teacher

Then Job said in reply:
 At least listen to my words,
  and let that be the consolation you offer,
 Bear with me while I speak;
  And after that you can mock!

Job 21:1,3

It was a Friday afternoon at Desert Center. The new guy, Washington was washing the windows at the weather station. I would have noticed him anyway because of his intensity. However, the rain that was falling at the time guaranteed that his actions would catch my attention.

"They look a lot cleaner," I said to him, trying to strike up a conversation. He didn't answer me and kept working. Well, I decided, some men are just naturally quiet.

Walking into the next room where the forecaster's area was located, I was happily greeted by Sergeant O'Keefe. "Charlie, how nice to see you." he exclaimed. "I'm glad you came down here when I phoned. I hope you weren't doing anything important this afternoon."

"No problem Sergeant. I was more than a little bored over at the barracks, and I was coming down anyway. I wanted to see how that new airman Washington was making out. I thought maybe he might need some extra help in this rain," I answered.

"Oh, no, not this one Charlie. He's good, I tell you. He's really good, responded O'Keefe excited. He's good because he has a degree in meteorology from the University of Wisconsin at Madison. They don't give those things away. He knows more about weather forecasting than anyone here except the Major. He even does the computations instead of guessing like so many forecasters do."

"No, Sergeant," I laughed. "You mean sometimes weather forecasters are just guessing," I questioned sarcastically drawing tears of laughter from O'Keefe.

"One thing I don't understand, Sergeant," I asked, "Washington is only an airman first class. If he has a college degree like you say, why isn't he an officer?"

"Well, responded O'Keefe, "He started out as an officer, but he flunked out of Officer Candidate School - because he's the nicest guy you'd ever want to meet.

"He's too nice a man, Charlie. He works like an animal. He should stop and think about things more. He knows how to read and write in ancient Greek. When he has time off, he just sits in the barracks and reads books on ancient Greek philosophy and compares it to the Bible. On his time off, all he does is read those books in the original Greek. He needs more rest.

"He's single. He needs to be taken up to the Las Vegas casinos like you go up to the casinos. He needs to let his mind run on ahead in life. He needs to be taken to some girlie shows and taught to gamble. He needs to be taught how to fight off a man whose trying to kill him with a knife, and then taught how to tell that man with the new bruises that you're keeping his knife as a souvenir, instead of calling the police and charging him with attempted murder.

"Another problem Washington has, Charlie. He wants to help everybody. Look at him. He's out there washing the windows in the rain in order to help the janitor. Yesterday I saw him sweeping the floor. If he's not careful he'll become the janitor.

"Last night when we walked out into the parking lot, he ran on ahead of me just to open my car door. I'm a grown man, Charlie. I don't like people doing things for me. He should know that Charlie. He should tell me to open my own car door, just like you do.

"I'm worried about him. I tell you, if he's not careful, he's going to drive himself nuts. Nice people do that, you know.

"See if you can help him. Be a Teacher to him. Follow him around. Work with him. Go over there and make a mess. He needs a teacher like you around to keep him from going off the deep end. Just do it for me as a favor, Charlie.

"You see, Charlie, the Major says that if you can teach him to stand up for himself, they'll send him back to OCS. Whether he knows it or not, his whole career depends on how much he can learn from you."

Laughing and bidding the Sergeant goodbye, I returned to the weather observing section of the station. Since Washington went to the University of Wisconsin, I figured he might be a football fan. Kicking over a chair on purpose, I greeted him, "How's it going, Washington? I'm Charlie. I'm the best football fan west of Green Bay."

Recognizing my presence at last, he put down his cleaning rag, he was dusting the furniture at the time, and returned my greeting. "Hi." he said timidly.

I continued, "I'm from Cambridge, Wisconsin, just southeast of Madison."

"Cambridge!" his eyes lit up. "I watched all the football games when I was attending the UW at Madison."

I could see that he and I were going to be the best of friends.

The weeks passed slowly. I put ideas in his mind, good ideas, and I worked them until they were accepted. It was a slow process, but I could see that he was making progress. Late one Monday afternoon we were both between shifts and otherwise alone in the barracks. He'd been in his room with the door closed all day, quietly reading Greek philosophy. Pounding on his door, I called out, "Hey, Washington! It's time for the evening meal. Come on. We'll walk over to the chow hall together. I heard a rumor that the Air Force has put some new nudie waitresses on the line." Then I stood laughing for a bit.

It took a while, but after a time, his door finally opened and there stood Washington, ready for chow. He didn't actually say anything, but from the serious look on his face I could tell that Sergeant O'Keefe was right. He certainly needed someone like me to help him rest.

It was a nice walk to the chow hall. He still hadn't spoken a single word. That was not a problem for me. I figured he was just a naturally quiet guy who might like to hear more about football. For the next hour, I told him about it. I figured he needed to practice interrupting other people, so I gave him plenty of opportunity.

Finally, half way through the meal, he started to come back to the land of the living. Seeing he was getting back to where he could talk, I asked him, "How did you do with gambling on your recent trip to Las Vegas, Washington? Did you play any blackjack?"

Then I stopped talking and waited for him to answer. His answer was some time coming, but the dam finally broke and his ideas started gushing from his mouth.

"I did just like you taught me, Charlie. I went to that casino where all of the dealers are beautiful young women wearing nothing but those see-through blouses. Man, some of those women were just incredible.

"As far as the money went, first I was ahead five dollars. Then I was losing five dollars. Finally, I got back even, so I quit, just like you taught me. Along the way, I must have gotten them to give me ten dollars worth of free whiskey and soft drinks. And I also got to watch the beautiful women for at least three hours." Finally, he had gotten back to where he could laugh.

"I'm really glad for you, Washington," I said, "I see you were talking to Payne for a while this morning. Tell me, how is Payne doing these days up at Mojave Wells?"

"Oh great," answered Washington. "Right now he's taking the afternoon wind measurements down at Range One. He really likes driving down there with his truck and playing around. I guess he takes one of the other range rats down there with him every time he goes."

"Every time?" I asked.

"Yes, every time," responded Washington. "At first he didn't. He'd just go down there himself. But he said that one day he saw something far out in the sagebrush. He's a little near sighted, you know, so, he started walking out there slowly, to see better what it was. I guess when it was still really far away, it started growling like a coyote. He figured it was growling at him, so he turned around and took off running. He doesn't know what it was but he doesn't think it was actually a coyote.

"Well, anyway, now anytime he goes out there, he takes one of the range rats with him. The range rat always stays outside and watches the sagebrush while Payne takes the readings. I guess it works out OK."

"I appreciate you telling me about Payne," I continued, "Did I understand that conversation you had with the Major this morning? Are you going up to the gunnery ranges after Payne?"

"Yes," answered Washington. "I asked the Major when he was going to send you up there again. The major said that you were far too valuable to send up there again. He said that he wanted you here at Desert Center so that whenever there was bad weather, you could come in and train the other observers. He said he needed you every time there was an airplane in trouble."

"But you're a very valuable person too, Washington." I stated.

"Oh, anyone could replace me here at Desert Center. But no one could replace you," said Washington sincerely. "The Major told me what he is going to do. He said he is going to leave Payne up at Mojave Wells for four extra weeks, while he gets together with his commanders. He's going to have me promoted back to being an officer. He says they'll start me out as second Lieutenant.

"Then, the very day the paperwork comes through, he is going to send me up to replace Payne at Mojave Wells, and leave me there for the next two or three years. I have a degree in Meteorology, and I know all about forecasting and observing the weather. The Major said that he's going to let me take complete charge of all of the weather stations out there on the ranges. After I've been up there a month and I've had a chance to get settled, he's going to have the Air Force training school send out six or eight new observers who are in need of on-the-job training, and station them with me. He says the new observers would be rotated up there for six weeks at a time, on a flexible schedule. Then they would be replaced with another set. That way, he says, the Air Force will be able to use all of those vacant facilities as a large training school with me in command. I might even make Colonel up there. If I had a sergeant to help me, like Dwight, a school like that could handle as many as twenty students.

The Major says they'll be sure to include observers who started their careers in other trades and are cross training into weather observing. He says that students like that always need someone who is unusually patient and helpful, to get them headed in the right direction," Washington paused for a minute, deep in thought. Then he continued, "There's something else way out there on the ranges which the Major wants me and Dwight to study too, but the Major didn't say much about what it was," concluded Washington slowly.

"Making you an officer is a wonderful idea, Washington!" I exclaimed. "I'm so happy for you."

"Thanks, Charlie," he said gratefully. "I'm happy, too. I'm just as excited as I can be, but there's one thing I don't understand."

"What's that?" I asked.

"The Major said that he came up with this idea right after he talked with you, one day when you and O'Keefe were working the day shift together. I was just wondering what you told him that got him started in the right direction?" Laughing some more, Washington continued, "You even have the Major believing that he thought up that part about Dwight."

"The part about Dwight?" I answered, playing dumb.

"Now don't go pulling that on me, Charlie." laughed Washington. "When the Major told me how he'd thought up this idea of sending Dwight up there with me, I knew you'd been up to something."

"But Dwight, would be a valuable person to have up there with you," I said. "You'd need a friend for company. Dwight would certainly keep all of the other airmen in line and maintain the proper level of discipline in the ranks. He has so much experience that he could handle many of the routine training sessions. He and his wife grew up in the country out in the far west. They're extremely close, and they enjoy doing all sorts of things together. He could move his family up to the town of Mojave Wells and settle down for a while. They're wonderful people. You, he, and his family would all be quite happy."

Smiling pleasantly, Washington replied, "You're right, Charlie. Of course, you were also right when you pointed out to the Major that such an assignment would guarantee me the eventual rank of Major, and Dwight the rank of Master Sergeant. You're the last person I'd ever argue with. Heck, if I won the argument, I'd be afraid that it was because you wanted me to win."

By now, the two of us had finished eating, and we began the long walk back to the barracks. We spent most of the time laughing. As we were approaching the barracks, I turned to Washington and said seriously, "There's one thing you need to remember about Mojave Wells, Washington."

"What?" he asked.

"Remember the story Payne told. Never leave the roads or the prepared places around the range lounges and go off into the desert by yourself. Never, never, never! No matter what! Even if you think you see people out in the desert starving to death. It's too dangerous. Just use your truck to drive into town for help. When you get to know the ranges, then you can decide for yourself. But remember, especially at first, never leave the road alone."

I thought I had made it clear enough, but I'm only human, I guess. I didn't realize that he wasn't listening. I didn't realize that once again, his mind was racing on ahead. Dumb to what was happening, I continued, "And remember Washington, when you're up there, you can tell me or Dwight or Steve anything, and we'll believe you. Remember, you can tell us anything at all."

We were just reaching the barracks when Washington noticed that Master Sergeant Walters was waiting for us. Since it was now past 6:00 in the evening, we were quite surprised. "What's up, Sergeant?" I asked.

Smiling, and apologetic, the sergeant answered, "I'm sorry to interrupt your evening, but there's been a problem with Payne up at the gunnery ranges. The Major and I have decided to send Washington up to Mojave Wells early to replace Payne. Washington, I'll take you up there tonight, and get you linked up with him. I'll come back up on Friday and bring Payne back to Desert Center. That'll give you a few days to learn the ropes. Tomorrow, I'll walk the paperwork through so you'll have your orders and get your extra pay. I may have to make a special trip up there on Wednesday to get your signature on some of them, but don't worry, Washington, it'll all work out. And don't worry, the Major has already begun work on your promotion to Second Lieutenant."

"What happened to Payne?" I asked, showing visible concern.

"Oh, he's not hurt, but he had an accident with the truck. He was driving back from range one, today. He was still ten miles from base, coming back on that gravel road."

"Yes, I know it well," I stated.

"Well, he must have been driving sixty miles an hour out there, and a safe speed on that road isn't any more than 35," continued the sergeant, obviously angry with Payne. "The truck hit a rock in the road and went into the ditch. The tie rod was bent and the truck couldn't be driven. Then Payne got out in the hot sun and started running towards town. The accident must have scared him something terrible. I mean, he grew up in the desert. He knows better than to go out running in the summer sunshine in such a hot dry climate. Anyway, he made it back to town only because the range rats saw him from far away and came to rescue him. I talked with him on the phone. He sounds half way calmed down now."

"Maybe something was chasing him," I suggested. "Both he and Sullivan have reported seeing occasional white coyotes and other animal like things out at range one."

"I find that hard to believe, Charlie." responded the Master Sergeant angrily. "Coyotes and other animals don't chase trucks, especially at 60 miles an hour. No, this is going to cost Payne a stripe. I'm going to ask the Major to prepare an article 15 tomorrow, and if Payne gives us any back talk, I'll ask the Major to give him a section eight discharge."

I could see the Sergeant's mind was made up, and there was little point in arguing with his six stripes. I helped Washington pack. By 7:00 in the evening, they'd left and I was alone in the barracks. I remember how happy

Washington looked as he and the Sergeant got into the sergeant's car. Even then, his mind seemed to be racing on ahead.

The rest of the week flew past, as did the next week. Then came Wednesday morning. I had just signed in. I was working the day shift at Desert Center. It promised to be a quiet day. The weather was clear and nearly calm. The ranges wouldn't be used again for another week. No one anywhere cared about the Mojave Wells winds today. The range winds were certain to be light and variable, hardly worth wasting a helium balloon to measure them. The morning forecaster, Sergeant O'Keefe, realized this and gave Washington the day off. When Washington called in the 4:30 winds, O'Keefe answered the phone. O'Keefe told him that no more winds would be needed that day and suggested that Washington spend the day in Palm Meadows having fun. Yet, Washington refused to lock the weather shack and spend the day relaxing in the city. Without telling O'Keefe, Washington decided to continue the day's wind measurement schedule, anyway. He'd brought his Greek philosophy books with him. There was no one else out on the ranges to disturb him. So in between these unnecessary runs he intended to do some reading.

The Major, Master Sergeant Walters, and the company clerk were away at a week long conference down in Los Angeles. So except for the forecaster, I was alone in the weather station. The duty forecaster was holding down the forecaster's area alone, so I had the rest of the building to myself.

Payne had been brought back from Mojave Wells in disgrace. He had spent the time sitting in silent depressed thought in the barracks while the Major considered whether or not to give him a section eight discharge. Payne hadn't taken the loss of a strip silently. He had argued with the Major. He'd claimed he had a good reason for driving the truck in such a panicky fashion - a reason he said he'd be happy to explain to the Major, if he could do so in private. The Major had refused the request. The Major said he already knew what the reason was and that Payne needed more discipline.

Washington had already phoned in the unnecessary 7:30 winds, so I was taken off guard when Washington phoned in, still again, at 8:15 a.m.

"Washington," I exclaimed, "I'm surprised to hear from you so soon." Washington was more emotional than I'd ever experienced. "Charlie, thank God it's you!" he exclaimed, screaming. "Thank God I have you to handle this."

"What's happened, Washington?" I asked in surprise.

"I'm out here at range three. I just saw a solid white airplane crash out in the desert. It appears to be the fuselage of a large airliner. It crashed at 8:13 a.m. It's about a mile northeast of the weather shack. Record the weather for the accident report. I'm going out there to help the people. That plane will be burning in a minute. I need you to send help as fast as you can. This is a real emergency! We'll need lots of ambulances, helicopters, and fire trucks."

"But wait, Washington!" I shouted into the phone. "Don't go out there! You must be wrong. You're the only one out there! Airliners aren't allowed to fly over that whole section of Desert! There aren't any planes flying anywhere up there today. There aren't any planes up there to crash! Stay where you are! Listen to me, Washington!" I screamed into the phone. "Please. Listen to me! You're all alone, Washington! Don't go out there alone!"

"I don't have time to explain now, Charlie," he continued, still not listening, his mind still racing on ahead of mine. "Those people out there need me. It looks like it's going to start burning. I see smoke and dust over there. It looks like a large airliner that has already lost its wings. Its tail section has already broken off. It looks big enough to have a hundred or a hundred and fifty people on board. I have to go out and save them, Charlie. I have to go! I have to save them from the flames! Send me help as soon as you can. You're the only person I've had time to phone. I need your help. I'm depending on you!"

With that he hung up. I could tell that he hadn't listened at all to me. I could tell his mind had already gone racing on ahead out into that huge, empty desert.

I quickly recorded the weather conditions. They could hardly have been better, clear skies, light winds. Then I walked over to the emergency phone to the Desert Center tower. Picking it up, I said, "This is Charlie. I'm the duty weather observer."

"Hi Charlie," answered the operator on the other end. "What can we do for you."

"I called to find out more about that airplane crash which just occurred up at Mojave Wells," I said.

"What crash?" answered the operator. "I've been on duty since six this morning. There haven't been any airplane crashes. Every plane out there is accounted for."

"Are you sure?" I responded, becoming more mystified with each passing minute.

"Of course I'm sure, Charlie," answered the operator. "I don't have anything else to do with my time on a day like today. I just sit and talk to the passing airplanes. Here, to make you happy, I'll check again with the air traffic control center at Palmdale." A short pause ensued. Then he returned, "I'm right. Every plane out there in the entire southwest is accounted for."

"But Washington, the weather observer up at the gunnery ranges just phoned me and reported seeing an aircraft accident about one mile northeast of the Range Three weather station," I implored.

"I don't know what he could have been looking at, Charlie, but I'm telling you, it couldn't have been an aircraft accident. We would have heard about it even if it had been some highly classified experimental model."

"Thanks," I said and hung up the phone.

I phoned the base hospital to see if they had heard anything. Like the tower, they were certain that no accidents had occurred on the Mojave Wells ranges. They were certain that if one had occurred, they would have been informed. I tried phoning back the Range Three weather shack. There was no answer. Now I had a real problem. Washington was obviously alone and out in the desert. So far, there was no help coming.

I tried phoning the barracks at Mojave Wells. There was no answer. I thought for a minute. Then an idea came to me. I phoned the Mojave Wells motor pool. My good friend Mark answered. As I expected, Steve and the range rats were playing cards in one of the buildings in the back of the motor pool. Mark promised to bring one of them to the phone. I could hardly blame the range rats for playing hooky on a day like today. Playing cards was much easier than picking up 25 pound practice bombs laying underneath some ragged sagebrush in this hot sun.

I waited patiently. After seven minutes had passed on my watch, Steve finally came to the phone. "Hello, Charlie." said Steve. "It's good to hear your voice. What do you want?"

"Hi, Steve, Washington seems to be having some kind of emergency out at range three. He phoned me and said that a plane had crashed about a mile northeast of the range three weather shack. He said that he was driving over there to help. He's out there alone. I was hoping that I could get you and some range rats to go out there and help him."

"No, sir, Charlie." replied Steve. "Not after seeing that thing that was chasing Payne a couple weeks back. Doug, Wayne, and I all saw it real good, up close and everything. Payne must've upset old Range Four Harry real good. We'd just as soon give old Harry some time to settle back down. The ranges are supposed to be closed for today. That thing is still out there, you know, Charlie. If Washington isn't careful, it'll be chasing him too!"

"Chasing Payne?" I asked. I wasn't sure I'd heard him right.

"Well, it wasn't really chasing him, if you know what I mean," said Steve. "If it had wanted to, it would caught him immediately. It was just scaring him so he'd go back to base.

"But just because it's you, Charlie, I'll tell you what I'll do. I gather up some of the boys and we'll take two or three trucks out to range three. We'll stay far apart for safety, like we always do when those things come in close. I'll phone you from the range three lounge when we get out there. Then we'll see what we're going to do next."

"Thanks, Steve. I'm sure that Washington will appreciate it, too.

"Don't worry, Charlie. I'll phone you as soon as we get out there." replied Steve.

With that Steve hung up the phone. I checked again with the command post. There simply couldn't have been an aircraft accident up at the gunnery ranges. Every single airplane was accounted for. Having nothing else to do, I went back to my weather duties and waited patiently for Steve's call.

Time passed. First seconds, then minutes, then a length of time that seemed like an eternity.

Mark phoned, and informed me that Steve and all of the range rats, using three trucks, had gone out to help Washington. He was in communication with them by way of the two-way radios the trucks carried.

According to Mark, Steve insisted that one truck wait at the range three gate and guarantee that the gate remained open. Steve ordered the second truck, driven by Wayne, to wait on the paved road about a mile down from the range three buildings. Steve insisted that the truck first turn around and wait while pointed back towards base. He also insisted that Wayne wait with the engine running. Wayne obviously understood why. Only Steve and Doug would go down to the range three weather shack. Mark said Doug was driving towards the buildings very slowly while Steve watched. He said other than that, he didn't have any information.

After still another long wait, the phone rang. It was now 11:45 a.m. It was Steve. He sounded very serious, "I'm sorry it took me so long to call, but first we had to talk to Washington."

"What is it, Steve?" I asked. "Was Washington there?"

"Oh, he was there all right, Charlie. It's a mighty good thing you called us to come get him. To begin with, you can cancel your aircraft emergency. There aren't any accidents up here," said Steve.

"What about Washington?" I asked.

"You better tell the major to send up an experienced replacement like you or Payne, and not to expect any more wind reports for today. Doug and I will bring Washington down as soon as he's able to travel," continued Steve. "He's not going to be able to make the trip alone."

"What is it, Steve? Has he been hurt?" I asked.

"Yes, Charlie, they hurt him real bad. They did something to him. It looks to me like they burned him, up on the forehead. Maybe his mind will snap out of it when he gets some rest with you down at Desert Center.

"Doug and I got here like you asked. When we drove up, his truck was parked in front of the shack with the engine running. He was hysterical with terror. The door on the driver's side of his truck was open. He was sitting in his truck on the passenger side, so I think they were the ones that drove him back here. He hardly knew us when we got here. He said that when they saw us coming, they took off running. He said if we hadn't come, they'd have killed him for sure."

"Who, Steve? Who drove him back to the shack," I asked.

"We went out there a little ways and saw what he saw. It was that same thing that was chasing Payne a couple weeks ago. It's still over there in a little hollow out in the desert. It's down in the sagebrush. You can't see it from here. It must not have known that Washington was anywhere around when he drove over there. He must have gotten on top of it before they knew he was coming. I think he surprised it pretty bad.

"He had his truck parked out back between the buildings like Payne and I showed him, so that nothing would know he was here, since Range Four Harry is always mighty curious, you know. Washington probably had all of the doors to the shack closed at the time too. All buttoned up like that, they must have decided the place was deserted, and felt it was safe to come in close.

"Just a minute! Doug in the truck says that thing's started to move. We have to get Washington out of here now! We'll bring him down to you! Be patient. It'll take us a while."

"But shouldn't you take him to the hospital first?" I asked.

"No, Charlie, No!" shouted Steve emotionally. In the background I could hear Doug laying on the truck horn, screaming, "Come On! Steve! It's coming this way! Let's get out here, now!"

With that, Steve hung up the phone.

I was stunned. I could hardly make any sense out of what had happened. After thinking about things for a while, I phoned the Desert Center weather barracks. Payne answered, with deep depression and repressed anger obvious in his voice. "Payne," I said pleasantly. "Washington is in some kind of trouble up at the Wells. They're bringing him down now. You're going to have to go back up there tonight. You'll have to take over the ranges until the major gets back. You'll have to get things back in order. They're really going to need a man with your experience up there. They couldn't possibly give you a section eight now. If they did, they wouldn't have anybody

303

with experience left to cover the ranges. Let's go to the evening supper at the chow hall together, as soon as I'm off duty. You know you never did tell me how that accident happened."

"I have to go back to the Wells?" asked Payne. His spirits were obviously starting to pick up. "I'm not going to be thrown out of the Air Force?"

"Yes, Payne. I believe that's right," I answered. "I'm pretty sure that Dwight will agree with me. As you know, the major left Dwight in charge of the weather observers while he and Sergeant Walters are away. By the time they get back, you will have racked up an impressive record for being the man of the hour. They'll think of you as the nice young man who worked hard and saved the day. The major will probably give you a little lecture for driving too fast, and probably have you wash the windows here at the weather station a couple of times. But I'm pretty sure this'll get you off the hook."

"But what about you? Why can't they just send you up there, discharge me, and ask for some new troop to help out down here at Desert Center?" asked Payne.

"Oh they could never do that," I said, "I've been having these bad stomach pains from eating the food at the chow hall," I responded, laughing. "I feel fine when I'm moving around a lot, like here at the Desert Center weather station. You know how, once in a while this flu I have, has been giving me dizzy spells. It wouldn't be safe for me to go up to Mojave Wells alone, right now. I won't be in shape to go back up there until after I can get in to see the doctor. When I do, I'm pretty certain that the hospital will want to watch this flu for two, maybe three weeks at least."

"Oh, right," said Payne, finally laughing for the first time since his accident. Then he continued, "You know, Charlie, some days you can't lie worth a darn. You'd better work on that one while I'm up there."

I said goodbye to Payne and checked with Dwight. He was in complete agreement and said he'd inform the major. I still remember how long Dwight laughed when he phoned me back. He said, "Charlie, I talked with the major. He agreed with our plan. He's really concerned about Washington. He said that Payne should thank God that he has a friend like you." Dwight continued laughing, "The major said there's no reason for you to pretend to be suffering down at the hospital just to convince him to let Payne of the hook. He said if you're not careful, they'll take your appendix out down there just for the fun of it." Dwight laughed some more, "The major told me, 'Have Charlie spend an evening inspecting some show girls down on the strip, and then have him show up for duty complaining about eye strain. I'll believe that one for at least three weeks.' He was laughing his guts out at the time."

Having finished talking with Dwight, I said good-bye and returned to my duties. The afternoon dragged on slowly as I waited for Washington.

Finally, at 3:10 in the afternoon, Washington walked slowly into the deserted front office of the weather station. Obviously dizzy, he staggered when he walked. Positioning himself next to a chair, in the middle of the open floor space, he stood there quietly, and waited for me to come find him. Through the windows I could see Steve and Doug driving off.

"Washington!" I exclaimed gently, "Are you OK?"

Obviously in intense pain, he tried to speak. At first he was totally incoherent. I offered him a chair but he refused to sit down. Finally, he found some words he could say. "I'm going to see the neurosurgeon!" he pronounced slowly and forcefully.

"Tell me about it, Washington," I said gently. "You know I'll understand. You know you can tell me anything. You know I'll believe you."

He stammered incoherently for a long time. Then he began crying intensely. His anguish was obviously too much for him to bear.

"You know I'll understand," I continued gently. "You know I've been out there myself, Washington. Whatever is out there, you know I must have already seen myself, from far off."

Washington stopped crying for a few minutes, and began breathing deeply. He started speaking very slowly, very deliberately, and very quietly. In between his stammering and his tears, he said, struggling to find his self control, "I was only trying to help them. I thought they were dying. I thought it was going to burn. I couldn't drive any farther. The sagebrush was too thick out there. I got out. I ran. I ran on ahead. I went to save them from the fire. I got to the rise. At last, I could see it. It lay there. It looked like a big airplane without wings or a tail. I shouted for them to get out of there before it burned. I shouted at it. I threw rocks at it. I tried to break the windows, so the people could get out before it burned, but when I threw the rocks, they wouldn't even reach it.

"Suddenly the door opened, and four monsters came running out at me. They were white and terrible. They were angry little mutants. They had claws and growled at me like angry coyotes. I couldn't run. They were all around me growling and jumping. They ran all around me. I was trapped.

"Then a young white woman came running out. The monsters must have kidnapped her and made her their slave. They were terrible. She shouted at me in English. Somehow she knew what I was thinking. She was shouting, 'they are only playing with you. Run away. Don't help me.'

"I couldn't leave her there. I couldn't leave her to those terrible monsters. I grabbed her arm. It was pure white and thin. They must not have even fed her. Then, she began fighting me. She began growling at me like a coyote, like the terrible little monsters. I tried to run. I tried to take her with me.

"Then two men came running out of the fuselage. They were so angry! They almost killed me! I couldn't fight them! They were screaming in English, 'you idiot. You stupid idiot! Run you idiot! Run for your life!'

"I tried. God knows I tried to run, but I couldn't! I let go of the girl. I was going to leave her behind! I couldn't fight them. They were too strong! They had claws and growled at me like angry dogs, and horses! I had to leave her behind. I tried to turn but the monsters were everywhere. There was nothing I could do! The monsters were in the way. I grabbed one of them and slapped him out of the way.

"Then the men got so angry. I couldn't think anymore. I was so helpless. One of the men took out a little square white pencil, and he burned me! He pointed it right at my forehead and he burned me. It hurt so bad. I was helpless. I couldn't think any more! I couldn't tell what was happening anymore. The men grabbed me and started dragging me towards my truck. Then they dropped me in the sand, and one of them went and got my truck while the other one screamed at me in English. I was lying there on the ground, crying. I was so terrified. I was begging them not to kill me. The one by me was screaming, 'you stupid pig. You are not even supposed to be out here today! They were only playing. You hit the little girl! We will kill you for that! You grabbed the teacher! Do you think she is helpless? Do you think we are fools? Do you think we bring her out here with no weapons? She should have killed you! I intend to kill you myself as soon as the Captain lets me.'

"They brought my truck and jammed me into the passenger seat. One man got into the driver's seat and the other one climbed into the back. They started taking me down the road towards range four. The girl saved my life. She ran over to the truck and growled something at the both of them. Then she shouted at me, "The little girl is going to be alright, so we are going to let you live. Don't ever come out here again. We will kill you if you ever come out here again. Do you hear me? We will kill you!

"Then the girl stayed behind. We have to find her. We have to rescue her. I was helpless. They had me in the truck. I was out of my mind. They looked all white with large blue eyes, blonde hair, and claws. They drove me back to the shack. They were screaming at me all the way. The man driving used the pencil on my forehead again and again. The pain was awful! I couldn't stand the pain. He was screaming, 'Are you going to get out of here? Are you going to get out of here?' I couldn't take it anymore. I was screaming. I was begging for my life! I passed out in my truck. When I came to, Steve was there. Thank God I called you, Charlie. Thank God Steve was there!

"I can't take the pain anymore, Charlie. I'm going to the neurosurgeon. Thank God you were here, Charlie! I'm hurt real bad, way down, deep inside my head. I can't think anymore. I have to go to the neurosurgeon. All I was doing was helping them, Charlie. All I did was run on ahead so I could help them. I just wanted to save them from the fire."

With that, he turned slowly and left the building. I could see him stumbling slowly across the parking lot towards the hospital. He seemed to be crying, still in abject terror.

That was the last time I ever saw Washington. The rumor on base was that the neurosurgeon gave him six months R & R leave to be taken in his hometown back in Ohio. According to the rumor, the neurosurgeon ordered him to locate six of his favorite high school girl friends and report on what they were doing now. The neurosurgeon was also rumored to have asked him to file a similar report on six of his favorite high school friends who were young men. As requested by the neurosurgeon, the Air Force promoted Washington back to the officer's ranks. They made him a second lieutenant. Then the air Force increased his salary an extra $30 dollars a day to cover his travel expenses. After six months, rumor had it that he still hadn't improved, so the Air Force gave him an honorable discharge. They also awarded him an 85% disability for mental reasons, non-revocable for life.

The evening meal came quickly at Desert Center. 6:00 p.m. found Payne walking beside me across the gravel covered vacant lot that formed the path to the chow hall. His spirits were soaring, and he now found plenty of topics to discuss. As we walked, I asked him, "Payne, what was it like up at the Wells when you were there?"

Payne thought for a minute or so. Choosing his words carefully, he responded, "You know how scary those buildings out at range three can be, especially on dark nights. I just can't believe that you were willing to go out there at 3:30 a.m. alone. When I was up there, I wouldn't go anywhere out on the ranges at night. Even in the daytime, I wouldn't stay out on the ranges alone in between balloon runs. I would just drive slowly out to the range, take the balloon readings quickly, and drive back into town real fast. When I am alone, I don't stay out there even to do the calculations. I drive back to the barracks on base and phone them in from there."

"Before my truck accident," Payne continued, "I used to go for short walks out in the sagebrush down at range one, but not anymore."

"What happened on the day you had your accident?" I asked.

Payne sat quietly for a few minutes before answering. Then he answered calmly, "One afternoon down on range one, after I had finished all of my balloon runs, I had just closed up the shack when I saw something small and white a short ways out in the sagebrush. I thought it might be a rabbit or a young coyote so I went walking out into the sagebrush to catch it. It started barking and yelping, and took off running through the sagebrush. I took off running after it. I chased it for a short time. I almost caught it, but it got away from me. Then, from three or four other places down in the range one valley I could hear a lot of barking and yelping, and I got kind of scared, and I took off running to my truck. Once I got my truck running, I spun the tires and got out of there fast.

"The next afternoon, I had finished taking the readings for the last run of the day, and I had just closed up the weather shack down at range one. As usual, I was going to drive back to my barracks on base, do the calculations, and phone Desert Center from there. As I was walking towards the truck, something tall and white stood up out in the sagebrush. It wasn't very far out there, maybe only a hundred feet or so. You know, Charlie, how I'm a little near sighted. In the bright sunlight like that, well I couldn't be certain what it was. I spoke to it but there was no response. As it stood there, it seemed to be waiting for me to come out and get a closer look, so I walked out towards it very slowly. I'd take a few steps at a time. Then I would stop and wait for a few minutes. It just stood there looking at me. After doing this a few times, I found myself, probably only 25 feet from it. Now I could see it very clearly. It appeared to be a lady in a nurse's uniform. She had chalk white skin and unusually large eyes. Then I saw that she had only four fingers on her hands and that instead of fingernails she had long sharp claws. I became frozen in fear. As soon as I had become afraid, she spoke to me using perfect English. She said that when I came down to range one, I shouldn't go chasing things out in the sagebrush. She said that I should do things more like you had. She even referred to you by name, Charlie. She said that you seldom went hiking out in the desert. When you did, you never went chasing after the things you saw. She said I should be more like you and be content to just look at things from a distance. By now I was so afraid I couldn't have even whispered an answer. Then she said that I had been chasing one of the children the day before. The lady said the child was so terrified that the child will have to rest for at least two weeks before it can be

311

taken on another field trip out into the desert. As my punishment she said, she wanted to make sure that I knew how it felt to be afraid. Then about a quarter of a mile behind her I saw this large white craft rise up out of a depression in the sagebrush where it had been hiding. It looked sort of like the fuselage of a passenger plane, only it didn't have wings or a tail or visible engines or anything. That's when I finally panicked. I just went berserk with fear. I almost tripped over my own feet as I turned around and started running towards my truck. I tell you, I ran faster than I have ever run in my life. I climbed into my truck, started the engine, and just floored the gas petal trying to get out of there. I could see it chasing me in my mirror. They could have caught me anytime, but they must have only wanted to scare me. They did a real good job of it too."

"That's why you were driving so fast and lost control of the truck on one of those curves?" I asked.

"Yes," answered Payne. "I won't go back out there to Range One. No sir, not even if someone was to put a gun to my head. From now on, every time Desert Center asks for range one winds, I'm going to just make them up like all of the other guys except you, used to.

"I can't believe all the things you did out there alone, Charlie." said Payne thoughtfully. "The range rats tell me that besides Ranges Three and Four, you go out to Ranges One and Two by yourself. Some days they'd even see you driving way out there, out beyond Range Four, all alone. Charlie, you've got some guts!"

"So when you go out there, you take someone else with you?" I asked.

"I sure do," answered Payne. "Usually I take Doug. Nothing will ever sneak up on Doug. When we go out there, we have to drive all around behind the buildings and everywhere before Doug is satisfied we're alone".

"Except for you, Steve is the best one to take out there. He knows the most about the ranges, and he never takes any chances."

"But I tell you, Charlie, nobody can compare with you. Every one of the range rats says that, you know. They all say that they don't feel safe out there when you're not there. I sure agree with them."

"That's a surprise, Payne. I wonder why they would feel that way?" I responded.

"It's because you think things through and keep your head about you when something unexpected happens. Everyone has noticed it. Like that day you sent the air policeman and the tow truck out to Range Two."

I answered. "Tell me, Payne, what did scare the range rats that day? They never would tell me. They always tell you more than they tell me."

"Range Four Harry," He answered. "The range rats said that when it came time for lunch, their truck wouldn't start. Then they all walked the mile or so up to the lounge to call for help. They say that when they got there they saw Range Four Harry standing inside one of those old aircraft hangers up by the mountains, watching them. They panicked and ran into the lounge and locked all of the doors and windows. The phone wouldn't work, and they didn't know what to do, so they all hid inside, shaking in their boots. They say he looked more like a young lady wearing a white nurse's uniform."

"Gee, now I'm really confused, Payne," I answered. "What kind of woman in a white nursing uniform is out standing in an old aircraft hanger, making sounds like a horse, scaring servicemen on a government base, 22 miles from the nearest town, on a hot summer day in this desert?"

"I can't make any sense of it either," Said Payne. "But Bryan, the air policeman, walked up there slowly and saw her from a distance. He thought it was the same woman who was waiting for you in the barracks, the night after you left and came back to Desert Center."

"Waiting for me?" I exclaimed in surprise. "Gee Payne, I never had any women in the barracks when I was up at Mojave Wells."

"Well, you know how you always stayed in that long double barracks down by the runway before Steve had you move into the barracks with the rest of the guys?" said Payne. "You know, it was one of those barracks where the range rats swear they've seen white ghosts?"

"Yes. It was that single story barracks with sections and a shower and bathroom area in between. Both sections were really long. Except for me, it was deserted. But it did have bunks for 76 men."

"Did anything unusual ever happen while you were staying there?" asked Payne.

"Sure, Payne," I answered. "Many things happened in that barracks that I have never told anyone. I never felt like I was in danger, or that I was threatened in any manner. But that was a mighty scary barracks to occupy. The lights in that barracks didn't light it up, and there were dark shadows all over the place. There were only a couple of windows in the entire barracks so you could never see outside. I tell you, Payne, it took courage to walk into that place alone at midnight.

"Since I was the only one in the entire barracks, I could sleep on any bunk I wanted to. When I moved in, I picked the bunk closest to the bathroom and showers. That was in section one. For a couple of days it worked out all right. Then things started happening in the section between me and the doorway on that end."

"Things?" asked Payne.

"Yes, unexplained things," I continued. One night I walked down the aisle to the bathroom. By the time I came back up the aisle, I discovered that more than two hours had passed, but I swear that I hadn't spent more than ten minutes in the bathroom. After a few weeks of these strange events going on, I decided to change compartments so that I'd feel safer. I chose the compartment closest to the door. That way, I reasoned, no matter what happened I would be able to get outside to my truck. This worked fine for a few days. Then, it started up again. It seemed like my mind started playing tricks on me. In one of the compartments in section two, every now and then it seemed like there was an intelligent sheet floating in one of its corners. I never had the courage to actually walk down into section two for a closer look.

"Then there was that aircraft mechanic who stayed in the barracks with me for a few days. They'd sent him up from Desert Center to repair that F105 that was forced to land at Mojave Wells when its engine quit. Well, he only stayed in there with me for a few days before he left the barracks one night in absolute panic. He claimed he woke up in the middle of the night, and there was something white standing in the aisle way. He never would go back into the barracks, even to get his belongings. Steve and I had to go in and get them for him the next day.

"After he left, things starting getting really scary. When I would walk from my compartment to the bathroom, sometimes it seemed like some of the dark compartments on both sides of the aisle held sheets of white cloth or white wall paper which I never dared to look at. Then in the mornings, when I got up at 3:00 a.m., sometimes it seemed like I wasn't alone. When I would be shaving in the bathroom, it seemed like something was watching me from the darkness. It seemed like something was just real curious about everything I did. But it didn't seem to be curious about me, so much, as it seemed to want to study everything I had. It felt like more than anything, it wanted to reach out and grab my razor, my soap, my after shave, everything I had, and look at my things up close.

"Then I noticed that whatever it was, it seemed like it knew what I was thinking. One night I had parked my truck in that gravel parking lot across the street. While I was still in the bathroom, it felt like it asked me in a playful spirit, "What are we doing next?"

Without paying much attention, I answered by thinking, "Now I'm going to walk to my truck." Immediately, it felt like it was really happy, I mean happier than I can describe, and that it was going to run on ahead of me so that it could watch me get into my truck. It seemed happier than any kid is when he's playing his favorite game. It seemed like it just went skipping out through the half open door to the barracks before I could even turn around to see what it was. Then I felt like I was alone again. I started wondering if I was losing my marbles. But then, when I got out to my truck, as I was opening the door, I became certain that I was being watched by that same something. It just seemed to be standing on the other side of the barracks, the one that Doug always says is haunted. It felt like it was just happy and playful and that it enjoyed playing games with me. When I looked over towards that barracks, I could see some soft white fluorescent light coming out from behind it. I tell you, Payne, I'm certain that there was something real playing games with me.

"One day I became certain that something had very carefully taken every item out of my duffel bag and very carefully put it back in. I was stunned. There was just no way around it. I had just done my laundry the night before. I had carefully placed all of my clean clothes in my duffel bag. When I got up in the morning at 3:00 a.m., I intentionally placed my duffel bag on top of my bunk. I'm certain that it was sitting on the bottom of my pillows when I left for the ranges.

"When I came back to my barracks at the end of the day, I can't explain my surprise. There was no question about it, my duffel, had been moved at least 6 inches. When I looked inside, I could hardly believe my eyes. Every single piece of my clothing had been removed from the bag, carefully unfolded, carefully refolded, and carefully placed back in my bag. A few of my clothes had been placed back in my bag in a different sequence than the sequence I used. I hardly knew what to think next.

"Then I started taking my flashlight with me whenever I went anywhere in the barracks. That way, I could shine some light into the dark shadows whenever I went to the bathroom or walked through the barracks. One night, it was way past midnight and I had already gone to sleep. I woke up suddenly because I had to go to the bathroom. Grabbing my flashlight, I quickly got up and went hurrying down the aisle to relieve myself. As I was walking back, I let the light of my flashlight fall into all of the dark corners in the empty compartments along the aisle way. They weren't all the same. As I walked past one of them, my heart nearly stopped in shock. I was too stunned to do anything but keep walking back to the end of the barracks where my bunk was. I was so shocked that I couldn't actually become frightened. I couldn't actually believe that what I had seen was real. It looked like there was a narrow white sheet hanging up against one of the walls, maybe six feet tall and three feet wide. I knew it hadn't been there before. My mind must have been playing tricks on me because the sheet looked like it was a vibrantly alive totally white young woman with intelligent blue eyes looking back at me.

"I was so stunned, I just kept walking back to my bunk and sat down. I remember thinking that there was no point in running. I remember thinking that I might as well lay down and go back to sleep because whatever it was, if it hadn't killed me yet, it probably wasn't going to.

"The next morning, I didn't use the bathroom until after the sun came up. When I checked the compartment, there was nothing there. But the thing that convinced me that I had seen something real is that there wasn't anything there that could have been mistaken for a white sheet, either. I tell you, that compartment was absolutely, totally, empty of everything except the metal bunk.

"That day, I changed compartments. I chose the compartment that was down at the other end of the barracks. I chose the last bunk down by the outside door to section two. Then, I would never use the bathroom or the showers after sundown, unless I was absolutely forced. Even so, many nights it still took guts to sleep in that barracks.

"Then I noticed that on many warm summer mornings, when I got up at 3:00 a.m., the door on the east end of the barracks would be propped open. That door didn't have any steps outside of it. It opened to the north. It opened out directly to the flight line. I began carefully inspecting the door before I went to bed. I'm certain that every night I closed it securely. Some nights I locked it, and stayed up until after midnight watching the door. Many nights I even left the lights on. Yet, morning after morning I would get up and the door would be propped open. One night, right after evening chow, I spent a half hour over in the airman's club before returning to my barracks. Then I went to bed early. I got up at midnight just to watch the door to see who was opening it. To my surprise, when I got up at midnight, the door was already propped open. I decided it meant that whoever was opening the door had to have a way of knowing if I was sleeping, before opening the door. But the reason it made me break out in a cold sweat, was because it also meant that whoever was doing it, also had to be monitoring my movements from some distant place out in the desert north of the base area. This realization really frightened me for a time, because my compartment did not have any windows, and the barracks does not have any windows on the north side.

"One morning, I was determined I was going to find out who was opening the door while I was sleeping. I got up at 3:00 a.m. Once again, someone had already propped open the door. I quickly shaved, brushed my teeth, and got dressed. Then I went over to get a closer look at the doorway. I noticed that my barracks was isolated from the other barracks. I also noticed there were no other buildings at Mojave Wells between my barracks and the desolate desert covered mountains and valleys stretching to the north of Mojave Wells. I started wondering about that, so I went to my truck, and started it up. I drove around the base checking every other door, before heading out to take the morning weather run. Every other door on Mojave Wells base was closed. Why, I wondered, would the only door that opened out into the empty desert be of interest to anyone…anyone except Range Four Harry?

"Then one night I was awakened by a noise in my barracks. I quickly got dressed, went outside, locked myself into my truck, and waited. I saw some white people like creatures run out from my barracks into the sagebrush in the desert northwest of my barracks. They were running twice as fast as an Olympic runner is capable. I was a bundle of nerves for a while. After a few days though, I decided that I had to protect my sanity - at any price. I decided to just force myself to forget everything that had happened. In order to protect my sanity, I taught myself to just close the door in the morning, shave and get dressed without asking myself any questions. I trained myself to just ignore any lights I saw out in the desert, and just walk to my truck singing my happy songs. Some mornings, I was praying to God every step of the way. This policy of denial let me finally settle down and enjoy being stationed at Mojave Wells.

"I believe you, Charlie," Said Payne. Remember the week you trained me, how you returned to Desert Center on Thursday afternoon instead of staying until Friday like we told Desert Center on the phone?"

"Yes," I answered. "You were trained and I wanted to leave early so I could date Pamela."

"That was perfectly fine with me, Charlie," answered Payne. "That wasn't any problem at all. I just thought you might like to know, that evening, about 10:00 at night,

Bryan was going through the barracks you used. He'd been driving by and noticed that door on the side by the runway was propped open, that same door that leads straight out into the desert to the north.

"Well, he went walking in slowly and making a lot of noise and singing loudly, in case there was some airman in there with his girlfriend. He wanted to be sure they knew he was coming. To his surprise, there was an attractive young lady standing in there in the aisle who greeted him when he came in. He was really surprised because she was standing in there in total darkness, as though she were waiting for someone.

"Bryan said she was well dressed, wearing a nice dress with long sleeves, and gloves. She also wore opaque white stockings, flat dress shoes, and she appeared to be about 19. He noticed that she was wearing quite a bit of makeup and a wig. She had an unusually light complexion. He said that she was naturally very quiet. When she spoke to him, she pronounced the words in English very carefully and very smoothly. He said she didn't have any accent whatever. She appeared to be holding something like a pencil in her right hand.

"Bryan asked her what she was doing there. According to Bryan, she identified herself as 'The Teacher'. She said that she was waiting to talk to you, Charlie, and that she wondered where you might have gone."

"Me?" I asked in surprise. "But, Payne, I don't know any woman like that. I don't know any woman who even knew I stayed in that barracks."

"I know," answered Payne. "But Bryan swears that she seemed concerned when he told her you had gone back to Desert Center early. She asked if you were OK and happy.

321

She wanted to know if you had been hurt or terrified in any manner. When Bryan explained that you were in perfect health and you were just going back early so you would have time to make the long drive up to Las Vegas, she seemed noticeably relieved. According to Bryan, she said she always enjoyed being around you because you were always so happy and interesting. She said you had always been so patient with her and the children. Then she said that the children loved being around you too, especially her little girl. She hoped they hadn't frightened you. She seemed to be really happy when Bryan told her that you liked it up here, and you would be coming back up to Mojave Wells next summer. Bryan said it felt like time wasn't of any concern to her. It felt like she had hundreds of years to work with.

"According to Bryan, she stood there silently as though she was talking to someone else with her mind. Then she told Bryan that she wished to leave and asked him to leave first so she had room to leave without brushing past him. Bryan agreed. The two of them walked out to the door. Bryan held the door open for her. He said she asked him to leave the door propped open for a few hours. Bryan agreed. She asked him to walk her back to her trailer in the Mojave Wells trailer park. Bryan agreed and they started walking side by side over towards the trailer park, which is a mile or so over there. Bryan said that for a long time when they were walking, she wouldn't say anything. Then, when they were just entering the gate to the park, she suddenly exclaimed, 'There's my trailer,' and went running on ahead of him.

"There wasn't any way he could have kept up with her. He said she ran faster than he's ever seen any human run.

She just ran away from him and kept running until she was out of sight, way up ahead of him. The thing Bryan says he finds so screwy is that he's certain she didn't go into any of the trailers. He's certain that she ran through the trailer park and just kept running down that dirt road out into the desert to the northeast. Bryan doesn't know where she went. He says that she just vanished out into the night, out into the sagebrush."

"Well," I answered. "I honestly don't have the faintest idea who the woman could have been, but you know, that Friday night about 1:30 a.m., I was playing blackjack in that new big casino on the strip. I was playing with Pamela. We were laughing and having a good time together. Well, there was this one young woman standing in the crowd across the casino. I became convinced that she was watching us and following us around. She matched the description of the woman who was talking to Bryan. She seemed really happy and playful. It was completely unnerving because I felt just like I used to feel in the barracks at Mojave Wells. It felt like she was studying my every move. It felt like she was intensely interested in every motion I made, whether it was with the cards, or moving my chair, just everything. After a while, I was so disconcerted I just didn't know what to do with myself."

"Perhaps," he responded, "but think of the time. It couldn't have been the same woman. It was about 10:30 when she ran on ahead of Bryan. It's several hundred miles from Mojave Wells up to Las Vegas, and to that casino where you were. Bryan last saw her running out into the sagebrush. She would have had less than three hours to make the trip. Then, in order for her to find you, she'd have had to been able to read your mind from a distance, through walls and everything. Either that, or else she would have had to know how you think, better than you know yourself. Otherwise, how would she have been able to pick you out of the Las Vegas crowds on Friday night? No human could do anything like that."

"You're right," I said. "It couldn't have been the same woman."

"Not unless she was very good at running on ahead," answered Payne.

The Happy Charade

…And now, compelled by the spirit,
    I am going to Jerusalem,
        not knowing what will happen
            to me there…

Acts 20:22

Washington's problems had a nuclear effect on the Major, Sergeant Walters, the Desert Center Base Commander, and on the Pentagon Generals. Officially, Washington was rated by the base neurosurgeon as having suffered a mental collapse. They said that he had been overwhelmed by the intense loneliness of the Mojave Wells environment and duty conditions. Responding to an order from the base medical commander, a one star general, every weather observer at Desert Center was ordered to report to the neurosurgeon's office, one at a time, one per day, for a full block of psychological testing. Only those observers approved by the base neurosurgeon would be allowed to pull a tour of duty at Mojave Wells. So, one by one, the detachment weather observers visited the base hospital as ordered. Yet, even that, I found alarming. While the other observers were not given precise appointments by the base neurosurgeon, I was. For the others a time slot was assigned, 2:30 to 3:30 every afternoon. Since the Major cared only that all observers eventually report as ordered, a great deal of schedule shuffling occurred.

Yet, for me it was different. Everyone else was scheduled to go first. Than two weeks would pass before my turn came. After watching observer after observer report for testing in catch-as- catch-can order, I became convinced that some type of error had occurred. I decided to switch with my friend Dwight and report in his place. Who would care, I thought.

I was in for a terrible shock. That warm march afternoon when I entered the front door of the neurosurgeon's reception area, the receptionist reacted as if I'd come to rob a bank. I was hardly inside the door when she jumped up in anger, and demanded to know what I was doing there so early. To my surprise, she recognized me immediately. She already knew me by face, name, rank, and serial number, even though she was a perfect stranger to me. I hardly had time to say my name before she angrily ordered me out of the reception area, and back into the street.

As she was physically pushing me from the building, I became especially confused. The date I was scheduled to visit the neurosurgeon was three weeks hence. I was scheduled for the Wednesday of the week of Easter vacation. Yet, according to the sign on the front door, the building would be closed and locked for the entire Easter week. All medical personnel were scheduled to be away on vacation. Above her angry orders, I asked her if the schedule was correct. As she was physically shoving me out the front door, she shouted, "Of course it's correct, Airman Baker. We never make mistakes. We know perfectly well who you are! You be here exactly at 1:30 on the day you're scheduled, and not one minute before!" Then she slammed the front door in my face and locked it to prevent me from reentering. As I walked away, across the gravel covered parking lot out front, I could hardly have been more perplexed.

I walked slowly back to the weather station to let Dwight know that he was still expected to report to the neurosurgeon's office. I expected to relieve him so he could report for testing as ordered. I really wasn't prepared for what happened next. By the time I arrived at the weather station, the Desert Center MP's appeared to be out searching for me. As I entered the front door the Major was just hanging up the phone. He called me over to his desk and said in fatherly tones, "That was the base neurosurgeon on the phone, Airman Baker. They really don't want you to report for testing until Wednesday of Easter week, three weeks from now."

"But I don't understand, Sir," I responded respectfully. "The sign on their front door says the entire medical facility is going to be shut down for that complete week. If I wait until then, the doors will be locked and the building is going to be completely empty."

The Major responded seriously, "As I understand it, Charlie, the head neurosurgeon will make a special trip and come back from vacation on that day, in order to be there to conduct your tests."

"But Major," I carefully protested, "The other observers who have talked with him say he's planning on spending all of Easter week in San Francisco. According to the schedule, he'll have to fly back here in the middle of his vacation just to talk to me for an hour or so. He could have just talked to me today and not had to screw up his entire vacation."

The Major chose his next words very carefully as he answered, "Charlie, the neurosurgeon is an officer with almost 30 years of experience. His schedule is his problem.

All I know is that they really don't want you over there even one minute early. That was the base medical commander on the phone. He made it explicitly clear to me that they think of you as being a very, very special individual."

Still protesting, I continued, "But Major, Sir, how do they even know who I am? That new guy Harris, the one with the wife and the two little kids, told me that when he went over for his turn last week, the neurosurgeon spent less than five minutes talking with him about himself and his family. Harris claims that the neurosurgeon spent the rest of the hour, that's 55 minutes, Major, just asking him questions about me. Harris claims that the neurosurgeon already knows everything there is to know about me. Harris claims the neurosurgeon wanted to know all sorts of ridiculous details about me…things like, did I enjoy playing with his kids, did I get upset when his kids got in my way; did I get surprised if his kids came up behind me suddenly? I don't know what's going on Major, but I tell you when Harris and his wife had me over for supper three weeks ago, I never even touched his kids. I mean he has nice kids and a nice family, but I let his wife take care of the kids while Harris and I played chess. I don't know what's going on Major, but the way they've scheduled me doesn't make any sense. It just doesn't make any sense at all!"

The Major sat quietly, absorbed in deep thought for a few minutes, before answering me. When he finally answered, he spoke very slowly and chose his words very carefully. "Charlie, the schedule doesn't make sense to you or to me, but I assure you, it does make perfect sense to the base medical commander. We, here, serving our country in the military, have to learn to trust our officers and to do as we have been ordered. The orders that we have received are very explicit. They come from the base medical commander and he is a one star general. The orders state very explicitly that it is OK for you to be as much as 45 minutes late for your appointment. However, these orders strictly forbid you from being even one minute early. Do you understand your orders?"

"Yes, Major," I answered respectfully.

The Major continued sympathetically, "The medical commander says he understands if you are afraid to go inside. The medical commander says he understands if you choose to wait outside for as much as 45 minutes to get up your courage to go in among them. The medical commander told me personally that he will understand if they have to come outside into the parking lot to interview you. He told me personally that you must come alone, and that only you may attend the meeting. But I promise you Charlie, that if you enter that building so much as one minute early for your appointment, the medical commander will not understand, and if you enter the building even two minutes early, you will be court-martialed."

"Court-martialed, Sir?" I responded in fear and surprise.

"Court-martialed!" responded the Major. This is a very special interview. You may come to this interview as much as 45 minutes late. You may say anything you want to. You may wait outside in the middle of the parking lot. You may make them come outside to talk to you. If their appearance or actions frighten you, you may end the interview any time you chose, anyway you chose, for any reason you chose. He gives you his word that no matter what happens, they will not pursue. But if you enter that building even two minutes early, the Base Medical Commander and I both guarantee that you will be court-martialed."

With that I was dismissed. I was too afraid to ask any more questions. The Major was obviously a man who meant what he said. I relieved Dwight as the duty observer so that he could report for testing. No one seemed to care that he was late. Yet, to my surprise, he reported that no one would have cared if he had been early either. Like Harris, Dwight reported that the neurosurgeon spent less than five minutes talking with him about his feelings, his family, or his children. Like Harris, Dwight reported that the neurosurgeon seemed interested only in discussing his observations about me. "Why me?" I wondered. "Why me?" It seemed as if the entire base medical facility was doing everything backwards. "Why don't they want me to come one minute early on a day when the entire medical facility is closed?" I wondered. "What would I possibly see outside or inside a deserted set of medical offices that would make them want to court martial me?"

As I waited for my appointment, the days and weeks seemed to drag by. Day by day, I waited anxiously. Finally, the day of my appointment came. When Easter vacation began, the base medical facilities shut down completely, just as the sign had promised. Although my appointment was scheduled for 1:30 in the afternoon, I was in uniform, waiting in my barracks, by 9:00 a.m. My nerves were so on edge that I skipped the noon meal. Using my radio, I checked and rechecked the accuracy of my watch at least a dozen times. When 1:00 p.m. arrived, I left my barracks and began the long slow walk over to the apparently deserted base medical facility. I carefully timed my route so that I arrived at the outside entrance to the neurosurgeon's office just over two minutes late.

As I was crossing the graveled parking lot out in front of the building, in the distance, through one of the darkened windows I could see the receptionist come out from a door to a back room, walk slowly and smoothly into the reception area, walk over to the entrance door, and unlock it. As she did so, I noticed that she didn't bend forward as most women would have. Rather, her unusually thin frame remained standing straight upright as she reached out and unlocked the door. Then she walked back behind the counter in the reception area, and sat down out of sight. At the time, I was actually relieved that she wasn't the normal receptionist who had ordered me out of the facility three weeks before. The whole thing did seem odd, though. The receptionist was wearing a wig, gloves, white nylon stockings, lots of makeup, and a dress with long sleeves, a lot of winter clothes for such a warm spring day. I judged her to be about my height, 5'11". She was also unusually thin, and had an unusually smooth manner of walking.

Arriving at the front door, I gently opened it and walked inside. To my surprise, the receptionist didn't rise up to greet me. Instead, she remained sitting, bent over behind the reception counter. In an unusually quiet pleasant voice, and an unusually well spoken manner, she directed me to have a chair. 'He' would be with me shortly, she said. Through it all, she sat generally facing away from me, and acted as though she really didn't want me to see her face, or any portion of her except for her wig and her right temple.

In addition to the receptionist and myself, I could hear three other people in the otherwise deserted building. One was sitting in an office all the way down a hall, on the other side of the double doors in front of me. The other two could occasionally be heard, apparently standing, just inside the doorway to a room which connected directly to the back of the reception area. Since I had never heard them sit down, I concluded that both of them were standing. I found this fact slightly unnerving. Men standing inside of doorways are usually well armed security guards. "But why would they be guarding a doorway that only a receptionist could use?" I wondered. I thought about it for a few minutes. I concluded that the two men, whom I had never actually seen, must be providing a safe haven for the receptionist. They must be standing there just in case she felt she needed protection from me. I thought about it some more. It still didn't make sense to me. If the security guards felt that I was a threat to the receptionist, why wouldn't they just walk out into the reception area and demonstrate that the receptionist was well protected?

I noticed that all of the lights were turned off. That seemed odd, but there were quite a few windows, and these windows let in some sunlight. Still, I wondered, "Why don't they want the fluorescent lights turned on?"

As I looked around the room, my gaze fell on the thermostat. Despite the fact that this was a warm afternoon and the receptionist was warmly dressed, the thermostat was turned up beyond 80 degrees Fahrenheit. "Why doesn't the receptionist turn it down?" I wondered. "With all of the clothes she's wearing, she must be roasting."

An answering thought seemed to appear in my mind. It seemed to come into my mind from nowhere in particular. I found myself thinking that the earth wasn't a warm place. I found myself thinking of the earth as a cold, desolate wilderness where the most intelligent people had to dress carefully in order to stay warm.

Then there was the matter of the parking lot. As I gazed through the window, an odd fact struck me. The parking lot was completely empty. "So how did the receptionist and the other three people get here?" I wondered. The only vehicle anywhere around, that I knew of, was a large step van which I'd seen parked out back when I was walking over to the building. Yet, the whole thing still didn't seem to make sense to me. A rich, high ranking military doctor with a highly paid nurse, and two assistants, all meet somewhere, all get in a step van and drive over to a deserted set of offices just to ask me if I loved my mother and my father? Why wouldn't they just bring their cars?

Then there was the receptionist herself. She still hadn't looked at me, even once. She sat behind the counter, bent over so far that only the top portion of her head, from the temples up, could be seen. She was sitting so still that I soon became convinced that she was listening to something. Yet, what? There were no radios to be heard. The loudest things in the entire room were the silent thoughts that roamed around in my brain. Then I noticed something truly confusing. When I moved, in order to get a magazine to read, the receptionist moved too. It seemed as if she was intent on keeping her right temple always turned towards me, as she sat there. Then I noticed that she seemed to be able to correctly anticipate my every move, almost as if she were able to read my very thoughts. Now my nerves were really getting jangled.

Then I found my thoughts wandering. I found myself remembering the experiences I'd had at Mojave Wells, and how much I'd enjoyed them. I found myself remembering the beautiful early morning drives out to range three, and pleasant afternoons down at range one. Then I found myself day dreaming about taking the balloon measurements with children playing around me, and having pleasant conversations with beautiful white coyotes and other animals. Then I remembered rescuing the lost little white girl with the big blue eyes, down at range one. Then I began to feel like my mind was no longer my own.

Getting hold of myself at last, I brushed all of the thoughts that I could, out of my mind. I sat quietly and patiently, waiting for the doctor to call me. I noticed that more than 15 minutes had passed. I worried that maybe I'd come too early. According to the Major, I would be in serious trouble if I had come early, and the Major was a man of his word. In order to reassure myself, I spoke to the receptionist, speaking clearly and gently, "I came at the proper time, didn't I. My orders said that I had to report at 1:30, and I arrived at 1:32." There was no answer, so I repeated my statement, "Excuse me, I came at the proper time, didn't I? I mean, I wasn't too early, was I?"

After a long pause, the receptionist replied, speaking carefully, still sitting bent over, looking away from me, keeping her right temple turned towards me, "Yes, You came at the proper time. Sit quietly. He will be with you in a few minutes."

Nothing seemed to make any sense to me. I sat there wondering "I'm ordered to report to a deserted set of offices, over Easter vacation and then forced to sit quietly in a chair, day dreaming every minute about past experiences, and wait for a long time, because the neurosurgeon is too busy to see me as scheduled ?"

Having no other choice, I sat quietly, as directed by the receptionist, and waited for the neurosurgeon to see me. Then an odd thought crossed my mind. If the neurosurgeon was the man waiting in the office down the hall, waiting to see me, and if I was waiting here to see him, the only thing keeping us apart was the receptionist. "Why doesn't he just walk up the hallway and get me?" I wondered. After all, this is his vacation that I'm screwing up. Then another odd thought crossed my mind. I became convinced that the neurosurgeon wouldn't come to get me because he was afraid to be around the receptionist. It was such an odd thought that it didn't seem as though I'd even thought it at all. Rather, it seemed like someone had placed it there in my mind for me to read.

I struggled with this odd idea for a few minutes. It didn't seem to fit anywhere in my mind, and it didn't seem to have come from within me. The neurosurgeon, after all, was a one star general. "Why would he be afraid of his own receptionist?" I wondered.

As I sat there wondering, I noticed that the clock on the wall now read 1:58 p.m. Without warning, and without moving her head towards me, the receptionist spoke, "At exactly 2:00 p.m., you are to go through the double doors. Walk directly down the hallway and talk to the man sitting in the end office," she said pleasantly. Then, without really standing up, she arose slightly from her chair and suddenly left the room - exiting through the doorway behind the counter. As I sat there, I could hear her meeting up with the other two individuals standing in the back room. They weren't saying anything. Only their footsteps could be heard. I was shocked. Through it all, she had acted as though she didn't want me to see any portion of her...not her dress, not her face, not her legs, only her hair and her right temple. It seemed as though she'd kept me sitting there for a full half hour, just so she could sit with her right temple directed towards me.

Having nothing better to do, I sat patiently watching the minute hand on the clock measure out the remaining two minutes. Then, at 2:00 p.m. sharp, I slowly got up from my chair, looked around the deserted reception area for anything I might have dropped, pushed open the double doors, and entered the long hallway beyond. Down a short hallway to my right, it was obvious that the receptionist and the other two individuals were standing out of sight in a darkened empty room. I thought it odd that the other two individuals, whom I had never been able to see, had been so willing to stand more or less still for a full half hour in a windowless room with no lights, when it would have been so easy to place chairs in the room, turn on the lights, and sit down. It seemed contrary to human nature.

In any event, I continued down the long hallway. I was glad to be finally seeing the neurosurgeon, whom I had waited so long to see. Reaching the last room on the end of the hallway, I knocked on the closed doorway.

"Come in," was the pleasant response.

I opened the door and went in. Sitting there in a soft chair, in a darkened room, was a pleasant man, probably in his early forties. He was neatly dressed, wearing a nice three-piece business suit with a narrow necktie. The bulge under his left armpit betrayed the gun he was carrying in a shoulder holster. From the size of the bulge, I concluded that the gun must be an unusually large caliber. The bulges in the pockets of his suit jacket looked suspiciously like extra ammunition clips. "Unusual tools for a neurosurgeon," I thought to myself.

"Have a seat," he said, apparently referring to a sofa positioned to the left of him. "And close the door so we can talk." I noticed that he never once made any hand or body motions as he said this, and remained sitting motionless through it all.

I found it odd that he was obviously unwilling to rise up out of his chair to greet me. Yet, his unwillingness didn't seem directed at me. Rather, it seemed as though he was just used to living in an environment where nobody greeted each other, or reached out to touch each other. It struck me as odd. I chose to pursue the matter. As I sat down on the sofa, I said in a calm, matter of fact voice, "I understand that the fruit trees are in bloom and that San Francisco is pretty this time of year," knowing that the neurosurgeon was from San Francisco.

"I don't know," he answered. "The cherry blossoms weren't open yet last week in Washington DC. Maybe they're open now in San Francisco."

I was stunned. The gun, the lack of immediate knowledge of San Francisco, the conclusion was inescapable. Whomever I was talking to, it certainly wasn't the base neurosurgeon. I interpreted his pleasant smile to mean that he expected this happy charade to continue. I didn't disappoint him. Smiling myself, I continued, "I suppose the leaves are just beginning to come out in southern Wisconsin. There were some trees out in front of my high school which always started to put out their leaves about this time of year."

"No. They haven't started opening yet," he responded, knowingly. "You're talking about those big old trees just across the street from the high school, where the roots have pushed up the sidewalk, aren't you?"

I was almost too stunned to answer. "Had he actually been checking up on me so closely that he'd traveled out to my high school just to see what it looked like?" I wondered. I thought about it for a minute. Men with guns, who investigate you by walking around your hometown, usually call themselves security agents. Such agents do not give psychological exams. They give debriefing sessions. I wondered, "Is that what's really happening? Was the half hour wait in front of the receptionist the actual exam, and am I now being debriefed by the government security agent?" It seemed so backwards from what I had been expecting.

I decided to continue probing for information. His pleasant smile betrayed his belief that all of the security bases were still covered. I let him think so. There was no point I decided, in upsetting him. I smiled pleasantly, myself, and speaking calmly and clearly, I continued my probing. Turning to him, I said pleasantly, "I see the lights are turned off. Do you want me to ask the receptionist to turn them on?"

The way the muscles in his upper left arm and neck twitched, along with the muscles over his gun holster convinced me that my question had struck home. "Was she still in the reception area when you came down here?" He asked showing both fear and surprise.

"No," I responded, settling him down. "But she and her aides were standing in that back room down the side aisle. I could easily walk down there and ask her to turn on the lights if you want." It was a clever trap. I was expecting him to say no. I wanted to see how he was going to do it.

Sitting calmly, almost motionless, and speaking in a smooth and well controlled voice, he responded, "No. Never disturb them. They always want to be alone. We should just stay sitting here and let them be alone. If they want to talk to us, they'll come to us."

His response really took me off guard. He clearly believed that he and I formed one group, and that the receptionist and her two aides formed another. Yet he and I had met only minutes ago. "Why does he believe that he and I are of a kind, and that the receptionist and her two security aides form a different kind?" I wondered.

Yes, confusing as it was, things were starting to make sense to me. Things were starting to add up. The security agent obviously believed that when I was sitting in front of the receptionist in the reception area, I was sitting in the presence of a person who was vastly different from both he and I. The receptionist was obviously a person whom he didn't want to upset. He almost certainly was afraid of her. I had spent time meeting with the receptionist. It was obvious to me that now, the security agent, posing as a psychiatrist, wanted to debrief me to see if I was still all right. It all made sense, except for one simple fact: the receptionist had never once asked me a single question. Apparently, nothing had happened when I was waiting in the reception area, except that my thoughts had seemed to wander a great deal. I sat there in confusion, wondering about things for a few minutes. Had nothing really happened when I was sitting in front of the receptionist, I wondered? How then, had I guessed that he was afraid of her when I was sitting in the reception area?

I thought for a minute more, and I decided to continue my probing. Turning towards him, I continued, as though I knew more about the receptionist than I was revealing, "I see the receptionist was wearing a dress with long sleeves, a wig and gloves. She must have been warm enough, wearing all of those clothes in this weather."

At the mention of the receptionist, the man in front of me flinched noticeably. Then he responded, in a warm manner, "Yes, it's just now becoming warm enough outside for her to move around, but she has to stay heavily dressed in order to do it. Actually, I was surprised that she agreed to be here, today, since it's so early in the spring. She must really enjoy meeting with you because she's risking another sickness with what she's doing. Ordinarily, she wouldn't go outside into the open air for another month or so."

I was too stunned to respond. I sat on the couch, mentally struggling to digest what he'd said. Then he continued, "Did everything go all right when you were in the reception area?"

"Yes," I answered, still struggling with my thoughts.

"Did she tell you about her little girl?" he asked.

"No," I answered, "I didn't know she had one. She didn't say anything to me at all."

"That doesn't matter," he answered knowingly. Then he asked, "What kinds of thoughts were going through your mind when you were waiting out there?"

I responded, "Well, while I was sitting out there, I did have an unusually pleasant daydream about being out on the Mojave Wells gunnery ranges in the early morning hours. In my dream, I was playing with an unusually intelligent little girl, while her mother stayed watching me from out in the sagebrush. The little girl in my daydream was sort of like a little second grader, who wore pretty white dresses and things, and who seemed to really enjoy riding ponies and playing games around the area where I was working. Sometimes she seemed like a playful little butterfly."

This seemed to make the man in front of me happy. Smiling noticeably for the first time, he responded, "I can see that your wait in the reception area was a success. I'll explain to you what's going to happen next. Then I want you to leave here by way of the back door. When you leave this room, do not, under any circumstances, return to the reception area. I want you to continue down this hallway to the exit door at the end of the hallway, and leave by going out that door into the back parking lot. Then I want you to walk directly away from the building toward the airman's club. You are not to look back at this building as you do so. Keep walking away from this building until you have reached Desert Center Avenue that is about a mile over in that direction. Then you may do whatever you want. Do you understand?"

"Yes," I answered. I knew better than to ask any more questions.

He continued, "I'm going to give your commanding officer, the major, the following orders. Only you may be stationed at Mojave Wells. You will be stationed up there alone, and you will be stationed up there until further notice. You will never be ordered off the ranges, even if the ranges are closed due to an emergency.

"You may go anywhere you wish on the ranges, at anytime you wish. That includes day or night, weekends and holidays. You are also allowed to go as far out as you wish, anytime you wish. No guard is ever allowed to say no to you, even at night.

"No other weather observer may be stationed with you. If you get sick, then no one may replace you. Taking the wind measurements will cease until you have fully recovered. If you have an accident when you're out there, then you must bring yourself safely home.

"If you need to be relieved for a few weeks to take your annual leave, then your friend Payne, and your friend Dwight, as a team may relieve you. This two-man team, Payne and Dwight, must be together at all times, even to visit the bathroom. They may relieve you for no more than two weeks, once every six months.

"Under any circumstances, no married observer, other than Dwight, may ever be stationed at the gunnery ranges. Only those single observers whom I have approved may be stationed at the gunnery ranges. In every case they must be part of a two or three man team, and in every case the team may not spend more than 3 days and 2 nights at Mojave Wells, with no more than one assignment per man per year. Under no circumstances is any weather observer except you, ever allowed more than one half mile from the immediate roads between the Mojave Wells base and weather shacks. No observer, except you, is ever allowed to visit places such as the ammunition bunkers out at range three or the arroyo at range one. In addition, no observer, except you, is ever allowed to travel beyond range three, or to be on the road to range four.

Every weather observer, except you, must report immediately to the Desert Center base neurosurgeon for debriefing. They must do so upon return from any trip or any assignment to the Mojave Wells ranges. They must be debriefed, even if the trip was only an afternoon trip to deliver supplies. Upon their return, as soon as they enter the Desert Center gate, they must report to the neurosurgeon.

That's everyone, including the Major and Sergeant Walters, no exceptions, except you."

"Except me?" I asked, sitting in quiet wonderment.

"Yes," he answered. "Everyone except you. Nothing about your assignment is classified, nothing whatsoever. You have total control over everything that you see, that you hear, or that you do. The only rule is that whatever you do, you must do it alone.

You are never to report for debriefing. Whatever you see, whatever you hear, whatever you experience, you need never tell anyone unless you wish to. You may tell anyone you wish, or no one if you so wish. You may tell them every single detail and experience, as often as you wish, or you may tell them nothing. It's all totally up to you. Just remember, if you ever feel overwhelmed, if you ever feel that you need to talk to one of us about your experiences, just phone the neurosurgeon, day or night, or phone the duty officer here at Desert Center. The base medical commander, or myself, will personally and immediately come to you. There will be no questions asked. The two of us, myself, and the base medical commander, are authorized to use the emergency medical helicopter for transportation. Ours is the highest priority. We may divert the helicopter or any other piece of transportation equipment we desire, from any accident or any emergency, just to come to wherever you are. We are ordered not to ask you any questions! We have been ordered not to keep any records of such meetings. You will never be criticized, reproached, or disciplined for asking to see either one of us. Do you understand your orders?"

Dumbfounded and sitting there in near disbelief, I answered, "Yes."

He smiled. Turning at last to me, he said, "Son, I hope to God for your sake that you are right. I hope you are as good at keeping your wits about you during difficult times as they say you are, because you sure are going to get tested. One last thing, remember, you have a name. When you are out on the ranges, if you are ever asked what your name is, respond by saying that you are "teacher's pet". You are also known as "the friend of the teacher". You may also say that you are out there on the ranges because the teacher asked for you.

"I'm teacher's pet?" I asked carefully.

"Yes," he responded. "It's a name to be proud of. You may tell your name to anyone and to everyone that you wish to. The individuals, who need to know your name, will also know you face to face. But just to be on the safe side, make certain that you remember the name. Now time is running very short, but there is still time enough for you to ask me just one question. Is there any one question that you would like me to answer?"

"Yes," I answered. "I'm looking forward to going back up to Mojave Wells. I really enjoy being up there, but I was wondering, why me? There's nothing special about me. The other guys here at Desert Center are good weather observers too. Payne grew up in the desert, and he's completely at home out there. Michael grew up here in Palm Meadows. He'd be an excellent choice. Then there's that new black guy, Harris. He's sharp and knows all of the ropes. I mean, why was I chosen over sharp, well qualified guys like that?"

He sat pensively, for a minute or so. Then he answered, "I'll tell you the truth, Charlie. For what you're going to be facing, you deserve the truth. Some on the committee, like the Teacher, picked you because they say you're more patient than the others. The Desert Center base commander picked you because they say you keep your wits about you better than they've ever seen or heard tell about. Others, back at the Pentagon, picked you because of your incredible reasoning ability, like the way you figured out that I'm not really a neurosurgeon. As for me, I picked you because of your courage. I still can't believe that you're sitting in here on the sofa beside me. I told the committee that even a brave man in your shoes, would be cut to ribbons by his inner fears and anxieties. I told them that after you were kept waiting for so long, after all you've already been through, alone, at night out on the gunnery ranges, the best we could expect is that we'd end up having to interview you outside in the parking lot from a distance of 100 feet or so. I can't believe the guts you have. You just walked into this building, said, 'Hello', and waited in front of the receptionist for a complete half hour. I wouldn't have believed it if I hadn't seen it with my own eyes.

"Driving out to the gunnery ranges, alone, in the darkness, every morning like you have been, and will be doing, takes a man with your kind of guts. I don't have the guts to fill any one of your shoes. Don't forget, anytime things get tough, there's always going to be someone here, on the other end of the phone.

"You'd better go, now, Charlie. They all must be getting cold by now, and I must get them back before darkness comes. She'll freeze for sure if she's out on a night like tonight, the way she's dressed. It's probably going to get down to at least 65 degrees."

With that the interview was over. I left the building by the back door as ordered, and walked the mile without ever looking back.

The next day, the Major called me into his office to deliver the same set of orders I'd received in the neurosurgeon's office. The first sergeant, Master Sergeant Walters was present. I remember how intent and fatherly they both were.

As I left the weather station to get my belongings, my mind was still spinning. I alone could go to Mojave Wells. I had to be alone. I would get extra pay. I had full use of the weather truck. The Mojave Wells weather stations would never be inspected by anyone except me. I could come back to Desert Center for Christmas and Thanksgiving. No one else would ever be sent unless I asked Payne and Dwight to relieve me. I could call the commanders anytime, say anything or nothing, no records of such conversations would ever be kept, they would divert the emergency medical helicopter from any other accident or emergency just to talk to me, and they promised that they wouldn't ask a single question about my experiences, and all I had to do in return was take five or six weather reports every working day, starting at 4:00 a.m., from the gunnery ranges, until further notice. All I had to do was drive 22 miles, or so, out into the desolate, deserted Mojave Wells gunnery ranges, through distant mountain passes into distant hidden desert valleys, alone, every morning Monday through Friday, in the darkness of 3:15 a.m. and measure the winds. It all seemed so simple. It all seemed so terribly simple. It hardly seemed like the U.S Air Force.

Summer Rain

Can you raise your voice among the clouds,
or veil yourself in the waters of the storm?
Can you send forth the lightnings on their way,
or will they say to you, "Here we are?"

Job 38:34,35

The desert is a dry place but sometimes it rains. This morning I was well rested and wide awake as I headed my truck north into Mojave Wells Valley, past the wet sagebrush and the dripping wet yucca plants. A late afternoon storm had blown in the day before. The desert exhibits a special beauty during a nighttime rain. I enjoyed its beauty, and I found the sound of rain on my barracks roof to be relaxing. I was in bed fast asleep by 6:30 in the evening. Consequently, it was a simple matter to be in my truck heading out to range three by 1:30 a.m. the next morning. Some thunder had awakened me. I was too well rested to go back to sleep. I've always been a night person, and I wanted to enjoy the beauty of the nighttime desert rain. Happy, then, I turned off my alarm clock, shaved and dressed, and headed on out to the ranges. Lightning was striking the mountains on both sides of the valley as I carefully brought my truck onto the Range Three road. I opened my window a little, turned on my headlights, heater, windshield wipers, and settled back for a nice easy, quiet drive out to my weather shack. I remember well the drive out to Range Three that morning. The rain seemed so cold, so relaxing, so beautiful, and so real.

I was looking forward to spending some time resting and reading in my weather shack before taking the balloon run this morning. Starting the diesel generators was straight forward, and once electricity was available for the fan on my gas heater, my shack would be warm, comfortable, and snug. Beside me in the truck was a large jar of drinking water, some soda pop, and four sandwiches I had gotten from the chow hall the night before, in case the rain prevented me from making it back in for breakfast. Beside me on my truck seat also were some candy bars, and a thick interesting history book. I expected that my weather shack would be a nice restful place on this cold, rainy morning.

The storm covered the entire valley, and it also covered all of the mountains on both sides. I relaxed even more. I was feeling quite brave, as I drove on through the rain. It was obvious to me that the ranges would remain closed today. The range rats would have a pleasant day playing cards on base, in the sheds out back of the motor pool. Because of the storm and the hour, I naturally expected to be alone out on the ranges.

Soon the buildings of range three loomed slowly up out of the mist and the rain. I parked my truck in front of the generator shack, left the lights on, the engine idling, and quickly started one of the diesel generators. I noted that all of the fuel tanks were full, so the diesel could run for months, if necessary. Then, getting back into my truck, for protection from the rain, I drove the short distance over to my weather shack. I turned off the engine, and the headlights as I parked the truck in front of my shack. In a few short minutes, I had opened the front door, turned on the lights and the heater, and was well on my way to having a very enjoyable morning.

When I had driven up to the range three buildings, I hadn't paid much attention to anything except the rain. It was dark, raining, and misty. My eyes had scanned across a large dull white object a half-mile or so out in the desert, northwest of the range three lounge. It was just barely visible through the mist and rain, and I supposed that it was just another part of the storm. After all, I was expecting nothing but desert out there.

When I drove out to the ranges, I seldom took the trouble to look all around. I seldom looked in all of the buildings, before going on about my business, but once in a while I did. Those mornings when I did investigate, usually everything was obviously deserted, but some mornings were different. Some mornings the hidden areas would give forth sounds, bumps, flurries of activity, and dull, white fluorescent glows that sped off into the desert, stopping to watch me from afar. One morning I tripped over a jackrabbit, so I supposed that all of the sights and sounds were due to rabbits, dreams, eye problems, or maybe loneliness. This morning, because of the storm, I saw no need to check the lounge, the tower, and the other hidden areas out at range three. The rain was heavy. The night was dark. The mist was everywhere. It seemed as if I were the only creature on God's green Earth with any reason to be out on the ranges on a night like this.

Entering my weather shack, I turned on the lights, started my gas heater, turned on my radio, closed the front door behind me, and opened wide my side door. Then I got my papers and my other things ready for the morning balloon run. Even though the balloon release wasn't scheduled for almost three hours, I inflated the balloon. I reasoned that it might be raining too hard at 4:30 to make the balloon run. However, if I had my balloon ready, and there was a break in the storm before then, I could release the balloon early, and still get a useable set of winds. It was a good plan, but it required that I periodically check the progress of the storm - a simple task for an experienced weather observer like myself. It was a steady rain, and it wasn't very windy, so I left my side door open and my front door closed.

Now that everything was in readiness, I checked the rain outside, and settled down to the next chapter in my American History book. The chapter I was reading, described how the family of settlers in the 1800s, had first entered Mojave Wells valley from the north. It described how they had brought their wagons down this very valley, apparently passing close to the spot where my weather shack stood, and continued down to the actual springs now named Mojave Wells. I found the chapter engrossing, and time slipped away on me.

As I sat there reading and wondering what the days of the old west might have been like, an image of how the settlers might have looked as they walked by this spot in the desert, formed in my mind. The image was pleasant and relaxing. In my mind's eye, I imagined myself sitting on one of the ledges in the mountains to the northeast, watching them as they and their wagons traveled down the Mojave Wells valley. I found myself wondering how the settlers would have felt if they had known that they were being watched from afar. Then, in my mind's eye, I imagined that I could see them sitting and eating around a campfire at night, just a mile or so from this spot, while some curious, non-threatening totally chalk white woman out in the desert, circled around them, watching their every move. I began feeling as though the image was real, accurate, and intentionally communicated to me by some woman who had actually sat on one of the mountain ledges to the northeast, watching the settlers from a distance. I became annoyed with myself, since my purpose had been to educate myself, not to daydream. With much effort, I finally forced the images from my mind. The images kept coming back, so, to get control of myself, I turned to one of the later chapters on the history of the city of Seattle.

Putting the book down at last, I turned suddenly towards the open side door behind me, and peered out into the mist and the heavy rain. My intention had been to check the progress of the storm. Consequently, my eyes immediately came to rest on a thick, rectangular, dull white patch of mist located no more than 30 feet out in the desert. The patch appeared to be some 6 or 7 feet tall, and 5 or 6 feet wide. Sitting in my well-lit shack, my eyes weren't used to looking out into the rainy darkness. Consequently, I wasn't surprised when it appeared to float away silently to the south. At the time, however, I was left wondering. It appeared to be too close, and far too solid to be a patch of clouds or rain, and the storm was moving towards the north. Most of all, I couldn't shake off the impression that it had been standing there, out in the rain, watching me, before it had drifted away into the wind.

Since I hadn't checked the weather outside for some time, I decided to go outside into the rain and take a good look around. Stepping outside through my side door, I gingerly strode around to the front of my shack. I made a lot of noise as I did - so at least the rabbits were scared. It was muddy outside, and the clouds were so low that there would have been little use in releasing the balloon. The rain was so heavy I could just barely make out the lounge building, the control tower, and the range billboards. The low clouds obscured the tops of the building. The Range Three outhouse, which stood out in the desert to the north, was totally obscured by the rain. However, the large white misty patch had returned. Now it was floating out in the sagebrush, a few inches off the desert, less than 50 feet from me, out in the skip bomb practice area to the northeast. I studied it intently for fifteen minutes or so. I became certain that the white patch in the rain was watching me back. In any event, whatever it was, it had made me very curious. It floated there relatively motionless, even though the storm continued to drift by. I decided to walk over to where it was, and get a closer look. Yet, as I walked towards it, I couldn't seem to close the 50 feet or so which separated it from me. I stepped across the cable into the skip bomb area, and walked slowly towards it. Feeling quite foolish, and beginning to feel apprehensive, I called out to it, "Is anyone out there? Who are you? Do you need help? What do you want?"

There was no response. It continued to fall back away from me, always in total silence. Soon I had followed it a great distance out into the tall sagebrush northeast of the graveled area, and the lights of my weather shack were becoming very dim in the rain behind me. The rain let up momentarily as I was looking back towards the range three buildings, now more than 400 feet away. To my surprise, it appeared that the lights in the range three lounge were on. Both rooms in the lounge were filled with a soft white fluorescent light that flooded out through the open doorway and the large glass windows, illuminating the cement walkway in front. A 7 foot tall misty fluorescent white patch floated by the northeast corner of the building, and it seemed to be always staying between me and the cement walkway out front. Two more misty fluorescent white patches could be vaguely seen through the rain, floating slowly from the lounge out into the desert towards the northwest, all in perfect silence.

"For an empty deserted building sitting 22 miles out in the desert, there sure is some party going on," I muttered to myself. As the rain closed back in, obscuring my view of the Range Three lounge, the problem finally forced its way into my cold rain soaked consciousness. I felt a certain momentary shock as I remembered replacing a 100-watt light bulb in the Range Three lounge a few weeks before. At that time, I'd checked all of the lights. I was certain the Range Three lounge didn't use fluorescent lights.

Deciding that I had gone as far into the desert on this rainy, stormy evening, as common sense would allow, I turned and started walking slowly back towards the graveled area. The white patch also turned, and for a time it followed me back, always maintaining the 50 feet distance between us. As I was reaching the cable fence, it finally floated slowly off, disappearing at last, in stately fashion, into the dark rainy mists a hundred feet or so to the north. The rain was getting steadily worse, and by now I was wet and cold. I slogged back across the gravel to the cozy warmth of my stove and my weather shack.

When finally I arrived back in my shack. I warmed myself by the stove. I left the side door open for fresh air and returned to reading my history book. As I reread the chapter on the history of the discovers of Death Valley, I noticed that this time my mind was not flooded with images of settlers and wagons, as it had been before. The change was quite dramatic and I spent a few minutes wondering why. It was the same book. It was the same night. It was the same me. Only now when I looked out the side door into the dark rainy mists, there was no white patch. I checked my consciousness some more. I turned to the chapter on Seattle. Still no images of northern forests, no images of the snow covered mountains, no images of sturdy unshaven settlers came into my mind, as they had done so before, and still no white patch out in the rain.

In my mind I struggled for a while. I decided that I must have been dreaming. I just couldn't accept the reality of the obvious conclusion. After all, for the images to have been placed in my mind by the white patch, that would mean that it would have had to be more than 150 years old. Then there was the problem of communication. In order for the images to have come from the white patch, it would first have to know what I was thinking, so the communication would have to work both ways. Then there was the question of its motives. The white patch's only possible motive would have been that it had wanted to entertain me, or to play with me in a childish, fashion. Logic no longer was the problem. Whatever the logic of the situation was, I just couldn't accept the reality of the obvious conclusions.

I closed the book, and put it back on the shelf in front of me. My mind was not up for reading anymore. I had to decide if the white patch had been real, if it had intentionally come out here to enjoy the beauty of the night rainstorm, as I had, or if it was just a drifting patch of mist and rain. I turned off my radio, and decided to just sit quietly in my chair, looking out the side door, into the cold, dark rainy mists. I wondered if the white patch would return. After waiting 20 minutes or so, my patience was rewarded. About 30 feet out in the desert, the white patch slowly floated back into view in total silence. This time it floated in from the southeast. It blended in so well with the darkness, the mists, and the rain that I wasn't at first sure that it had returned. Once again I spoke to it, calling out loudly, "Is that you? Whoever you are, what are you? What do you want? You frighten me. I'm only a weather observer. I only come out here because I have to report the weather to Desert Center. What do you want? Why are you watching me?"

Again there was no response. The only sound was the sound of the cold heavy rain falling steadily on the roof of my weather shack. Standing up slowly, and still wondering if I wasn't just talking to the rain, I decided to step outside and try to get a better view of it. As I did so, I spoke to whatever it was, "Don't worry. I won't hurt you. You frighten me. I just want to see what you are." Yet it made no difference. As I stepped down from the side doorway into the mud outside, once again it floated slowly away from me. Again it retreated out into the desert, this time down towards the southeast. The rain was lighter in that direction. It wasn't until the white patch was some 200 feet from me that it finally disappeared out into the darkness, the rain, and the mists. Still, my mind wouldn't let me accept the reality of what I had just seen. "It must be the rain," I said to myself out loud. "It must just be something to do with the rain."

I went back into the warmth of my shack, and sat down to think about things. Then I remembered the white patch that I had seen vaguely through the rain as I had driven up

355

to the range three buildings. I wondered if it was still there. This patch had been much larger than the one I had just seen. It had been the size of a building larger than the range three lounge. I decided to drive over there. Maybe that large white patch was still out there. I went out to my truck parked in front of my weather shack. Try as I would, it just wouldn't start. Even though its V8 engine was in perfect working order, and the battery was new and fully charged, it behaved as though the battery was totally dead. Swearing to myself, I got out of my truck, out into the cold hard rain. I decided to walk over to the northwest, towards where I had seen the large white patch. There were no outside lights on, and my flashlight was my only companion. Now my flashlight, and the new spare batteries I always carried with me, failed too. Undaunted by these startling developments I continued walking slowly through the darkness and the rain towards the western edge of the graveled area. When I reached the edge of the thin sagebrush on the western side, I decided I had come as far from the warmth of my weather shack as made sense. I wanted to continue on, out into the sagebrush towards the northwest, and I was swearing to myself because my usually dependable truck hadn't started. Common sense dictated that it wouldn't be safe for me to go any further. I stood there, in the driving rain, by the edge of the sagebrush, for 15 or 20 minutes, studying the darkness in front of me. My vision was perfect, and I found my conclusion somewhat unnerving.

There was no question about it. Something large and white was parked less than a quarter mile out in a small depression in the desert, parked out there in the darkness, in the mists, and in the rain. Smaller fluorescent white patches, some only 3 or 4 feet tall, others 5 and 7 feet tall would periodically float between this large white object and the Range Three lounge. I was certain that my conclusion was correct. Yet, the shock of it all somehow prevented me from fully grasping the situation I had accidentally stumbled into. Between the large white object and me, some 70 feet or so in front of me, floated another 7 foot tall misty white rectangular patch. It appeared to be similar to the first, only this one refused to fall back when I stepped forward.

Feeling cold, and wet, and noticeably afraid to go any further, I quickly retraced my steps back to the warmth of my weather shack. Once inside, I noticed that my flashlight was now working perfectly again. My spirits were buoyed by this discovery, and my fears began subsiding. I decided to try my truck again and it too now started perfectly. After revving the engine for a few minutes, and convincing myself that it would start again, I shut it off and got back out into the cold hard rain. It was now going on 4:00 a.m. The rain was subsiding, and I decided that I would be able to release the balloon on schedule at 4:30. As I was standing there, checking the progress of the storm, once again I noticed the first white patch. This time it was floating in the rain, over behind the range three billboards. Feeling braver, now, believing that my truck would start again, I decided to once again close on the small white patch. I still wondered what it could be. Keeping the range boards between me and the white patch, I walked quickly to the north, toward the western end of the range billboards. It didn't seem to know that I was coming. I closed the distance as fast and as quietly as I could without actually running. Coming even with the western end of the range billboards, now some 10 feet from me, I was finally able to see into the misty fluorescent white patch which floated in the heavy rain on the other side. The rain didn't seem to actually fall into the white fluorescent area, but rather, the rain appeared to just fall in streamlined patterns around it. My eyes hurt when I looked into the fluorescent white light, and I could look into it for only a few seconds. It reacted to my presence almost immediately. Standing there in the white fluorescent mist was a chalk white woman-like creature, very thin, maybe 6 feet tall, clad in what appeared to be an aluminum-canvas suit, with an open helmet, and aluminum like gloves and boots. The creature felt pleasant, friendly, fully-grown, and totally feminine; but it didn't actually feel human. Instead, it felt as though I was looking at a beautiful feminine animal, such as a horse. I was stunned by the fact that as I looked at it, I felt the same as I had felt when the images of a beautiful white woman studying the settlers passing through the Mojave Wells valley, had flooded through my brain. In my mind, she seemed to be laughing and teasing me in a friendly girlish manner. She seemed to be laughing, "Now that you've caught me, Charlie, what are you going to do with me?" Then, still laughing, she retreated from me, disappearing once again, out into the darkness, and out into the cold hard rain, out into the empty desert to the northeast, all in total silence.

"Am I still sane?" I grimly muttered to myself. I stood there in the rain for a long time, in numbed shock, denial, and disbelief.

After a long time, the cold hard rain falling on my face brought me back to my senses. Grimly, I turned, and trudged back through the rain, toward my weather shack. I couldn't accept the reality of what I had just seen. I decided that I must be dreaming, or going nuts. I decided that the best thing for me to do would be to just release my weather balloon, take my measurements, phone Desert Center with the results, and head back to base. Without further ado, I unlocked my theodolite, removed the protective cover, got my balloon from my weather shack and released it. Then I began taking the wind measurements. As I had expected, after less than 2 minutes of flight, the balloon disappeared into the base of the rain clouds. It meant the run was over. I covered and locked my theodolite, collected my things, and trudged back to my shack.

The calculations took only a minute or so. The phone to Desert Center had lots of static, but worked sufficiently. Reading my report to the Desert Center night shift observer went by in a flash. The observer gave me the happy news, the Desert Center Base Commander had decided that no weather reports from the Mojave Wells gunnery ranges should be taken today, including the one I was just phoning in. "Great," I muttered to myself, as I hung up the phone. "Isn't that just like the military. I come out here early, go through three hours of God knows what-all, just to take two wind measurements which they throw in the wastepaper basket!"

With a practiced hand, I turned off my stove, secured my radio, turned off my lights, and locked up my weather shack. Then I started my truck, and turned on my headlights. Since I wouldn't be coming back out again today, I decided to check the rain cover on my theodolite one last time. I pulled my truck up alongside the theodolite stand and left the engine running, and the headlights on. I got out and double checked everything. I had just finished doing so when I looked up in the direction of the Range Three lounge. Floating there in the rain some 50 feet away from me, just out of the edge of my truck's headlights was once again, the seven foot tall, fluorescent white patch. Occasionally, between the waves of cold rain, I could make out the image of a thin, tall, chalk white man, standing there inside of the fluorescent patch, intently watching me. I was suddenly struck by the way he seemed to anticipate my every move. He obviously intended to block any route that I might take, were I to decide to walk over to the Range Three lounge and inspect the fluorescent lights inside.

For an instant, I stood frozen in fear, in the driving rain, watching his every move as he watched mine. The two of us, were obviously of a kind, protecting the doorway between two different worlds, worlds that connected out there in the night. He was forced to defend his world, as I was forced to defend mine. His defense required that he confront me, but for me, I had a much simpler defense. I could pretend that he wasn't real. I could retreat. I could back slowly away from the doorway. I wasn't protecting anything physical. I didn't have to block anyone's path. I was protecting only my own happy innocence. I could think about God and His love. I could call on God for help. I could cry out suddenly, in a momentary terror, "Not out here! Not out here in the rain!" Then I could break and run. My defense allowed me so many ways to deny the white mist's reality, and the reality of the tall white man standing inside.

I turned aside and refused to look in his direction. Then I convinced myself that he wasn't there at all. Suppressing my momentary panic, I began my retreat. Carefully, I got back into my truck. I backed away from the white patch and drove over to the generator shack. Leaving the truck engine running and the lights on, and in total denial, I hurriedly shut down the diesel and quickly returned to the innocent safety of my truck, locking the truck doors after I had gotten back inside. I was relieved when I glanced back and saw that the white patch hadn't followed me, hadn't pursued. As I brought the truck back onto the pavement, shifted into high gear, and headed back on into town, I breathed several deep sighs of relief. I was now in the business of protecting myself. I was now in the business of pretending to myself that I was alone when I was out on the ranges. I was now in the business of pretending to myself that I was God's only intelligent creature that enjoyed the beauty of a nighttime desert storm. I was now in the business of pretending that the white patches, which I had seen out there in the rain, weren't real. I did such a good job of pretending that as I drove on into base, I turned off my windshield wipers. I began singing one of my made up sunshine songs. "…Oh, God, don't let the rain come down…, "and I proceeded to pretend that even the cold hard rain, even the very storm itself, wasn't real.

All That a Man Has

…Once again, the sons of God came
    to present themselves before the Lord,
       and Satan also came among them.

And the Lord said to Satan,
    "Whence do you come?"

Then Satan answered The Lord and said,
    "From roaming the earth and patrolling it."

And the Lord said to Satan,
    "Have you noticed my servant Job…?"

And Satan answered the Lord and said,

    "Skin for Skin,
      all that a man has,
      will he give
        for his life…

       …Job 2:1,4

Once again I needed to go in to Desert Center for supplies. Once again I checked out the two and a half ton truck from the Mojave Wells motor pool. I loaded my empty helium tanks, collected my log and inventory books as before, and began the long run into Desert Center. It was a beautiful day and there was much to be considered. The logbooks contained many entries. One entry was from an observer named McPherson. Four years before, he had written, "Range #3, 0615 hours. I was late phoning in the morning report. The lights came again this morning. They came in closer than ever before. I released the morning balloon on time at 0430 hours. After I took the readings, I began walking back to my weather shack. I thought I got a glimpse of some child playing in the weather shack. Then I thought I saw some adult step out from the alley by the supply sheds, and point something at me. I don't know what I was doing for the next hour and ten minutes. The range #3 area seems deserted now, but I'm terrified of this place."

When I reached the supply depot at Desert Center, I parked my truck, went inside, and checked out my supplies. The chief master sergeant was waiting to talk with me. This time he greeted me with a smile and a friendly manner. Once again we took seats at the nearby table. The sergeant turned towards me and asked, "What do you think is going on up at Mojave Wells, Charlie? I knew all of those men who served up there before you. That's how I proudly earned these eight stripes - by keeping in touch with the men and making certain they had the supplies they needed whenever they needed them.

The gunnery ranges up there are beautiful places. Driving out onto the ranges and reporting the winds on a nice day like today, is a fine job. All you have to do is drive out into the beautiful desert sunshine and release a balloon five times a day. It beats the crap out of sitting around a dirty warehouse like this, working indoors in the dust and fumes. Out there you're free. There are no officers or sergeants to give a man any crap. What I want to know is: Why would 59 men before you, each in his turn, desert the ranges? Why would they do such a thing? You've been up there for quite a few weeks now. You've already taken more wind measurements than all of the observers before you, and you're still going out there. What is it that ran all of the others off the ranges, but hasn't bothered you?"

"I don't know, Sergeant," I responded.

Looking over the records, he continued, "The only observer who was anywhere close to your supply requests was that observer several years ago with a drinking problem. Yet he requisitioned less than one third of the quantity he should have been requesting. He and I shared a beer now and then, down at the Airman's club. He always swore that he stayed stone sober when he was up at the Wells. He told me that if he had even a single drink and went out onto the ranges, he'd start seeing things. Things like distant lights and chalk white people, little children with claws that floated up around the rocks and cliffs and stuff. One time he claimed that he had seen a radioactive horse he called 'Range Four Harry'.

"He wasn't the only one to claim that either. Dozens of those other observers would come in here and tell me the weirdest stories. They used to claim that a man would have to give up his very sanity, just to stay alive for even one night out there on the ranges. But you know Charlie, I never paid any attention to those stories until you opened my eyes with these supply requests."

"Do you remember an observer named McPherson?" I asked.

"Yes, the sergeant responded. "I remember him well. He was a staff sergeant, a four striper. He was another one that used to tell me more of those stories," answered the sergeant.

"How so?" I asked.

"I remember the first day he came in here. He was on his second enlistment. He'd just made staff sergeant. He was so proud of those four stripes. He was telling me how he was going to do a better job up at the ranges than any man before him. He checked out 50 balloons, 2 tanks of helium, some office supplies, and 500 blank forms. Then just three weeks later, he came in here looking like a whipped dog. He was so nervous and edgy. He would have fainted if I had shouted at him. I tell you Charlie, McPherson was one fine airman, but he didn't have a cutting edge on him. He didn't know how to mark out his own piece of ground, and stand there and fight. I tell you Charlie Baker, he wasn't the tough nosed soldier that you are."

I smiled pleasantly and took the sergeant's words as a fine compliment.

The sergeant continued. "On his second visit, McPherson requisitioned another 500 blank forms. Imagine that, Charlie. He'd driven all the way down here just to requisition another 500 forms. I was surprised. When I was filling out the paper work, I explained to him that he was welcome to as many blank forms as he wanted, but I wondered why he needed another 500 so soon. I mean, 1000 blank forms in only three weeks is a lot of forms.

"McPherson explained that the other blank forms were out in the range three weather shack. He needed these new forms to keep with him in his barracks. So I asked him why he didn't just drive out to range three and pick up a couple hundred or so of the other forms. It seemed to me that would beat driving way down here, just for more forms.

"But McPherson didn't see it that way. He told me that he had abandoned all of the range weather shacks. He wouldn't go out onto the ranges again, even if the Air Force were to court martial him. He said there was something out there that would wait for him. He swore that at first it would just stand out in the sagebrush and watch him from a distance. Then it got braver. It would hide in around the buildings, and follow him around wherever he went. There was a night he called 'The Night of white Terror'. He said it was a night when the lights came right in around the buildings, and wouldn't go away. Whatever it was, it came up behind him in perfect silence, and just stood studying his every move. He was breaking down in tears when he was spilling his guts to me. He said that night it had come in so close behind him that when he turned around, he could have almost touched it. He became hysterical and left the ranges in a panic. He wouldn't drive back out there again, even to pick up his personal belongings. McPherson finished that one TDY and immediately put in for a transfer."

The sergeant took a sip of coffee and continued, "Then there was Jackson. He was a tech sergeant, a five striper on his third enlistment. He was a black man who had grown up in the slums of Chicago. You know he had to be one tough soldier. They sent him up there because the guy before him had run into something out on range four and had gotten burned real bad. He said the first couple of days he was up there, he worked like a dog and took all of the balloon runs as scheduled. Then on the third day, just after breakfast, as he was releasing the balloon, he said that three of them stepped out from behind the range three lounge. I guess it was two men and a woman dressed up white as sheets. It scared him. He was afraid they might be members of some white racist group. He said they just stood there watching him, as though they wanted to talk to him from a distance.

Well, I tell you, Charlie, Jackson took out of there and he hasn't been back to Mojave Wells since.

"Then there was Taylor. He was a young Airman First. The day he came in here four years ago, all he wanted was some ink pens and forms. He was real nervous and cagey. I was trying to break the ice, so I asked him if he'd ever seen anything unusual up there. He turned white as a sheet. He said he always kept a sharp lookout, trying to make sure that nothing surprised him, the way it had the others. He said on the third morning he was up there, he was taking the morning run out at range three. He heard something behind him. He turned around. Standing there was Range Four Harry, smiling at him, big as life. He said he screamed in terror and took off running for town. Taylor claimed that as he left, he could hear old Harry laughing at him, as though all Harry wanted to do was prove he could surprise him. Taylor was another one that would never go back up to Mojave Wells again."

"But none of those men were ever actually threatened were they?" I asked.

"No," replied the sergeant. "But they were all terrified just the same. Some of the other weather observers, however, have been attacked and burned, out there on the ranges. Several of them have been given medical discharges." Then turning to me, the sergeant continued, "How about you, Charlie. I want to know why you've lasted when they didn't. In the weeks you've been out there, has anything like that ever happened to you? Why haven't you become frightened, too?"

"I wouldn't say I was any braver than those men," I responded. The ranges can be mighty scary, especially at night. I've seen lots of unusual things, but nothing has frightened me so bad that I couldn't say my prayers, shrug it off, trust God to protect me, and carry on with my orders."

"Things? What things?" asked the sergeant.

"Well, I've seen those lights way up the valley. They seem to be intelligently controlled as McPherson reported. I've seen them coming part way down the road which connects range four with range three. But so far, they've been stopping quite a ways off, before they get to range three."

"Do you see them often?" asked the sergeant.

"Yes," I answered. "On most nights I first see them way up on the northwest side of Mojave Wells valley, between about 11:30 p.m. and 1:00 a.m. There are always five or six of them. Usually they float down towards the buildings at range four. They play around the range four buildings for a while and sometimes come down the road towards range three where I am. Then they go back up the valley just before sunrise. At first they made me a little edgy, but then I shrugged it off. 'Life's too short,' I said. 'to be scared.' They obviously know I'm out here. If they wanted to hurt me, they would have done it by now.'"

"I see you're a different young man then McPherson was," Stated the sergeant matter-of-factly.

"Then there's that flying train engine which I've been seeing lately," I continued. "At least that's what it looks like. I first noticed it early last week. I was out at range three about 7:30 a.m. in the morning. I was sitting in my weather shack getting the forms ready when I saw it following along the landscape up the valley towards range four. It was three or four miles away at the time. It was solid white and looked very similar to the diesel engine on a passenger train. Of course, the sides were a lot rounder and they molded smoothly into the bottom. It didn't have any wings or wheels or anything, and it didn't make any sound as it traveled. It was flying along about ten or twenty feet above the sagebrush. At first I didn't think anything of it. But the next morning it came by again at the very same time, so I became curious. I came back out from breakfast early. I wanted to see if it came a third time. Sure enough, the next day, at 7:30 a.m. sharp, it appeared following the terrain through that pass in the mountains just a few miles northwest of the town. It followed the terrain towards the east until it was just over the low point of the valley. Then it terrain followed up the valley towards range four, skirting the buildings at range three in the process. When it got up by the range four buildings, it skirted around the southern and eastern edge of the buildings. When it was at a point about a quarter mile southwest of the range four buildings, it paused in its flight and floated in mid air for about thirty seconds, obviously studying the buildings in intelligent fashion. The way the vehicle maneuvered convinced me that it was intelligently controlled. Then it sped up and terrain followed up the valley towards the northeast. The entire flight took about five minutes. The closest it ever got to me was about a mile and a half. That day I had been watching it from inside my range three weather shack.

"The next day, I wanted to get a better look at it. After going in for breakfast, I returned to range three early, as before. I parked my truck out in the open by the generator shack as I always do. Then I stood out in the open, on the west side of the range three lounge waiting for it. At 7:30 a.m., just as before, it appeared terrain following through that low pass to the west, and began entering the valley. But this time, it acted as though it saw me standing there watching it. Whoever was on board must have eyes as good as those of an eagle or a cat because it was almost ten miles away at the time. This time it appeared to abandon its flight plan. It retreated to the very base of the mountains along the far west side of the valley. Then it terrain followed north up the valley. This time it never got closer than four or five miles from me. The next morning it started following a completely different path. Now it enters the valley using a pass twenty miles or so northwest of me. Then it speeds across the valley much faster than it used to. Now I can't see much of anything, so I just gave up following it."

The sergeant sat thinking for a minute or so. Then he spoke in fatherly tones. "On those first trips, it terrain followed a distance of about thirty miles in less than five minutes. That's an average speed of approximately 350 miles an hour traveling only 20 feet above the sagebrush. That's one awful high performance vehicle. There's no way the U.S. Air Force or anyone else on this earth could have built it! Didn't it frighten you?"

"No, sergeant," I responded. "Should it have?"

"Yes! A vehicle like that could have come down on you the way an eagle comes down on a field mouse," replied the sergeant. "It would certainly have scared those observers before you."

Stammering some, and off balance, I responded, "But it never got very close to me. A mile and a half is still a long ways off."

"At 350 miles an hour, it could cover that distance in less than 15 seconds, Charlie," responded the sergeant. "You would barely have had time to fall to the ground before it was on you.

"Tell me, Charlie, how close does danger have to come to you personally before you feel threatened? How close before you decide that your God isn't watching, and you feel forced to break and run?"

"I don't know sergeant," I answered thoughtfully. "Yesterday morning the lights came from up the valley again, they way they have on so many mornings. Yesterday, they came down the road from range four closer then they ever have before. At first they made me a little nervous, but they appeared to stop when they were still over a mile distant. I guess that distance for me is just over three quarters of a mile. There's a ridge out in the desert north of range three which is just under three quarters of a mile. It's about 1200 yards out. I guess when it comes down to it, I'm willing to ignore the lights, trust in God, and go on about my business until the lights come closer than that ridge - until the lights come in closer than three quarters of a mile."

"So, you believe that the God you pray to, can't protect you from danger if it comes closer than that ridge at three quarters of a mile?" asked the sergeant.

"Yes," I answered. "I guess when it comes down to it, that's what I believe - but so far they've always stayed back of that ridge, so I don't believe they'll come any closer."

"Well, remember Charlie," said the sergeant, "when you are standing out there at range three looking at the lights, those lights are out there in the desert looking back at you. Whatever those lights are, they have come more than 25 miles down that valley, across gullies, sagebrush, rocks, canyons, and arroyos, just to see what you are doing. They sure are willing to close in on you. They sure are willing to come that last 1200 yards and confront you out in the open, face to face, they way they confronted the men before you.

371

When that night comes, I pray that your God stands closer to you than three quarters of a mile."

It was late. I thanked the sergeant gratefully, loaded the supplies onto my two and a half ton truck, and told the good sergeant good-bye. By now, it was late in the afternoon. I was feeling a slight fever and a little nausea - perhaps from the flu - or perhaps from the stress of it all, so I decided to skip the evening chow at Desert Center. I rested for a little while at the base library. Then I began the long drive back to Mojave Wells. Night was falling as I headed back across the Desert Center valley and found the entrance ramp for the newly built freeway. As I pulled onto the freeway, I could hear the belt breaking on the truck's generator. Having no safe place to turn around, I decided to keep heading towards the Wells. I hoped the truck's battery would last long enough to get me there. By the time I was passing the exit to Silver Canyon, it was obvious that the truck's battery was not going to be up to the task. With the engine misfiring and running rough, I finally reached the rest area at the top of the grade. The engine lasted long enough for me to bring the truck into the rest area, and park it along the right side of the pavement. There it quit altogether. I took an auto flare from out of the glove compartment and jumped out of the truck into the warm early evening air. The rest area consisted of a two-lane stretch of pavement that ran parallel to the main freeway for a few hundred feet. An ordinary steel chain link fence and a few feet of desert sand were all that separated the main lanes from the rest lanes. I raised the hood on the truck, walked back behind the truck 50 feet or so, and lit the flare. It burned a bright red flame for about twenty minutes while I waited patiently for someone to stop. The flare was just burning out when a state trooper pulled into the rest area with his lights flashing. He stopped his patrol car next to me, and got out. I was sitting on the back of the truck at the time.

The trooper approached me, "Good evening soldier. Some woman who calls herself 'The Teacher' notified my dispatcher that you needed help. You're named Charlie Baker, right?"

"Yes," I responded. "The generator belt on the truck gave out on me. I drove it until the battery went dead. I need Mark from the motor pool up at Mojave Wells to come down with the wrecker and a new belt, to get me out of this mess."

"Right, soldier," replied the trooper. "That's what the teacher said. My dispatcher has already notified the air policeman, Bryan, up there. He and Mark are getting a belt and getting the wrecker ready now. I stopped by to let you know they were coming. They'll be here in a half hour or so."

"Thanks, officer," I responded. "I have plenty of water in the truck. I'll be fine until then."

The trooper got back into his squad car, turned off the flashing lights, and headed back out onto the highway. From my vantage point near the top of the grade, I could see across the valley towards the northwest and into the next north-south valley. Far to the northwest, I could see several of the dull white fluorescent lights that had terrorized McPherson so many years ago. In the distance, they seemed to be floating on the warm evening desert air. They also seemed to be out unusually early this evening. As I watched, they moved in military fashion, several miles down the valley towards Mojave Wells. I noticed a second set of dull fluorescent white lights down in the valley through which the freeway ran. The lights were probably two miles away, partially hidden down in the sagebrush margin that bordered a dry lakebed. There were five different lights down there. As I watched, the lights slowly kept closing the distance until they were less than a mile away. I felt safe enough, parked next to a busy freeway.

My musings were cut short by the arrival of the wrecker from Mojave Wells. Mark took the wrecker down the highway a shot distance before cutting across the central median strip. Then he brought the big wrecker back up the freeway to the rest area where I sat waiting. I jumped down from the back of my truck as he arrived, and greeted Bryan and Mark. They pulled the big wrecker the rest of the way up into the area. Mark realized my truck's battery and generator were located on the passenger side of the engine, so he instinctively pulled the wrecker off the pavement to the right. He continued on down the gravel and sagebrush on the right shoulder, until the working part of the wrecker was adjacent to my truck's engine. Amid a cloud of dust and gravel and flying pieces of sagebrush, he let the wrecker roll to a stop, and turned off the engine. I supposed he was planning to tow my truck into the Mojave Wells motor pool, so I took up a military position standing next to the front bumper of my truck on the driver's side. I remained standing upright, a foot or so away from my truck, to the left of my truck's front bumper. Because of the dust and gravel kicked up by the wrecker, I stood facing the freeway, hoping to protect my face and eyes from the debris. Mark, however, an excellent mechanic, announced his intention to replace the generator belt right where the truck stood. I stood listening to him, watching a new

Cadillac on the freeway as it approached the entrance to the rest area. It appeared to be traveling much faster than the other traffic. I stood there transfixed as the Cadillac left the freeway and entered the rest area without so much as letting up on the gas. The Cadillac appeared to be traveling at more than 80 miles an hour. I stood stationary, exposed, stunned, in shock, in the path of the oncoming car, unable to move a single muscle as the Cadillac barreled down on me. While I stood transfixed, the Cadillac drove past me at perhaps 80 miles an hour, missing my body parts by no more than ¾ of an inch - less than the length of any one of my fingers. The realization of what had just happened was slow in flooding over me. Not a single hair anywhere on my body had been touched. Not a single thread of cloth anywhere on my cloths had been touched. The polish on my leather military shoes had not been so much as dulled. Yet the car had passed me so close that I was at first unable to believe it had missed me. For a few minutes I stood there, still transfixed, wondering if it was just my soul that was standing there waiting for God, and believing that perhaps my earthly body, now dead, was being dragged off by the speeding car. It wasn't until my eyes had intensely searched every square inch on the front hood of the retreating car, searching for patches of my blood and pieces of my various body parts, and finding none, that I finally realized I was still alive and untouched. For me alone, God had stepped out from behind the mist and answered the good sergeant's question, "How close could danger come before God could no longer protect me?" I felt as though God, in person, was standing there beside me, next to me on my right, smiling, laughing, confidently chiding me, "Silly Charlie. You thought I

375

needed three quarters of a mile. Ha, ha, ha …See - I don't even need three quarters of an inch."

Catching my breath at last, I stepped back away from the open lane in the rest area, my mind grappling with the truth that God had just shown me. My concentration was broken by the sound of my truck engine roaring to life. Mark had obviously completed the repairs and was testing the engine. I hurried over to the truck door and began thanking him and Bryan profusely. Neither Mark nor Bryan, however, would take any praise. Mark, jumping from the truck, shouted over the roar of the engine, "The best way you can thank me, Charlie, is if you can get this truck unloaded and back to the motor pool by 7:00 a.m. tomorrow morning. The sergeant who runs the Mojave Wells Airman's Club needs it to get supplies from Desert Center tomorrow, like you did today. We'll all be put out if you keep him waiting."

I could hardly refuse. Late as it was, I promised Mark that I would unload the supplies at range three tonight, and return the truck to the motor pool before sunrise.

I had just barely finished speaking when the sudden movement of the lights down in the valley caught my eye. Now they were moving intently back across the distant dry lakebed. I climbed into my truck, placed it in low gear, and begin pulling back out onto the freeway. I glanced over at the distant lights down in the valley as I did so. The lights were retreating rapidly across the valley towards the northwest. I thought nothing of it at the time, but the lights were retreating back towards the buildings at range three many miles in the distance.

Mark and Bryan followed me for a few miles to make certain the truck was running properly. Then they hit the gas and sped on past me, heading back into Mojave Wells. I was already plenty tired and driving slowly. It had been a long day. I found myself wishing I could get a cup of coffee and a hamburger somewhere. Everything in Mojave Wells was closed when I got there. I had to make do with several cans of cola and a few bags of corn chips from the vending machines outside the administration building - not much in the way of nutrition, but I needed something. After giving the matter careful thought, I decided that my best bet would be to deliver the supplies out to my weather shack at range three before turning in. Then I could sleep the rest of the night on the comfortable floor of my weather shack, take the 4:30 a.m. run, and return the big truck to the motor pool before breakfast. It seemed like such a good idea. The fact that I would be spending the entire night alone out on the ranges - out where the so many observers before me, had refused to venture in broad daylight - never crossed my mind.

As I headed the truck out into the desert towards range three, the clock was running towards 11:00 p.m. I was already having trouble staying awake at the wheel. By the time I arrived at range three, I was much too tired to notice anything. The dull white fluorescent lights coming towards me from a mile or so down to the south east, the second set waiting over by the mountains to the northeast, the third set converging on me from the sagebrush a couple of miles off to the northwest, the lights now showing themselves down towards the southwest by the range three gate, did nothing to alarm me. I parked the big truck with its headlights shining into the generator shack. I left the lights on and the engine running as I stumbled out of the truck and opened the door to the generator shack. Tired as I was, I flooded the generator's diesel engine with the ether starting fluid. I counted myself lucky when the diesel finally started, but it took a while. The pounding diesel didn't help my concentration any. It took me an unusually long while to complete the electrical adjustments. Tired, now, and edgy, I stumbled back out through the open shack door, towards the waiting truck. The truck's headlights or something fluorescent white blinded me suddenly as I came out through the door of the generator shack. Something seemed to touch me momentarily, on or inside my right temple. I got a brief glimpse of something chalk white behind me and on my right. The muscles in my stomach tightened suddenly. It felt like I took a sharp blow down low in my guts. I missed a step in the doorway. I stumbled and went down on the hard sharp gravel, falling on my hands and on my knees. My mind fuzzed over and stayed fuzzed over for what seemed like a long minute or so. I found it hard to focus on much of anything. Several chalk white people seemed to be standing around me, talking to each other in quiet and whispered tones. One of them, a young woman, was saying, "You must speak English. He is the weather observer. His name is Charlie Baker. He speaks only English." Another, a young man, was saying, "He is very tired. You must readjust your electronics. He will remember this for sure. Be careful when you are around him. If he becomes more tired, none of our electronics will have the slightest effect on him."

When my mind finally cleared, I swore some, blamed the whole episode on breathing too much of the ether starting fluid, and brushed off my scrapes. I carefully began getting back up. I noticed that I was not getting up from exactly the same place to which I had previously fallen. That spot was clearly marked by my handprints, and some bloodstains. That spot was 3 feet or so off to my left. The place I was getting up from was a softer place. I paused for a minute to consider my situation. Something seemed terribly out of place. I glanced at my watch. It had stopped for some reason, even though it had been running when I had entered the generator shack. I was used to the ranges and used to being alone in the night. I was also used to trusting my feelings. Something felt terribly wrong. It took my tired mind a minute or so to figure out what it was. Finally it came to me. I became certain that I wasn't alone. There seemed to be some tall, white person, hidden behind the glare of my truck's headlights. Slowly I returned to my feet, and carefully retreated until my back was up against the wall of the generator shack. "Is anyone there?" I called loudly out into the darkness. "Is there anyone out there?" There was no answer.

I waited a few minutes. My mind cleared. The fluorescence seemed to retreat silently into the desert to the west. Blinded by the headlights as I was, I couldn't get a good look at it. I decided that I would be better off if I concentrated more on my work and less on worrying about things in the night. So I shrugged off my fears, and decided that my mind must just be playing tricks on me.

I cautiously returned to the safety of my truck and placed it in gear. Then I began slowly maneuvering the truck over the soft rough ground and through the mesquite behind my weather shack. The moonlight was bright and the truck's headlights cast unusual shadows through the mesquite. Concentrating on my driving, I paid no attention to the two dull white fluorescent lights, previously hidden by the mesquite that went speeding off towards the southeast.

The truck was heavily loaded with helium cylinders. It took all of my concentration and several tries before I finally got the big truck through the thick mesquite and backed up to the rear door of my weather shack. It was hardly perfect but when I had it sitting at a 30 degree angle to the back door, I called it good. I was already too tired to struggle any further with the heavy steering wheel. After killing the engine, I jumped out onto the soft dirt. With a practiced hand I unlocked and opened all three of the doors to my weather shack, turned on the light and the radio, and reset my watch. It apparently had been stopped for twenty minutes while I was in the generator shack, or on the ground outside. Then I slumped into my chair to rest a minute, nurse my wounds, and enjoy the cool evening breeze that swept gently through the open doors. I tried calling the Desert Center weather station. It had an observer on duty around the clock. I wanted to request a wake up call at 3:30 a.m. The line was heavy with static, making the phone useless. I sat for a minute wondering why. It was a beautiful warm summer night with a nice moon. There was no obvious reason for the phone connections to be messed up.

I sat resting for a while longer, listening to the radio. The music was soft and dreamy, although it too had a great deal of static. Out back of my shack I could hear something moving quietly in the night. I supposed that it was probably just some sagebrush or tumbleweeds blowing in the gentle evening winds. In the center of my desk, right out in the open, lay my favorite pencil - the one that had been missing for several weeks. Tired and already sleepy, I gratefully picked it up without thinking and returned it to its normal position in my desk drawer. I was just closing the drawer when my mind stumbled across what had just happened, and I was numbed back into consciousness. The pencil could not possibly have lain in that obvious open position every day for the last few weeks. I had, after all, searched high and low for it. Getting to my feet and settling myself down, I decided I should forget about the pencil's re-appearance, and get the truck unloaded as quickly as possible. I put on the heavy leather work gloves which I kept in the shack, removed my fatigue cap and placed it neatly on top of my wind plotting table. Then I set about the business at hand.

It was obvious that unloading the big truck was going to be an extremely difficult task. Each steel helium tank was 5 feet 8 inches tall and weighed more than I did. I began by unloading the light stuff, the boxes of balloons, the batteries and lights, the blank weather forms, and the other office supplies. There were at least three dozen boxes. It took a good many trips between the cab of my truck and the weather shack to get it all. I piled the supplies on my desk, on my wind plotting table, on my empty shelves, and anywhere else I had room. Without thinking much about it, I noticed that my fatigue cap was now missing. I shrugged, and supposed that it had probably fallen somewhere on the floor. I looked high and low for it, but to no avail. I couldn't find it anywhere. I sucked in a deep breath, ate a few corn chips, and took quick drink of cola. Then I set about the exhausting task of unloading the 12 helium cylinders. First I had to set up a makeshift ramp from the high back platform of the truck down to the soft ground. Then I had to set up a second makeshift ramp from the soft ground up to the back door of my shack. For this I had several long thick 8-inch wide planks. I kept these planks stored over in the alley between the storage sheds. They were extremely heavy. I didn't relish the thought of dragging them into position. Singing to myself, with feelings of fatigue already laying heavy on me, I went out the back door of my shack, and trudged over across the soft sandy dirt to that alley way. The moon was bright, so I didn't think much about the soft white fluorescent light that was glistening from between the buildings. I was watching the ground as I walked, so I was unprepared for the sight that confronted me as I rounded the corner of the building. Standing there about 20 feet away, looking directly at me, was a solid white human like woman. She had solid chalk white skin, large blue eyes, and blonde hair. She had a flat non-protruding nose and similar flat ears. She was wearing a pleasant expression on her face. She was my height, 5' 11". She had a boyish figure and she was much thinner than most human women. On each hand, she had only four fingers. The gloves she wore suggested that she had 2-inch long claws. She was wearing an aluminized canvas chalk white jump suit with an open, white, motorcycle-like helmet. The suit and the helmet emitted a field of soft white fluorescent light that was perhaps 3 inches deep. The light wasn't particularly bright, but it hurt my eyes to look into it. Three or four feet in front of her, was a little girl who appeared to be her daughter. Her daughter's eyes were larger in proportion to her face than her mother's. Her daughter also wore a solid white suit and helmet. The little girl was floating some 3 or 4 feet above the ground, and remained stationary watching me.

I had obviously surprised the two of them. However, tired as I was, I did not conclude that they were actually real. With the little girl floating directly above the heavy planks which I had come for, it was an easy matter for me to decide that my mind was playing tricks on me. For that reason, I was not actually afraid. I decided that I must be just experiencing the effects of the fatigue which was rapidly overtaking me - and maybe the lack of good nutrition caused by my diet of cola and corn chips. I stood motionless myself, watching the two of them as they stood there. I was waiting for my brain to return to normal. I was expecting the two of them to vanish before my eyes the way a ghost might have. After a long two or three minutes passed, the little girl floated over to the other side of her mother and drifted down until she was standing on the soft ground. Then, apparently on a silent command from her mother, the little girl stepped silently and quickly away from me, down the alley, and disappeared from view around the side of the building to the left - towards the generator shack. Then her mother, still wearing her pleasant expression, stepped quickly sideways, away from me. She also disappeared around the side of the building to the left. As they did so, I stood there calmly thinking to myself, "So this is what insanity is like. I see what they mean, it's quite painless."

After the two of them had disappeared around behind the buildings, I stood motionless for a few minutes, believing I was letting my brain return to normal. I watched the white fluorescent light proceed around behind the generator shack, and decided that my body must be very low on vitamins. I resolved that in the future I would get more sleep, take high potency vitamin pills, and eat more nutritious food. Then, supposing my brain had returned to normal, I decided to continue on with my work After all, I said to my self, isn't hard work the best therapy for problems like mine?

The planks were extremely heavy, and had to be lifted carefully and dragged into position. I walked down to the far end of the alley to roll the first one off the others. As I bent down to grab onto it, I noticed that both the mother and the daughter had left a large number of boot prints in the soft dirt. I shrugged off what I'd seen. I needed to get back to work. I grabbed on to the heavy plank. It was with great difficulty that I dragged it back to my truck and finally positioned it to form a ramp up into the back of my truck. I took a deep breath, ate some more corn chips, took a drink of cola, and continued on with the brutal work at hand. As I was positioning the third plank, I noticed the little girl float out from behind the generator shack. She was 3 or 4 feet off the ground. She floated there for 2 or 3 minutes watching me. Her mother stepped out from behind the generator shack and obviously communicated with her in silence. Then the two of them both returned behind the generator shack. This time, I got a much better look at the two of them. I noted how completely real they appeared. Still, I wasn't afraid. I had convinced myself that I was suffering from the effects of poor nutrition and extreme fatigue. I considered them to be hallucinations.

With my ramps now in place, I sat resting on one of them for a few minutes. I noticed some more white fluorescent patches down by the mesquite to the southeast, and over by the mountains, and over by the ammunition bunker to the east. I took another sip of cola, put my work gloves back on, and began the brutal task of unloading the helium cylinders.

Cylinders 1 and 2 weren't too bad. I still had a few reserves of energy, and I wasn't shaking too much from fatigue. I walked up the ramp onto the platform of the truck, and grabbed each one in turn. I carefully walked them down the truck ramp and up the other ramp into my weather shack. Cylinder 3, however, was a near disaster. Coming down the ramp, I slipped and scrapped my leg on the plank - nearly dropping the cylinder in the process. Swearing and limping I finally got the heavy cylinder up the next ramp into my weather shack. It took a long time to get it safely stowed in its place in the corner. Then I sat down and nursed my wounds. My left knee, especially, was in bad shape. I always kept a first aid kit and some rubbing alcohol in my shack. This night, they served me well. Then, munching some more chips and sipping another cola, I returned to my work.

For cylinders 4, 5, and 6, I tried a new approach. I carefully laid them down on the bed of the truck, with their bottoms pointing towards the back of the truck. I carefully slid them until their bottoms were even with the end of the truck bed. Then I got down from the truck and, standing on the ground, I slid them, one by one, down the ramp. It was brutal tiring work, but at least I didn't have to limp up and down the ramp. I had just finished lowering cylinder #6 to the ground. I had just leaned it against the back of the truck, and stepped back to rest. As I turned around, back towards the open rear door of my shack, my view passed though the open rear door, on out through the open front door, and out towards the open square beyond. Standing there, bent over at the waist watching me, was another solid chalk white creature. He appeared to be the male version of the young woman which I had previously surprised standing in the alley. He was about 60 feet away. We both stood frozen for a minute or two, watching each other. I wasn't afraid. Even though he appeared to be perfectly real, I supposed that he was just another hallucination caused by my fatigue. He was about my height, but very thin. He probably didn't weigh more than 110 pounds. Like the woman, he had chalk white skin. He was wearing an aluminum canvass appearing jump suit that gave off a soft white fluorescent light. He had blue eyes that stretched further around the side of his head than any human's and also stretched further around the side of his head then did the woman's. Suddenly, he seemed to realize that I was watching him, and he quickly stepped back from the open door way and out of my line of sight.

I stood somewhat confused for a minute or so. I wanted to believe he was just another hallucination, but he looked so real. Then I decided that maybe he was one of my range rat friends playing tricks on me - a friend who might be able to help me unload the truck. Singing a little then, so as not to surprise him, I began walking slowly around the east side of my weather shack. As I passed the open side door of my shack, I noticed my missing fatigue cap sitting in plain view on the floor in the middle of my shack. It sat upright, as though intentionally placed there. It's appearance caused me to feel a certain amount of alarm. I had looked high and low for it only a short time before. I estimated that it had to have been placed there sometime within the last ten minutes, maybe even within the last five minutes, and hallucinations don't move caps around. I reached in, picked up my cap from the floor, and placed it carefully in an open area on a nearby shelf. Then I continued walking slowly and carefully on my journey around my weather shack, singing at moderate volume as I did so. Reaching the open area in front of my shack, I continued on, still singing, walking diagonally towards my theodolite and towards the range three lounge. The white male creature had, in the meantime, retreated behind the lounge building. I was about half way across the open square when I paused to consider the situation. Soft white fluorescent light could be seen glistening from behind the lounge, and also from behind the generator shack and the nearby storage sheds. I remembered the stories that I'd heard about Range Four Harry. I wondered if he really was a hermit who made a living by prospecting for gold. He might be the one causing the light to shine from behind the range three lounge – and gold prospectors are not necessary friendly. My head and all the muscles in my body were already aching from fatigue. It was becoming difficult for me to reason things through. I had no way to get off the ranges until my truck was unloaded. I had no place to run to, no place to hide. This definitely wasn't the time to challenge whoever was hiding behind the lounge. Still, I needed help to finish unloading the truck. I stood for a few minutes thinking things over. Then I shouted loudly out into the darkness, "Hello in the lounge." There was no answer. I continued, shouting loudly, "Whoever is over there, I could use a little help over here at the weather shack." Still, there was no answer. I continued, "I'm in the middle of this brutal job of unloading these helium cylinders. I have 6 more of the things to unload. It sure would be nice if I had another man or two to help me." Still, there was nothing but silence. "I don't have any money to pay you with, but I'd owe you a big favor. I have some cola and some corn chips we could share. Maybe sometime you'd need some help when you are out here and then I'd be here to return the favor." Still silence. "Look it's a big desert out here and it only makes sense for us men to cooperate." Still silence. "Now if you don't want to help me do the brutal heavy labor I understand - but it'd be a big help if you could just keep me company while I work. At least you'd be there to calm me down so I don't get too over-worked and totally collapse or something." For a few minutes, from over behind the range three lounge, I could hear quiet sounds that reminded me of a horse laughing. Then from over behind the generator shack I could hear soft muffled sounds that reminded me of a happy dog barking. Annoyed, I shouted back, "Fine! Just fine! If all you want to do is laugh at me, then just fine! Well, I'll just show you. The men of my family - we're one tough bunch of guys. No way have we ever given up easy. We learned at a young age how to work until we dropped. I'll unload that whole big truck all by myself, and then I won't owe you any favors. You'll see. I won't owe you anything - not a thing! Then, when you need help, you won't be able to proudly ask me to return the favor, like you could have if you'd helped me tonight when I need it. No! Then you'll have to pay me big time! Remember, when that day comes, you could have helped me tonight - you could have helped me tonight for free!" The distant winds carried more soft horse laughter and muffled happy dog barking until after several minutes, at last, the empty stillness of the beautiful moon light night returned.

Disappointed that no help was coming, I turned slowly back towards my weather shack. I was concerned for the safety of the last helium cylinder that I had unloaded - cylinder #6. I stepped naturally sideways towards the east, until I was able to look through the distant front door of my weather shack, on through the brightly lit interior, on out through the back door where cylinder #6 stood leaning up against the back of my truck. The brightly lit interior of my weather shack made it impossible to see anything whatever in the darkness out through the distant back door. I found this to be quite alarming because I knew my eyesight was excellent. I was standing where the white creature had been standing when he had been watching me. Yet, the glare of the lights inside my weather shack prevented me from seeing anything whatever out through its back door. The conclusion was inescapable. If the white creature were real, he had better eyesight than any human. This conclusion made me feel a certain nervousness. Under the circumstances, I decided that I should get back to work immediately, and get my truck back into driving condition as soon as possible. I therefore put aside all thoughts of anything else, focused on my need to get my truck emptied, and began hurrying back across the open square towards my weather shack. Reaching it, I munched a handful of corn chips, took another quick sip of cola, and proceeded with my work.

Moving cylinder #6 over the soft ground was a job so brutal that I'm certain I'll remember it for the rest of my life. Finally, after a horrible ordeal, and ripping open some more of the blisters forming on the palms of my hands, and further bruising my left knee, I got cylinder #6 up the ramp and into my weather shack. I caught my breath, swore some, nursed my wounds, and went back for cylinders #7, #8, and #9. Chanting and singing to myself to help get oxygen into my lungs, I climbed the ramp up to the back of the truck. Carefully I laid the next three cylinders down on the bed of the truck as before, and slid them back towards the make shift ramp. I had just finished sliding cylinder #8 so that it lay with its bottom even with the back platform of the big truck, when my telephone began ringing. Considering that it was nearly 2:30 a.m., I was surprised to say the least. Cautiously I got down from the back of the big truck, entered my shack, and slowly approached the phone. After it had rung perhaps 20 or 25 times, I carefully picked up the receiver and answered, "Range three weather shack, Charlie Baker here."

The voice on the other end was master sergeant Walters. The phone had a good deal of static, but I could hear him reasonably well. "Charlie," he began, showing obvious surprise. "You are actually out there working like they said. You are one brave dedicated soldier."

Taken aback by his praise, I stumbled for words, "Thank you, sergeant. It's 2:30 a.m. I'm surprised that you are up at this hour. I'm up only because I have to finish unloading my supplies. I need to get this two and a half ton truck back into the Mojave Wells motor pool before breakfast. What has you up at this hour?"

"The Desert Center base commander," replied the sergeant. "He personally phoned me at home here a few minutes ago. He got me up out of a sound sleep. He wanted me to make certain that everything was all right with you. He wanted to know if you needed any help with the truck or anything."

"Everything up here is fine, sergeant," I responded. "Don't get me wrong. I'm tired. I could use another man to help me unload these last six helium cylinders. That's just life in the military. Really sergeant, I have everything under control. I'll have my truck unloaded in another hour or so. It won't keep me from making the 4:30 run as scheduled. Then I'll lock up, return the big truck to the motor pool, hop over to breakfast in my pickup, and be right back on my normal schedule."

"Well, the base commander had more praise for you and your bravery than I ever thought possible, Charlie," continued the sergeant. "He is also worried for your safety."

"How so?" I asked. Then laughing, I continued, "I mean, these ranges are MINE, sergeant. I know every rock and every piece of sagebrush out here, even in total darkness. I'm even getting to know the white things that I see, by name. There's nothing out here I can't handle all by myself, sergeant. God help me. I love this place so much!" Then I laughed some more. "Tell the general he can go back to sleep. I got everything covered."

"You sure are the bravest soldier either the general, the major or myself have ever seen, Charlie," answered the sergeant soberly. "We're all glad that you still have your sense of humor. However, the general had some worries, some wishes, and some concerns that he wanted me to personally convey to you."

"What possible concerns could the general have at this hour? He must be an awfully light sleeper," I replied respectfully.

"Well, first the general wants you to know that he has phoned Mark in his barracks, and ordered him to give you the highest priority on the use of any of the vehicles in the motor pool. That includes the two and a half ton truck that you are driving. So, take all of the time you need to unload the truck, even if you don't get it unloaded by morning. The order applies only to you, not to me or the major, or any airman who might replace you.

"The general also personally phoned Bryan, the air policeman, and ordered him to convey the same orders to the sergeant who runs the airman's club there at the Wells.

"Next, the general has ordered all of the ranges closed up tighter than a drum tomorrow. No one can come out to help you, so take your time. Rest whenever you need to. The general has also canceled all balloon runs for tomorrow. He has left it totally up to you which ones you take and which ones you skip. If I were you, Charlie, I'd skip them all and spend the day resting in the barracks."

"But sergeant," I slowly stuttered, "I don't understand. Taking the wind measurements is an easy job. It won't be any problem for me to take all of tomorrow's runs as scheduled."

"I know, Charlie," replied the sergeant soberly. "But you're one hard working dedicated soldier. The general, the major, and myself are all in agreement. We don't want to work a good horse to death. The general wants me to reassure him that you'll get proper medical attention for all of those scrapes, bruises, and blisters on your legs, and on your hands and knees. They must be hurting you pretty bad. You know the ones you got when you fell coming out of the generator shack."

"The general knows about that too?" I exclaimed in surprise. "Who could have told him about that? I'm the only one out here!"

"Well, as I understand it, Charlie, the Pentagon did. I guess someone up there reported seeing lights or your lights or something out in the desert at range three and reported it to the Pentagon. They're the ones who woke him up tonight. Whatever they did, the general made it clear, I am ordered not to ask you any questions about anything. I am only to verify that you are personally healthy and safe," responded the sergeant.

I was speechless. Then the sergeant paused for a moment, thinking carefully about his next words, before continuing. "The general also had something unusual to request of you."

"What Sergeant?" I responded.

"He expressed his wishes that you wouldn't go chasing after any ghosts or white butterflies while you are out there tonight? He said that he doesn't have the authority to order you to stay in close to the weather shack, or to close your weather shack immediately and drive back into base. However, in a very emotional manner he expressed his wishes that for the rest of tonight, you wouldn't go over by the range three lounge. He specifically asked that you not go further in that direction than the theodolite stand. He says that you are free to go over there if you choose to, but he hopes you won't. He hopes that you will respect his wishes."

"What?" I asked in total disbelief. "Sergeant, I'm totally alone out here. I'm 22 miles out here in the desert. It's just past 2:30 a.m. I mean no disrespect, sergeant, but there's something about this whole evening that doesn't seem to be making any sense. I missed evening chow. I'm hungry as the devil. I've been eating junk food, and I'm low on vitamins. I'm so tired that I must be going nuts. Sometimes I think I'm seeing ghosts or somebody white around every corner. I can't go over to the range three lounge because I'm physically too tired to walk that far. Now I'm told that the Pentagon woke up the two star Desert Center base commanding general just so he could ask you to ask me, pretty please, not to go walking around any corners over by the range three lounge. If he wants me to stay away from the range three lounge all he's got to do is order me not to go over there. And another thing! How does the general even know that I tripped coming out of the generator shack? There weren't even night hawks out here to see me."

The Sergeant paused for a minute or so, thinking things through. Then he continued soberly, "I agree with you, Charlie, but enlisted men like us have to learn to trust our officers. The general made it perfectly clear that I was to deliver his messages with no questions asked. He made it clear that I could listen if you felt you needed someone to talk to, but he specifically ordered me not to ask you any questions about what it's like out there on the ranges tonight - or ever. He was very insistent when he was talking to me. The finest doctors in the Air Force examined you. To a man, generals and bird colonels alike, they all swear that you're in perfect physical and mental condition. You are the man they want for this duty. The general very specifically ordered both the major and I, to totally disregard any suggestion that you were hallucinating, or suffering from any kind of medical condition. The general was very explicit. If the major or I were to send any other observer up there to replace you, he would immediately court martial the both of us. You have to handle the ranges, Charlie, and you have to handle them alone. You can handle them any way you want to. Whatever is over there by the range three lounge, or out there in the desert tonight - whatever it is - you have to handle it - totally alone."

"Yes, sergeant," I answered, tired and respectful. "Tell the general not to worry. I've got everything under control, and tell him thanks for caring about my safety." With that I hung up and turned my attention back to the difficult task of unloading the last six helium cylinders.

Pulling cylinder #7 off the back of the truck was a shockingly brutal operation. The cylinder came down faster than I was expecting. It banged sideways against the back of the truck, momentarily pinning my bruised left knee against the hard steel bumper. It came to rest just narrowly missing my left foot. I swore a great deal as I walked off the pain. Then I manhandled the cylinder up the second ramp into my weather shack. I limped back for cylinder #8.

As I worked with cylinder #8, I screamed and shouted obscenities in anger, trying desperately to get more oxygen into my lungs. I finally got the cylinder slid off the back of the truck. Then, in a near fit of rage, and hurrying while my adrenaline was still flowing, I brutally dragged it up the second ramp into the back of my weather shack. In similar fashion, I forced cylinder #9 from where it stood on my truck, to where I left it in the back of my weather shack. Ignoring my cuts, my bruises, and my many blisters, screaming in rage, and shaking, and swearing at the Air Force and my lot in life, I half ran up the plank into the back of the truck, grabbed cylinder #10. Blinded by the dirt and sweat dripping off my face and brow, and beyond sanity, I screamed and yelled like a raging animal as I banged #10 down on the bed of the truck and shoved it to the back edge of the truck bed. Shaking almost uncontrollably, I jumped down to the ground and jerked #10 off the back of the truck, guiding it as it fell to the ground. I let it rest up against the back of the truck bed. Fatigue and nausea finally overtook me. I stepped back from my work, and stepped backwards across the cable fence that separated my weather area from the skip bombing range to the east. Using one of the wooden posts to steady my hysterical, shaking body, I bent over at the waist and began vomiting my guts out into the sagebrush, into the rocks, into the gravel, and into the soft dirt. As I was doing so, out of the corner of my eye I caught a glimpse of something white running along the side of my weather shack, back out towards the open area where my theodolite stood. I was far too nauseous at the time to care what it was.

After many long minutes of vomiting, and swearing, and sucking in the fresh night air I was finally able to straighten up some. Down to the southeast, perhaps a quarter mile distant, three more of the white fluorescent lights could be seen deployed in a skirmish line, approaching me slowly. When I finally got my vomiting controlled, still shaking, I stepped back across the cable fence, and steadied myself against the wooden post, my head pounding, gasping for breath in the fresh night air, and swearing to convince myself that I was still alive.

After many long minutes, I started feeling a little better. I limped my way back into my weather station and collapsed into my chair. After a few more minutes I carefully sipped some water and washed the dirt and sweat out of my mouth. I picked up my phone to call Desert Center for help, but it was useless with static. My radio was little better. Out in front of my weather shack, just out of sight around the corner of my front door I could hear someone walking carefully on the gravel. I was far too exhausted to be afraid, but it roused me to action. "Is anyone there?" I called out loudly. "Stay back. I'm very sick. My eyes are blinded from the dirt and from my sweat. I frighten easily and I need to rest," I called out loudly. It sounded like the person outside retreated back between the buildings a short distance. Standing up slowly and making a lot of noise as I did so, I carefully closed the side door to my shack. With my eyes closed, and signing loudly as I did so, I gingerly reached out and got hold of the front door and swung it closed. Feeling safer now, I sat back down in my chair, put my arms and head down on my desk, closed my eyes, and began resting. I was too exhausted to move. I ignored the sounds of several people walking quietly on the gravel outside. After a long time, I started feeling a little better. I knew there was only one way off the ranges. That way was for me to finish unloading the truck. Slowly I roused my self. I called out loudly and made numerous loud sounds. I was careful to give whoever was out side, all of the time they needed to go away. I carefully took another drink of cola, munched a few more corn chips, and washed them down with some clear water. Still tired, stumbling, and talking loudly to myself, I carefully went out the back door, and began the brutal task of getting cylinder #10 into my weather shack. I was sore from the top of my head all the way down to my very toes. Every muscle in my body ached. It took a long time, but I finally had inched cylinder #10 into the back of my weather shack. I went to get cylinder #11, dreaming of how nice it would be to get back to my barracks, and into bed. I was so exhausted that I wasn't sure I could make it up onto the back of my truck. I stood there for a long time, trying to decide what to do next. I was so tired that I nearly went to sleep standing up. Off to the southeast, about a half of mile distant, the skirmish line of three white lights remained on station.

With extreme difficulty, I finally made it up into the back of my truck. Once there, I rested for several minutes, breathing deeply. Then I grabbed cylinder #11 and began the process of laying it down on its side on the bed of the truck. I was far too tired to do so safely. Halfway down, I lost control of the cylinder and it slammed down onto the wooden truck bed, bouncing some as it did so. It tore open some more of the blisters on my hands as it fell. I screamed in agony for a while. After many minutes of cursing and swearing and shaking my hand, I finally got hold of myself. Using my feet, I slid cylinder #11 into position with its bottom even with the back of the truck. Then I carefully tried to get down from the truck. Too tired to hold my own weight, I slipped part way down and fell into the rocks and the dirt and the sagebrush below, opening more cuts on my hands and knees. Bruised, screaming in agony, I finally got to my feet. My fatigues were torn. My knees were scraped, and my right hand especially, was bleeding from cuts. Wrapping my cut right hand with my handkerchief, and screaming in rage, and in agony, I grabbed the bottom of cylinder #11 and dragged it off the truck, guiding the cylinder as it fell upright into the soft desert dirt. Then leaning it against the back of the truck, once again I stepped to the side and vomited whatever little was left in my stomach into the desert across the cable fence. Every cell in my body was screaming in pain. It was only with great difficulty that I could straighten up. I stood there for many long minutes swearing, and coughing, and shaking, and trying to get control of my dry heaves.

Setting down on a nearby wooden post at last, I decided that I had to get help with the last two cylinders - at any price. With my phone not working and my radio useless with static, I decided that I had no choice but to hobble over to the range three lounge, hoping the phone over there worked. I decided I would ask anyone I found over there for help. I began slowly hobbling and limping along the cable fence heading towards the front, northeast corner of my weather shack. It was a slow process. I stopped next to each post in turn to steady myself. I finally arrived at the northeast corner of my weather shack. Then I proceeded out into the open and stopped beside the next wooden post. As I stopped to steady myself, I saw her standing out there in the moonlit darkness. It was the chalk white woman whom I had previously surprised in the alleyway. Now she was standing naturally on the ground, in familiar fashion, next to the front door of the closest supply shed. She stood barely 25 feet away, watching me in silence. Her little girl was standing on the ground behind her. Both of them were wearing happy expressions, obviously unafraid of me. The power to the suits that they were wearing, appeared to have been turned down, but their suits still gave off a small amount of soft white fluorescent light.

When I first saw her, I wasn't startled or afraid. At the time I was actually disappointed with myself. I considered her to be a figment of my imagination. I was disappointed because I believed that my brain had begun to malfunction again. I steadied myself against the wooden post, and began studying her carefully. I was waiting for my body to rest, settle down, and return to normal - at which time I expected her to vanish into thin air. I stood there in silence watching her for at least fifteen minutes, while she remained pleasantly standing at her spot, in total silence, and watching me back. I marveled at how real she appeared. I remember saying out loud to myself, "I never knew that hallucinations could appear to be that real. You look as if I could just reach out and touch you." She seemed to find it amusing.

My body was still shaking from exhaustion. I had to endure more attacks of the dry heaves. After one of these attacks, as I was bent over, my stomach in aching spasms, I noticed a small square block of dry wood lying on the ground. Out of curiosity more than anything, I picked it up with my left hand, and, after straightening up a little, I gently tossed it underhand over towards the young chalk white woman. I expected the piece of wood to continue its normal path on through the space where she stood. I expected to prove to myself that she wasn't real, but just a figment of my imagination. As I watched, she smiled pleasantly, reached out smoothly with her right hand and caught the block of wood in mid air. Then she visually inspected it for a minute or so, and using a gentle underhanded motion, tossed it back to me. I was too stunned to catch it. I stood there transfixed as the block of wood bounced gently against my left chest, then my left knee, and fell to the ground at my feet. It took a few minutes for me to get hold of myself. "That's a pretty good trick." I finally muttered out loud. "Can you do that with your left hand?" I asked. Then I picked up the same small block of wood and gently tossed it underhand back towards the young woman. This time, still smiling pleasantly, she reached out with her left hand and caught it in mid air. Then, appearing to be almost laughing in silence, using a smooth under hand motion, she gently tossed it back to me. Once again, I was far too stunned to catch it .It struck the right side of my chest and fell harmlessly to the ground. The nerves in my neck and stomach began tightening in fear. Another spasm of dry heaves and vomiting set in. Steadying myself against the wooden post, I turned to my left, towards the south, and spent the next ten minutes or so bent over, and on my knees in dry heaves. Every coughing spasm hurt so much my mind would flood over in spells of dizziness and pain. Sometimes, coughing and choking, I would mutter, "You can't be real. You just can't be real." She seemed to find it very amusing.

After a long while, the spasms slowly subsided, and I was able to get hold of myself. Slowly I got back on my feet, bent over at the waist, and steadied myself against the wooden post as I took stock of my desperate situation. While I had been down on my knees, the tall white young woman had closed the distance. Now she stood in silent, friendly, and familiar fashion, next to the opposite corner of my weather shack, barely a dozen feet from me. The skirmish line down to the southeast had closed to less than 50 feet. Now I could see that it was a line of three similar chalk white creatures - apparently two young men and another young woman. To the south, next to my truck, stood another tall white young male carefully inspecting helium cylinder #11. The soft white fluorescent lights coming from behind my weather shack convinced me that several more such creatures were behind it, and out of sight. To the south, several miles in the distance, I could see two other much taller chalk white fluorescent patches posted in military fashion, down on the range one road at its junctions with the range two and the range three roads. Off to my right, standing by the back southwest corner of the range three lounge stood another such creature - apparently a young girl about the age of an eighth grader. Straight down at the end of the cable fence to the north, some 70 feet away, another fully-grown young male creature stood watching me intently. Behind me, off on a small ridge in the desert, less than 50 yards to the northeast, I could see still another older male adult creature slowly closing on me. As soon as I saw him, my heart went into my mouth, cold with fear. He was older and sterner than the rest. He was obviously heavily armed, obviously intent on closing on me. He appeared to be the same creature I had previously glimpsed momentarily before falling to my knees on my way out of the generator shack. Too sick to panic or run, I turned slowly towards the young woman. I was bent over at the time, and holding my sides in agony and exhaustion. 'Well, aren't you one beautiful hallucination." I said pleasantly. "And I see you have friends. You know, I haven't ever seen anything with your kind of beauty before." A large smile flashed across the young woman's face. I continued slowly and pleasantly, trying to get hold of myself, coughing and heaving as I spoke, "You don't frighten me. You're the one I trust. You could have killed me before now, if you'd wanted to. Anyway, the men of my family, we're one tough bunch of guys. We don't ever quit. We haven't ever been afraid of women. But that big white male coming up behind me, is another story. He scares me. I can see he's armed to the teeth and tough as nails. He must be one of your generals. I'm no match for him, and what's more, I'm sure he knows it. He can take me anytime he feels like it. I figure that he must be taking his orders from you because you're the one that's come in close. You must be one beautiful high-ranking lady. So I figure I'm better off if I just keep talking to only you. I wonder if you wouldn't ask that general of yours to back off a ways, back towards that bunker road behind him. It'd make me feel a lot better. He can still kill me from there if he takes a mind to. That would at least give me a chance to settle down and collect my thoughts, and talk to you for a while. You see, young lady, the men of my family have always been good with words. You never know, I might just get lucky. If you give me the chance to talk a while, I just might succeed in talking my way out of this mess I'm in."

Another broad smile flashed across the young woman's face. She and the others appeared to spend a few minutes laughing pleasantly, all in total silence. The well-armed adult male off to the northeast retreated suddenly, falling back to the desert ridge that lay along the bunker road, some 200 yards distant. Then the white male standing by my truck quickly retreated out of sight behind my weather shack. The skirmish line of three fell back to the southeast perhaps a quarter of a mile. The young woman glanced quickly off to the northeast, visibly checking the new position of the tall white general. Then she returned to studying me intently and smiled, as if to say, "Sure. Let's hear it?"

I spent the next several minutes vomiting and waiting out some more coughing spasms. When they finally subsided, I spent a few more minutes catching my breath. Then I continued slowly, coughing, stammering, and sometimes pausing, waiting out more dry heaves. "Well, I promised you an interesting conversation, so I'll begin with some jokes." For the next 3 or 4 minutes, I recited a series of 3 short jokes that I had made up myself. They were such bad jokes that I was shocked when the white lady creature standing in front of me suddenly broke out in near hysterical laughter, as did every other white creature I could see. Even the two tall white guards positioned in the distance, down on the range one road, appeared to be laughing intensely. In addition, the sound of several humans laughing could be heard coming from behind the range three lounge. One of them was laughing, saying in muffled tones, "Colonel, he's the one we need." And another one was saying, "General, he sure has guts!"

A good many minutes passed as the others laughed and I stood waiting. The entire range area was covered with hysterical, electric, uncontrollable laughter. Both the chalk white woman and her little girl were knelt down with their backs against the shed, laughing until they were shaking and dizzy. For my part, my mind was now totally flooded over with confusion. I had expected the laughter to make my hallucinations go away, but the opposite seemed to be happening. I was now extremely confused. I didn't think any of my jokes were particularly funny, but my hallucinations found them to be hysterical. I wondered how it could be that my hallucinations could find my own made up jokes to be funnier than I thought them to be. After all, they're both figments of my imagination - - aren't they?

Exhaustion began overtaking me, again, and another round of uncontrollable dry heaves set in. Soon I was down on my knees on the sharp gravel and sagebrush, barely able to keep from falling totally flat on my face. My hallucinations appeared to believe that I was laughing too.

I had been down on the rocks and gravel for a very long time when the laughter finally subsided, and the gentle stillness of the nighttime desert air finally returned. I spent a few more minutes suffering through some more coughing spasms. When they finally subsided, I spent a few more minutes catching my breath. Then I continued, slowly, coughing, stammering, and sometimes pausing, waiting out more dry heaves, "I'm very sick, and I'm not able to tell you any more stories. I'm totally exhausted. I have to rest, or I'll die. I have to get help. I can't move my truck until I've unloaded that last helium cylinder, and moved those last two cylinders to a safe place. I can't get back into base until I can move my truck." Then I paused some more, fighting off another coughing spasm. I waited until the dizziness from the coughing passed, then I continued. "My phone in the weather shack isn't working because of all the static. My radio isn't any better. I need to get over to the lounge. I could use the phone over there to phone Desert Center and ask for help. Then I could sleep on the sofa over there until I was rested or until help arrived."

The young woman stood in silence, pleasantly smiling at me, apparently listening to every word I spoke. I rested for a minute or so, thinking through my next words carefully, and collecting my nerves and my thoughts. I continued, "I'm too tired to walk across this open area in front of me. It's too wide. I intend to follow along this cable fence towards that young man up at the end. I need the fence to steady myself. Please tell him not to panic. I figure he must be armed, and I don't want him to fire on me."

Another happy smile flashed across the young woman's face. The young male at the end of the cable fence made a friendly gesture, and showed me the palms of both of his hands. He obviously wanted me to see that he didn't have any weapons aimed at me at the time.

Breathing a little easier, I continued. "When I get up close to him, about four of five posts up, I intend to turn towards the lounge, and try to make it across that open area up there. It's narrower up there, and I might be able to make it without falling, if I'm careful." The young woman smiled at me, and then turned her gaze towards the northeastern corner of the lounge. There was obviously something up there that she wanted me to see. I followed her lead, and turned my gaze to the same place. Out from behind the range three lounge stepped another young adult white male creature, about my height. He stood in silence, looking straight at me. Then, from behind the lounge, stepped an American Air Force colonel - his silver eagles clearly visible in the faint moonlight. The colonel, stepped to the left and north of the white creature and said in a low voice, "I'll handle this Harry." The white male then stepped back behind the range three lounge. The colonel remained standing, not actually facing me, but rather facing the section of the cable fence that I had said I intended to walk to.

As soon as the sight of the American colonel sank into my exhausted brain, a wave of relief flooded over me. I considered him to be a figment of my imagination, like the others - after all, I was 22 miles out in the desert. He had no obvious method of transportation, and I had seen him talking to a white creature - but he was an ordinary human. That convinced me that my brain was starting to return to normal. As I stood there, feeling tremendous relief that my hallucinations were at last starting to look like ordinary humans, the phone in my weather shack began ringing. Turning towards the young woman, I happily exclaimed, "That's my phone. It must be working, now. I need to answer it. If I'm careful, I might even live through this." While my phone continued to ring, the young woman remained standing next to the northwest corner of my weather shack. I slowly hobbled over to its front door. With the young woman standing smiling, less than 6 feet from me, I carefully stood up, and opened the front door of my weather shack. It opened out and to my left; away from the where the young woman was standing. Turning my back on her, I carefully climbed into my weather shack, climbed into my chair, and answered the phone, "Range three weather shack, Charlie." I was greeted by an ordinary dial tone, and virtually no static. My radio was now playing loudly as well. It also had no unusual static. I sat for a few minutes resting. I took some water, opened the side door, rinsed out my mouth, and spit the wastewater out into the desert. I rested in my chair some more, while slowly sipping some more water. According to the radio, it was now 4.00 a.m. I was feeling totally exhausted, but now I was able to relax. Soon I started feeling noticeably better. Outside, the colonel and the young chalk white woman remained on station, while the other white creatures slowly retreated from their exposed positions, and disappeared out of sight behind the range three buildings.

With some music now to help me, and feeling better, I formulated a plan of action. Tired as I was, I obviously needed to conserve my energy. I decided that I would move cylinder #11 to a stable position next to the rear door, up against the outside of my weather shack. The cylinders had a protective thick steel screw-on cap that protected the valve assembly from the sun, the wind, and the rain. It could safely wait outside for a few days until I could rest up and move it inside. Then I would take the 4:30 balloon run. Afterwards, I would decide what to do about cylinder #12. I began by stepping outside through my side door, and hobbling around to the front of my shack to close the front door - since it opened out. The chalk white young woman remained standing by the corner of my weather shack as before. Slowly I hobbled towards her, until I was standing directly in front of her. Then I carefully closed the front door. I still believed she was a hallucination. Looking her in the eyes, I said pleasantly, "You sure have been helpful for a hallucination."

Where-upon she startled me. She replied in playful feminine fashion, laughing and speaking perfect English, "Remember Charlie, next time you have to help us for free. You and the men of your family promised." Then she appeared to skip backwards several steps, in playful fashion. With her little girl next to her, still laughing, they both turned the corner into the alleyway and disappeared from sight behind the buildings. I was startled and surprised, but I was not stunned or afraid. With all of the white creatures now out of sight, and only the colonel visible - still on station by the corner of the lounge - I was actually quite happy. I believed that my brain was rapidly recovering and that with a bit more rest, things would soon be right back to normal. Singing and laughing, myself, I hobbled back around my weather shack. Then taking a deep breath, and shouting to fill my lungs with oxygen, I carefully inched cylinder #11 across the soft dirt towards the back wall of my weather shack. The cylinder was still three feet or so away, and standing in a precarious position when I had to quit to rest.

It was now 4:20 a.m. I decided to take the morning balloon run before continuing. I hobbled back into my weather shack, filled a balloon, attached the tracking light, and began taking the morning weather report. I released my balloon, picked up my clipboard, recorded the time, and hobbled and limped out to my theodolite. Tired as I was, taking off the heavy aluminum cover was quite a problem. Three minutes had already passed when I was finally ready to take the first reading. The readings for minute four, and five went as planned. As I was taking the fifth reading, I heard the characteristic clanging of a helium cylinder from behind my weather shack. I swore some because I supposed that cylinder #11 had fallen over. There was nothing to be done, but to continue with my wind measurements. As I was taking the reading for minute number eight, it was obvious that I had lost the balloon against one of the star fields in the Milky Way. This meant that readings six and seven were no good. Swearing some, I realized that I needed at least two more good readings in order to have a useful wind measurement. With a practiced hand, then, I went searching for my balloon against the bright star fields that concealed it. It was intense work and I didn't take my eye off the eyepiece and look around as I usually did. I finally located my balloon after fourteen minutes had passed. For the next three minutes, I tracked it carefully and recorded the readings. Satisfied that I finally had a decent set of wind measurements, I broke off the tracking process and put down the clipboard. I began breathing deeply, and sucking all the oxygen I could into my lungs. Then I picked up the heavy aluminum cover and locked up the theodolite. I was watching the American colonel as he remained on station, standing just out from the northeast corner of the lounge. As usual, he wasn't watching me directly. Rather, he remained standing in the dim moonlight, perhaps 100 feet from me, facing the mountains off to the east, and just looking my way once in a while. As I watched, an American Air Force sergeant, wearing eight stripes, stepped quickly out from the darkness behind the range three lounge. He approached the colonel on his left side. I could hear the sergeant say to the colonel, speaking in muffled tones, "We're finished, sir. He sure is one brave tough soldier to have unloaded 11 of those, out here alone, surrounded by our white friends." Then both of them stepped quickly backwards until they were out of sight behind the lounge - leaving me at last alone in the dimly lit nighttime.

Believing myself to be back to normal - exhausted, but normal - I decided to hurry with my remaining tasks, unload cylinder#12, and get back into base while I could. Taking a deep breath, I hurriedly replaced the aluminum cover, locked my theodolite, and hobbled back to my weather shack. Once inside, I hurried through my calculations as best I could, sipped some more cola, and phoned Desert Center. Sergeant Adams answered. The Desert Center base commander had asked him to come in early. He recorded my weather report, reminded me that the ranges were closed, told me that no more wind reports were needed for the rest of the day, and suggested that I head immediately into base to get breakfast and rest.

I was just hanging up the phone when I noticed that the back door to my weather shack was closed. I was shocked - while I had been taking the balloon measurements someone had closed the door. Calling out loudly, I gingerly stepped out through my side door. Singing loudly, I hobbled along the side of my weather shack to my truck in the back. I was stunned by the surprise I found when I got there. While I had been taking my wind report, someone had unloaded cylinder #12 from the back of my truck. Cylinder #11 and cylinder #12 now stood securely, side-by-side, directly up against the back of my weather shack. The heavy wooden planks had been taken down and were now laying neatly side-by-side in the dirt along the back of my weather shack. The rear door to my weather shack had been neatly closed and locked. My truck now stood ready to take me into base.

Exhausted, and nearly ready to drop, I didn't have the faintest idea what to make of it all. After overcoming my surprise, I took the truck keys from my pocket, climbed into the driver's seat, and gratefully started the engine. Then, with the motor running, I maneuvered the big truck back through the mesquite and around to the front of my weather shack. With the engine idling, I climbed out, turned off the shack lights, and locked up my weather shack. Then I pulled the big truck over to the generator shack, got out, and shut down the diesel. Climbing back into my waiting truck at last, with the early sunrise turning the sky pink in the east, I gratefully put the truck into low gear and began heading back into base, leaving range three behind. As I was leaving the range three area, in the mirror I could see the colonel briefly step out from behind the range three lounge and watch me as the truck headed into base. I didn't stop or slow down. I was quite happy. I felt that through hard work and concentration, I'd won a victory. I'd won, a victory over hallucinations, a victory over sickness and disease, a victory over things that go bump in the night. I believed that I had temporarily surrendered my sanity in order to stay alive. I believed that I was now an expert on hallucinations and bad dreams, an expert on desperate mental trade-offs, an expert on the figments of one's imagination. I believed that I now understood completely the tricks that a man's mind plays on him when he is exhausted and alone. The stress of that evening had been extreme. "It had to have been the stress", I repeated to myself. "I had to have been hallucinating. What other explanation could there be?" As I drove back into base, it was with great pride that I pushed the memory of that evening completely from my mind. It was with great pride that I convinced myself that the entire evening had been just a simple bout of mental exhaustion. Yes, I got control of my consciousness and my fears. I convinced myself that my brain would be all healed up and everything would be right back to normal, just as soon as I got a good meal and a good nights sleep. As I drove back into base, young, innocent - a mind trained to forget - yes - ignorance was certainly bliss. I believed that I had given everything I had, just to stay alive.

Rite of Passage

...today I fulfilled my vows.
So I came out to meet you;
I have looked for you
and have found you!...

...Proverbs 7:14 - 15

In many ways Mojave Wells was an enlisted man's paradise. Weeks could go by without seeing any officers or sergeants. Yes, it was true that some days the empty ranges were filled with fall rains, cold winter nights, and loneliness. But other days were much different. I was well supplied, had midnight chow in the barracks, a long comfortable bus ride up to the far away Las Vegas casinos on weekends, inspections were unheard of, and I could go anywhere I wanted to, anytime I wanted to. I had my own pickup truck and extra TDY pay. Some days, it seemed as though friends in high places surrounded me.

It was a warm Monday morning out at range three. The sun was rapidly heating up the desert floor. I had just finished the 9:30 a.m. balloon run and was walking across the open square towards the range three lounge. The ranges were in use, and I was expecting to have fun joining in the poker game which Steve and the range rats had going in the lounge. I had just reached the northeast corner of the lounge building, and was heading towards the open front door when the phone inside rang. Steve answered authoritatively, "Lounge three! You're even with Steven. Uh huh, uh huh.

Right general. Right away …Yes sir, yes sir." He hung up the phone, jumped up from his chair and announced to the rest of the range rats, "Condition yellow. Somebody wants to play with Charlie. We have 10 minutes to be in the trucks and heading out of here. Shut down everything and head into base. The ranges are closed for the rest of the week. Doug, go tell the range officer to order all planes to return to Desert Center in a direct and normal manner. Wayne, move the range boards to their red positions. The rest of you men, get the two power wagons and bring them around front while I close up the windows and pick up our cards, TODAY, Gentlemen. We're closing this place down, TODAY!"

I paused as the men double-timed past me. Then I nervously asked Steve, "Do the pull-out orders apply to me too, Steve?"

Steve laughed and responded, "No, of course not, Charlie. Whoever is coming out here to play, wants to play with you."

"Me?" I responded nervously.

Steve laughed some more as he was picking up his deck of cards, "Just stay calm, Charlie. We're all pulling out, officers and everyone. Everything out here is yours to play with for the rest of the day."

Steve was quite right. It was a beautiful day and everything out at range three was mine to play with, apparently alone, for the rest of the day.

The next day, Tuesday, began as another warm beautiful morning out at range three. Nothing fearful had happened but for some reason my nerves began to get the best of me. It wasn't like me to be that way. I enjoyed being alone. Usually I wasn't the slightest bit afraid of the dark but for a while, I was jumping at my own shadow. Then I became convinced that I was hallucinating again. Every time I went anywhere outside my weather shack, it looked to me like some young girl or young woman would silently float up behind me and follow me around. Sometimes she appeared to be about the size of a seventh or eighth grade girl. Other times she appeared to be a young woman my height, about the age of 21. Once the young woman appeared with a little girl by her side. Another time all three appeared floating side by side. Soon I wasn't sure if I was being followed by one woman or two, or three, or seeing double or even triple. Usually, the woman, or the girl, would hide behind me where I couldn't see her. When I turned around suddenly, she'd be there, maybe 6 or 8 feet away, floating a foot or so off the ground smiling at me. She was very thin with chalk white skin, large blue eyes, and blonde hair. Always she wore a white aluminum canvas like suit that gave off a zone of soft white fluorescent light. The young woman with the little girl, and the young girl appeared to be the same ones I'd seen close up, the night I'd had such a difficult time unloading my shipment of twelve helium cylinders. For that reason, when they came, I wasn't terrified or even afraid. I had come to believe that they were just my special personal apparitions. I was having this medical problem, I supposed, because I didn't eat right, get enough rest, or because I'd spent so much time alone out on the ranges. I wondered if I would ever recover.

On this Tuesday night, pleasant thoughts would form slowly in my mind, thoughts such as "Hello Charlie. Do you enjoy being called Charlie? Do you enjoy being out here alone in the dark? Thank you for saving the life of my little girl down at range one. You aren't afraid, the way the others were." Soon my heart was racing and my temples were pounding. I became certain that my mind was going and that the cells in my brain had given out on me. At first I tried singing to myself to control my fear. Then I gave up on singing and started talking to them as though they were human. I'd say things like, "Now please don't go getting in my way, little girl. I'm a busy man, and I have lots of work to do before I can go in for breakfast. You never want to come between a working man and his breakfast." It seemed to settle me down. The woman and the girls responded by smiling and giggling silently in return. That moonless night, out on range three, I was standing, leaning against the sturdy metal theodolite stand. I was enjoying the beautiful starlight and checking on the weather. The young woman was floating some 9 inches off the ground in total silence, some 8 feet or so from me, watching me intently. She looked so totally real that for a few minutes, I was actually too scared to move. I knew that no matter what she was, if I panicked, I'd never get back into base alive. I said my prayers and got my emotions under control. I began by slowly thinking things through and counting my blessings. I had an easy job and I liked doing it. I decided that I was one lucky airman. Why waste it all by letting a few silly things in the night scare me out of a good thing? Yes, as I stood there, I got my mind right. I decided that since she hadn't harmed me yet, she wasn't going to. Therefore, I should learn to relax whenever she was around, happily go on about my business, go right on singing my sunshine songs, and trust that she would be friendly in return.

I began my new lease on life by asking the young woman politely to step aside so I could walk back to my weather shack and get my balloon. She smiled and floated off to one side to my right so I could go by. I smiled in return, and told her, "Thanks". I walked slowly and directly to my weather shack. I got my balloon, confident that I finally had my senseless nameless fears under control. I was quite proud of myself, really, the way I was learning to work around my apparitions. Yes, of myself, I was very proud. The young woman watched me from a safe distance, twenty feet or so, while I got my balloon and took the morning run. Later I could see the young girl playing happily over by the range three lounge.

During the following nights, the eighth grade girl, the young woman, and the little girl would come whenever I was out there. Usually they came one at a time. There seemed to be a pattern to it - two days on and two days off for a while. Then they'd miss a day. Then they'd begin a new cycle of two days on and two days off. I frequently wondered about the cycle because I knew of nothing about my human body that operated on such a two-day cycle. Always they came from over behind the range three lounge. When they left, that's where they would return. Soon I wasn't the slightest bit afraid whenever I would see the young woman or the young girl over by the range three lounge, because I had come to believe that was where my mind stored all of my apparitions.

Over breakfast, one morning, I told my friends, Steve, Wayne and Doug about the chalk white women I was seeing. I began by laughing at myself, expecting them to join in. They never did. Instead, they silently exchanged serious glances. Then Steve pleasantly suggested that some afternoon when I had nothing else to do, I should check the soft ground over behind the range three lounge for boot prints. Perhaps, he suggested, I might find a set that matched the boots worn by the eighth grade girl. He pointed out that her boots would be smaller than any man's and therefore, would leave a distinctive set.

I objected, saying there couldn't possibly be any boot prints over behind the range three lounge because I couldn't possibly create even small boot prints by hallucinating. Steve smiled and responded, "That's my point, Charlie. Remember, when you do find small boot prints over there, the way me and the boys have in the past, that's exactly my point."

The whole conversation made me very nervous. Once again, I became afraid they didn't understand how difficult my duties were, how difficult it was to get up every weekday morning, alone in the darkness at 3:00 a.m. and drive some 22 miles completely alone out into the nighttime desert, how easily a man's fears could get the best of him in the nighttime as he tried to perform even a simple task, like reading a thermometer, once he became certain that some young eighth grade girl was playing games behind him - a young girl with two inch long claws, who could come up behind him so fast that she could kill him with impunity anytime she felt like it. I wanted to make them understand that it mattered not whether the girl was real or only a figment of my imagination. If I panicked, I would be dead either way.

Nervous because of their continued silence and furtive, knowing glances, I responded to Steve, stammering, "Don't look at me like that Steve. There isn't anything the matter with me. Maybe I could use some rest, and some more vitamins or something, but I'm just as sane as any man here! I enjoy being up here with you guys. There isn't anything out there in the empty darkness that I fear!"

Steve smiled, good friend that he was, and responded, "I know Charlie. I agree there isn't anything whatever wrong with you. What worries me is that the darkness out there isn't empty! Just remember, you'd have to be some kind of super human to create boot prints in the sand just by hallucinating out there in the darkness."

The next day the ranges remained closed. As usual, I was the only one allowed to go out onto them. Out of boredom I went in for the noon meal early. I was surprised to find that the base was almost deserted. Only the new cook was manning the chow hall. He had prepared the noon meal for only himself and me. He had plenty of work waiting for him, so I wolfed my meal and hurried back out to the ranges.

The mid-day run went fast enough. I was killing time until the last run of the day, the one at 2:30 p.m. It was a hot summer afternoon with light and gentle winds. I had both the front door and the side door of my weather shack open. I had just finished phoning the winds in to Desert Center. I was standing just inside the front door of my weather shack, with my back sort-of towards the open front door. I had taken off my sunglasses, hanging up the phone with my right hand, just laying the completed wind report down on my desk with my left. It was such a beautiful day, and I was really happy. I had been singing songs and even dancing around a little in the bright sunshine. It was hot, very hot. I had measured the temperature at 114 degrees Fahrenheit in the shade. I'd taken to carrying double and triple canteens of water. I was being extra careful with my water supplies. I heard a slight sound outside on the gravel behind me. The phone in my hand began tingling with electricity, and my radio suddenly fuzzed over with a light static. An unusual, gentle gust of wind came in through my weather shack and then blew on through the graveled range three area. Without thinking much about it, I turned around to see what was going on outside.

As soon as I turned, and my gaze had passed out through my open front door, I saw her. It was the young woman. She was standing out there alone on the soft gravel, just past my theodolite stand, probably 60 feet from me. Only this time, she wasn't wearing the fluorescent suit that she always wore at night. Consequently she was not floating as she frequently did at night. This time she was standing naturally up straight on the soft graveled soil watching me. She was wearing what appeared to be a relatively ordinary white aluminum canvas jumpsuit with white nylon rubber boots, standing alone, out in the bright, hot, noonday sun, with her solid chalk white skin, unusually thin, animated frame, large intelligent bright blue eyes, the gentle southeast wind blowing her short, nearly transparent white, blonde hair to one side, smiling pleasantly at me. It was a sight that I will never forget. I wasn't afraid or even startled. I had become certain that she was just a figment of my imagination. I felt a certain disappointment with myself, believing that the heat was starting to affect my brain. The glare from the bright sunshine was intense and hurt my eyes, which had adjusted to the shaded interior of my weather shack. This caused me a great deal of confusion because it meant that in order for my eyes to feel pain while actually focusing in on her, the light rays reflecting off her had to be real. Therefore, she had to be real.

The young woman stood there for perhaps another 10 or 20 seconds. Then, with a happy smile on her face, in a smooth fluid fashion, she turned to her right and took off sprinting towards the range three lounge. It was one of the most beautiful sights that I have ever seen. She was in full stride, the way Greek statues usually depict Mercury, the messenger of the gods. When she approached the northeast corner of the range three lounge, she covered the last five feet or so by putting both feet together and jumping towards it, the way a baseball runner might approach second base. She covered the short distance to the range three lounge at more than 25 miles per hour. The whole event happened so fast that for a while, I stood numbed and wondering what had happened.

After giving the matter extensive consideration, I remembered Steve's words from the breakfast table. Since the dirt was soft over behind the range three lounge, perhaps I should go over there and carefully check for boot prints. Cautiously, then, I put on my canteen belt with two full canteens of water. I took a good drink of water from my third canteen hanging from a nail in my weather shack, and very cautiously stepped outside through my front door. It was a beautiful day outside, in spite of the intense heat. The desert floor was sizzling hot and getting hotter every minute. The day before I had brought two eggs out from the chow hall. Just for fun I had fried them on the hood of my truck. With salt and pepper they had tasted quite good. Today, the desert floor was even hotter.

It was with a great deal of caution that I approached my steel theodolite stand and found a spot which I could lean against, enjoying its feeling of emotional security. I was hesitant to progress further towards the range three lounge. It wasn't the intense heat that made me hesitant. It was the sight of Range Four Harry standing out in the open, about a quarter mile down on the bunker road to the northeast. He was a young male about my height, with chalk white skin, and large bright blue eyes that stretched part way around the sides of his head. He had very short nearly white blonde hair. In his hands he was carrying a solid white pencil like object about 18 inches long. He stood there naturally, watching my every move. He obviously intended that I should see him. "So, even my hallucinations have guards," I remarked grimly to myself. I stood there by the theodolite thinking things through for a long time. "How can a hallucination of a young woman be so intense that it includes her own set of guards?" I wondered.

After a long time, probably more than a half hour, way up the valley towards range four, I could see the young woman, the eighth grade girl, and the little girl playing happily, hiking, circling towards the mountains to the northeast. As they approached the mountains northeast of me, Range Four Harry, still standing on the bunker road, finally began falling back along the pavement. Then, he suddenly turned away from me and melted into the sagebrush behind him. I waited by my theodolite stand for a long time, probably another fifteen or twenty minutes. Apparently alone again, I cautiously walked over to the spot where I had seen the young woman standing. Clearly visible in the soft dirt and gravel, were her boot prints. I followed them step for step over to the soft dirt behind the now deserted range three lounge. I noted that from the depth of the boot prints, even though she stood as tall as I did, she weighed only between 90 and 110 pounds. Numb, hot, sweaty, and a little afraid, I carefully retraced my footsteps back to my weather shack. Virtually every step of the way, I recited to myself the words, "It can't be real. Whatever happened, it just can't be real!" By the time I had returned to the safety of my weather shack, I had succeeded in convincing myself that nothing unusual had happened and that this was just another ordinary hot summer day in the desert. It was the only way I could feel sane, secure, and comfortable again. Singing my songs to myself, I took the 2:30 p.m. run early, phoned Desert Center as usual, locked up my weather shack, shut down the diesel as normal, and drove my truck back into town, completely convinced that nothing unusual had happened that day.

I felt I needed more rest, so I took the afternoon easy. I was walking over to evening chow, crossing a large vacant area on the Mojave Wells base, when my casual friend Greg, running hard, caught up with me. Emotional and intent, he caught me by my right elbow and stopped me out in the open.

"Charlie!" he exclaimed, nearly out of breath, "I'm glad I caught you. I have to tell you about this coming Tuesday."

"Oh? What about next Tuesday?" I asked, waiting for him to breathe again.

"I've got to tell you, Charlie," Greg continued emotionally. "Steve made me promise. He said that you had to be told. He said he'd die before he let those Desert Center generals surprise you as they're planning. Something's up, Charlie, something real big. Steve said if he told you, they'd suspect him. He said they'd break him down for sure and court martial him. Me, now, they'll never suspect me. I can tip you off and get away with it."

"Tell me what?" I inquired.

"About this Tuesday's inspection," gasped Greg. "Those Desert Center generals are out to get you, Charlie. They're planning a big surprise inspection to get you next Tuesday."

423

I chuckled. "I'm always ready for anything, Greg. They can come inspect my weather stations anytime they feel like. You must be mistaken, though. Not even my own commanders are allowed to come up here and inspect me. They must be coming up here to inspect you guys."

"No! No!" exclaimed Greg emotionally, grabbing my elbow harder. "You don't understand, Charlie. It's not the Desert Center base commander. It's the Pentagon generals who are coming on Tuesday. It's those generals from back east that must be out to get you because they're the ones coming."

"How do you know?" I asked, stuttering and betraying my inner nervousness.

"Today, it happened right after breakfast," answered Greg, "Right after you got in your truck and started driving back out to range three. I tell you they must have been watching you. That Desert Center base commanding general had it timed perfectly. You were just heading out onto the ranges when he phoned up here and ordered everybody to immediately head in to Desert Center for an emergency briefing. Everyone except for that new cook and you, had to go. Charlie, the way he did it, we all thought that nuclear war had been declared.

"Once the air policemen had us standing at attention in that briefing room down at the Desert Center command post, the base commander himself came in and personally delivered the orders. He ordered all of us except you to spend this weekend and Monday morning, preparing this base here at Mojave Wells for inspection. He said the base doesn't have to be clean, or even military. It only has to be safe. Any safety hazards have to be repaired or clearly identified and marked. Only the chow hall and the airman's club have to be spotless. He ordered that you were not to be used for any clean up duties. He wants you to be well rested and looking just the way you usually are. You are not even supposed to be told in advance of the inspection. He swore that he would court martial any man who disobeyed his orders.

"Everything else up here is to be left looking just the way it normally is. He said that four specially chosen air policemen would be posted on the Mojave Wells front gate at 4:00 p.m. on Monday afternoon. They will remain continuously on duty all through Tuesday, until midnight in the evening. The air policeman will be lead by some special young eight-stripe chief master sergeant named Smith. They are ordered to guarantee that the Mojave Wells base is empty and secure. He said only you will be allowed to come and go as you please. His orders were that every one of the rest of us are to begin leaving this base and heading in to Desert Center immediately after finishing our noon chow on Monday. We're to check into the visiting airman's barracks down at Desert Center. There will be hourly roll calls and bed checks starting at 10:00 p.m. on Monday evening, continuing all day Tuesday, until midnight on Tuesday evening. The air policemen will accompany us wherever we go. On Tuesday morning, after escorting us to breakfast at the Desert Center chow hall, they will escort us to the Desert Center base theater where we will spend the day watching Air Force training films."

"But, I don't get it, Greg," I protested. "What's any of this got to do with me? It sounds like it's you guys who are in hot water and getting inspected. It doesn't sound like the generals care at all about me."

"That's not how the rest of us see it, Charlie," responded Greg. "If only you had been there, standing at attention with us. When the general finished speaking, he asked if any of us had any questions. Steve, Doug, and Wayne were in the front row in the middle, next to Smokey. They all took one step forward at the same time, and Steve requested permission to speak. The general agreed. Steve got real emotional. He told the general how he, Wayne, and Doug had been out on the ranges so long, there wasn't anything out here they hadn't seen many times over. He said that at least he and Wayne and Doug had never had to face them alone. He told the general that it wasn't right that they should expect you to go out there alone just to stand for some white wolf inspection. He begged the general to let him or Wayne or Doug go with you to guard your back, or at least to let one of them wait for you at the range three gate. He said every man in the room owed you his life. He said this whole place was safer because of you, and now it was our duty to protect you the way you'd been protecting us.

"We all thought that Steve was going to get put in the brig, but the Desert Center commander just listened politely. He told Steve that the orders had come from the Pentagon and weren't his to change. Then he ordered Steve, Wayne, and Doug to remain silent and not to ask any more questions.

"Then Smokey took one step forward and requested permission to speak. That Smokey, you know Charlie is one intelligent person. He knew just how to take the general. He began by laughing a little bit. He pointed out to the general that he is the senior cook in the Mojave Wells chow hall, and that you and he are brothers. Then Smokey asked the general what they expected you to eat for chow during the white wolf inspection.

"The general replied that you would be issued a double set of K-rations to cover you while everyone else was at Desert Center.

"Then Smokey laughed. Charlie, I wish you could have seen old Smokey at work. He knows that general. Smokey pointed out that you are a big eater. He said that you considered those tiny K-rations to be little more than appetizers. He told the general that what you needed was real food, fried eggs, meat and potatoes, if you were to be expected to show off that lion-like roar of yours. Smokey asked the general to leave him alone in the Wells chow hall to make sure that you get fed proper with good coffee and good meals. That way Smokey said, the general could be sure the inspection would go the way they planned. That way, if anything went wrong, your brother Smokey would be right there with the hot coffee, fried eggs, and hamburgers just the way you like them. He'd get you right back to your lion-hearted self, so you could be right back out there for another one of them white wolf stand-ups, just like they wanted. You could see he had the general thinking.

"Then he worked his ideas deeper into the general's brain. He told the general that if they let him stay up here with you, the Pentagon generals and their white wolf friends could inspect you when you were eating your meals with Smokey. He said that he would be sitting at the table right there beside you, with his back to everyone, generals, white wolves and all. I tell you Charlie, soon Smokey had that Desert Center base commander laughing and agreeing to everything. Afterwards, Steve, Wayne, and Doug were

427

outside hugging Smokey and rubbing his hair saying, "Thank God you were there. Charlie is going to need all of the help that he can get."

Greg paused for a minute, catching his breath. Then, he stated quickly, "I'd better get out of here, Charlie. Just remember, we were all in agreement that you needed to be warned." Then he took off double timing towards town, before I could ask any more questions.

The days passed quickly enough. Inspection morning was another clear, hot, beautiful day out in the desert. The morning run went smoothly enough. Smokey and I had the time of our lives over breakfast. The entire base was deserted except for us. We laughed until our sides hurt. How could Air Force generals hold an inspection in a sillier manner? Yes, inspection morning was sure fun. I bid Smokey good-bye, and headed on out for the 8:00 a.m. balloon run. As I was leaving the base area, I noticed that the special guards had already taken up their positions on the front gate. Two other inspection teams were already beginning to go through the barracks and the buildings on the base of Mojave Wells. Another guard was heading on up to the chow hall, obviously to get Smokey out of the way of the inspection teams. I was laughing to myself at the time. I didn't pay much attention to the inspection teams, but as I was heading past the motor pool, looking back at my barracks, I noticed that two people with an unusual appearance, and with unusually white skin were inspecting it.

The morning balloon runs were also uneventful. The ranges certainly seemed deserted. I came in for the noon meal singing my sunshine songs, and parked as always in front of the chow hall. When I entered, Smokey already had one of the tables in the front of the dining area prepared for the two of us. It was set with food and everything. The back half of the dining area had been closed off with a curtain. One air force guard, a sergeant Smith, minded the curtain. After Smokey and I had taken our assigned places, with our backs to the curtain, the curtain was opened part way. Smokey and I laughed like brothers, ate our food, discussed fast cars and wild women, totally ignored whoever was seated beyond the curtain, and generally had a wonderful meal. When we had finished eating, the curtain was closed. I said good-bye to Smokey, left the chow hall laughing, and headed back out to the ranges.

The last wind measurement for the day was a simple matter. I turned my radio up loud, filled my balloon with helium, and wondered how an enlisted man's life could get any better. The desert, by one o'clock in the afternoon, was 114 degrees Fahrenheit and getting hotter. The humidity was less than 1%. Even a short walk in the hot sunshine would push a man to the limits of his endurance. My theodolite had become hot enough to burn my hands if I wasn't careful. There were the usual gentle breezes, light and variable from each of the distant mountains in turn. The balloon run was little more than child's play. I kept a sharp eye out for anything unusual, but the ranges appeared to be so deserted that soon I felt foolish for even checking.

I daydreamed my way through the last three theodolite readings, and carefully locked up my burning hot theodolite. Then, singing, I casually strolled across the hot, dry, graveled, desert pavement to my weather shack beyond. I adjusted the volume on my radio, completed my calculations, and phoned Desert Center. Dwight answered. I expected to laugh a while with my friend. On a day like today, how could there be any hurry, but Dwight was anxious, and highly agitated. He insisted that the Desert Center base commander was waiting on the command-post phone line, not for the readings, just for news on how the run was going. Dwight claimed the Desert Center base commander was highly concerned that the range three lounge might not be ship-shape. He insisted that I check on it as soon as possible.

Dwight refused to accept my wind measurements. He said the base commander didn't want him wasting my time by even writing them down. Flabbergasted, I reassured Dwight that I would double check the lounge immediately and phone him back before heading in for the day. Then, Dwight really confused me. He said that the base commander, a two star general, had virtually begged him, an enlisted man like me, to ask me to phone Desert Center again as soon as I got back from the lounge. Dwight said he needed to reassure the general that I was all right. The whole thing seemed so backwards to me that I could hardly restrain my laughter. "Doesn't the general have a spare colonel to come up here and slap me into line?" I mused. Dwight was deadly serious and didn't seem to be putting me on. Laughing and happy, I exclaimed, "Don't worry, Dwight. I'm a taxpayer. Tell the general that I own this place and everything out here is mine to play with for the rest of the day. Tell him I'll walk right over there to the lounge and set everything I own, straight." Then, I hung up the phone, still laughing and still confused.

One of my songs came on the radio. I spent a few more minutes dancing around in the hot sunshine, singing along with the song and sometimes tossing my cap high in the air and catching it. Then, happy and laughing, I stepped back into my weather shack. I put on my canteen belt with its two full canteens. I took a big drink of water from my third canteen. The day sure was hot. I hung my third canteen on a hook on the wall and turned off my radio. I closed, but didn't lock my weather shack and strolled happily off across the open graveled square towards the range three lounge. I was wondering how I could ever be happier.

A few minutes later and in the fullness of time, I arrived at the northeast corner of the lounge. My runs for the day were over. On a nice day like today, how could there be any hurry. "Forgot the general," I laughed. "He's got his problems. I've got mine."

I rounded the northeast corner of the lounge singing loudly. For a brief moment I heard a gentle fluttering or scurrying off in the dry desert on the other side of the lounge. It meant nothing to me. I continued singing and walking. The front door to the lounge stood wide open. I stopped and wondered for a few minutes. I had checked it earlier, just after breakfast. I distinctly remembered closing it. The ranges were deserted, weren't they? Unable to resolve the question, I shrugged it off, and casually walked on inside.

Inside, the lounge had two large rooms with a large, tall doorway in between. The ceilings in the lounge were high, but not unusually high for the hot desert. Except for the open door, virtually the entire north wall of the lounge consisted of a nearly continuous row of large picture windows with a second row of ventilation windows below them, at chest height. The ventilation windows opened inward. There weren't any windows or doors on the other three sides. Thus, once inside, nothing could be seen to the east, to the south, or to the west.

431

The floor of the lounge was smoothly poured concrete. Out in front of the lounge, running east and west along the north side, was a concrete sidewalk. It adjoined the building and the desert beyond. In addition, the roof of the lounge hung out over the sidewalk on the north side, creating a reasonably cool shaded area. Currently, all of the windows that could be open had been opened. Consequently, the lounge was swept with occasional cool breezes. On a hot day like today, it was a pleasant oasis sitting on the edge of a brutal cauldron.

A heavy wooden desk with a telephone, and a simple padded metal chair with padded metal arms, sat against the far south wall of the first room. Around the desk sat several other similar chairs. I noticed that the chairs had been neatly arranged against the walls. The entire lounge had been swept and dusted since I had checked it after breakfast - and all of the windows had been opened. I thought about that for a few minutes and wondered. Maybe it was just my memory, I decided, and shrugged it all off.

Still singing, I proceeded into the second room to close the open windows. The second room contained a steel-legged couch neatly aligned along its inner east wall. Next to the couch, facing the windows and the door was a large old wooden legged padded chair with padded exposed arms. The chair was positioned at a 45 degree angle to the sofa, in line with the sofa's far end. It spread out about 5 feet from the end of the sofa. The chair sat empty, facing me. As soon as I saw it, its position made an immediate impact on me. I was certain that I had positioned the chair against the far wall when I checked the lounge after breakfast. Looking at the chair, I became immediately convinced that someone had recently been sitting in the chair waiting for me.

I remembered that a few weeks earlier, my friend Doug claimed that when he, Steve, and Wayne had come out here one morning, they had found the furniture arranged as it is now, with an ordinary nylon hammock, typical government issue to cargo plane load masters, tied neatly between the arm of the chair and the arm of the sofa which now stood directly in front of me. The furniture was in the same position now that it had been then. Doug said the hammock was only 5 feet long and therefore, only big enough to have held a young child. Steve had insisted that the hammock be folded neatly and left on the chair. Then they had all headed back into base. Doug said that the next day when they came out, the hammock was gone. At the time, Doug wanted to make certain that I hadn't accidentally taken it. I stood there stunned. The only logical explanation was that someone must have sat in the chair, and used the sofa to secure a hammock style baby bed. I walked over to the chair and tested it and the sofa. Both the sofa and the chair slid easily on the smooth concrete floor. Such a cradle couldn't have supported much more than 30 pounds before the furniture slid and the supports collapsed. Everything seemed so impossible, so incomprehensible and backwards.

I wrestled with these contradictions for a few minutes. I put the chair and the sofa back the way they had been, complete with the 45 degree angle. I went back to singing one of my songs, and began the process of closing down the open windows. I was just closing the second one when the lounge phone began ringing. It startled me, but I supposed that it must just be my friend Dwight from Desert Center, calling to check up on me. I crossed over through the inner door, back across the first room, and answered the phone laughing, "Lounge three, airman Charlie Baker." I instinctively faced the phone, the south wall, and turned my back to the open door, to the outside, and to the windows behind me.

There was nothing on the phone, but a dial tone. I supposed that maybe Dwight hadn't waited long enough for me to get to the phone, so I began dialing the Desert Center Weather Station, but after only 3 or 4 of the numbers had been dialed, the line went dead. "Military equipment!" I laughed to myself, and put down the receiver. I had decided to let nothing ruin my perfect afternoon.

I decided to wait by the phone for a few minutes in case Dwight called back. I took off my cumbersome canteen belt, laid it down on the desk and sat down in the chair. I was in the process of opening one of my canteens when my eyes were drawn to something white moving outside in the bright sunshine. Casually, I finished my drink of water and put down my canteen. Another soft breeze rustled through the lounge as I sat there. While I watched through the windows, outside, the chalk white eighth grade girl smoothly took up a position in the thin sagebrush. She had silently come up over a sagebrush covered ridge a thousand feet or so to the northwest. Deliberately choosing an open area in the thin sagebrush, she came to a standing position some 50 feet northwest of the doorway to the range three lounge. While I watched, she remained standing there, completely at ease in the hot, bright sunshine. She stood looking at me through the windows. I sat on the chair inside the lounge, watching her in return. She obviously wanted me to see that she was out there. The chalk white aluminized canvas jumpsuit that she wore, matched the chalk white color of her skin. It did not glint in the bright sunshine. With her large bright blue intelligent looking eyes and her short blonde-white hair, she appeared to be the very personification of a hot, bright, summertime desert afternoon. She appeared to be a creature created entirely out of sunshine.

I remained sitting casually in the chair by the desk. Despite the fact that the chalk white girl appeared to be perfectly real, I still considered her and all of the chalk white creatures to be nothing more than hallucinations. Considering that I had closed a couple of the open windows, I supposed that perhaps my brain was suffering from the effects of the heat. Under the circumstances, it seemed only natural for me, after reciting a few prayers, to stand up slowly and stroll casually over to the open front door. There was a nice breeze through the doorway. Using my left forearm, I leaned naturally against the left door jam and studied the chalk white eighth grade girl for a few minutes. I was hoping that with the fresh air, my brain would soon return to functioning normally, at which time I expected she would go away. As I stood there, I spoke to the young girl as I had trained myself to do. I said pleasantly, as though talking to myself, "Well, you sure are having fun out there in the sunshine today."

The chalk white young girl didn't answer me. Instead, moving smoothly, she closed the distance between us to about 25 feet, obviously intending to attract my attention. Despite her silence, she appeared to be reacting to my words. I studied her for a few minutes. She seemed happy enough, but she appeared to be noticeably more nervous than normal. Remembering the words that Steve had spoken, I noticed that the molded aluminized nylon boots that she was wearing, left visible boot prints in the soft dirt where she was standing. This made me curious. I partly closed the door behind me and casually stepped out onto the concrete sidewalk. I said to her, as though talking to myself, "Don't be afraid. I'm not going to touch you. I just want to see you close up. I want to get a better look at the boot prints which you are making in the soft dirt over there."

I had taken only 3 or 4 steps in her direction when she appeared to panic. She began by running backwards for several steps. Then she turned and went crashing through some small thin sagebrush. Then she took off running at full speed until she had disappeared back over the sagebrush-covered ridge, which lay about 1000 feet northwest of me. I stopped and stood still for a few minutes. I shouted loudly, calling after her, "Don't be afraid. I didn't mean to frighten you. I wasn't going to touch you. You can come back. I won't hurt you." There was no response. I stopped and thought for a few minutes, timing her as she ran. She had been traveling more than 35 miles an hour when she arrived at the ridge. To run that fast, her nervous system would have to be operating some 2 and a half times faster than the nervous system of any human. This convinced me that she had just been a figment of my imagination. "Oh, Well," I shrugged, "I'll just have to be more careful in this hot sun."

I walked casually over to where the young girl had been standing and inspected the boot prints that she had left in the soft dirt. Their reality frightened me. Using my left boot, I carefully spread the soft dirt around and erased her boot prints. It made me feel much better.

It was a hot day, and I wasn't in any hurry. Military duty is such a constant thing. I casually retraced my steps back to the lounge doorway, wiped the sweat off my brow, and strolled back into the cooler, shaded lounge. I needed to get my canteens, phone Desert Center, and rest a few minutes before heading back into base. I reopened the closed windows, left the front door wide open, and returned back to the chair by the phone. The phone was still dead.

As I sat there, I noticed the chalk white eighth grade girl carefully circling out to the west, way out along the sagebrush-covered ridge. After a few minutes of circling and searching, way out to the northwest of the lounge, she appeared to locate an open path through the sagebrush that led back to the open spot that she had vacated earlier. This time, she was much more nervous than before. With a series of slow cautious moves, frequently retracing her steps, she deliberately returned to the open spot where she had previously been standing. I was shocked by the precision with which she unerringly returned to the very same piece of earth. Had I not wiped out her previous boot prints, she would have once again been standing in them. I wondered, "How can my hallucinations care about such precision, and know the desert better than I do?" The young eighth grade girl waited where she was, watching me through the window. She obviously intended once again that I should see her.

I sat waiting for a few more minutes. I was still supposing that my brain was playing tricks as a reaction to the day's heat. I decided that I had no choice but to go back outside and face the figments of my imagination. I took another drink of water, stood up, and attached the full canteen to the belt on my military fatigues. Then, after saying some more quick prayers, I went out slowly and deliberately to face whatever lay outside in the sunshine … real or imagined.

Reaching the front door, I waited for a few minutes, enjoying the gentle breeze. Then I spoke slowly to the young girl. Once again, she cautiously closed the distance between us to about 25 feet. "I'm glad you came back." I stated, as though talking to a young girl. "I didn't mean to frighten you. I know I don't like it when other people frighten me, so I try not to frighten other people in return."

She smiled at me nervously but didn't say anything. Then I heard a gentle bumping sound coming from beyond the hidden west side of the lounge. Before I could react to it, I heard a similar bumping sound behind the hidden east side of the lounge. "Who's there?" I instinctively called out. I was greeted only with silence. "That's a lot of noise for a deserted stretch of desert," I openly muttered. The chalk white girl remained on station and seemed to smile and shake her head in agreement with me. I decided that I should move to a more defendable position. I reassured the chalk white girl not to be afraid. Then, while singing one of my songs, I gingerly stepped outside. I positioned myself so that I stood next to, and just west of the front door. I placed my back hard against the narrow section of the wall between the door jam and the first window. I stood there for a few minutes, waiting to be attacked. Ignoring the girl for a minute or so, I began visually checking the immediate vicinity for danger and for an escape route. Not finding anything of note, I continued visually checking the ridgeline straight north from the lounge. The girl obviously wanted me to pay more attention to her. With a swift fluid motion, she suddenly skipped to her left and began making a series of soft meadowlark like sounds as she did so. She continued doing this until she was about 20 feet in front of me, directly in my field of vision. Then, dancing some more and making a few waving hand motions, along with the meadowlark sounds, she skipped backwards and sideways, back to her previous position, watching my eyes as she did so. This took me by surprise. "So, you want me to look in your direction?" I inquired. She smiled in return and continued skipping and performing a little dance, obviously intending to keep my attention.

A gentle wind came through the shaded area, moving a few dry bits of the amber dust and sand as it journeyed on its way. Then, I heard a more substantive sound out in the sagebrush behind me and to my right. I turned my head slowly, trying to comprehend the sights before me. Diagonally off to my right and just a little east of north from the lounge, stood the other young chalk white woman. She had just finished taking up a position some 30 feet from me, in an open spot out in the thinly spread sagebrush. She was smiling at me, and watching me intently. She seemed more nervous than usual. Down by her waist, she was holding a square chalk white pencil like object in her hands. Off to her left, and diagonally off to my northeast stood Range Four Harry. Like the young woman, he was standing fully upright, holding a chalk white pencil like object in his hands. They both smiled pleasantly at me. Straight east of me, I could see an American USAF sergeant wearing six stripes, double timing from the end of the bunker road, diagonally across the graveled square, in the direction of my weather shack. Behind him, another USAF sergeant wearing eight stripes, double-timed in the direction of my theodolite stand. As I watched, too surprised to react, they both disappeared out of sight, hidden by the edge of the lounge building. I could hear the last sergeant barking muffled orders to his men, "Brown, take his truck. Jones, shut down that generator and guard that generator door. Johnson, take that supply shed. Anderson, take that side door to his weather shack. I'll cover the theodolite stand and his front door. Brown, when he comes, we'll drive him your way. Remember men, when the said airman comes out of there; he's going to be hysterical. Don't waste any time! Immediately knock him cold anyway you can, and let the medical colonel worry about putting him back together."

I turned to the young woman and remarked calmly, "That's quite a reception party they have planned. I wonder who they're expecting." The young chalk white woman nervously returned my smile. It seemed like she was going to say something to me, but then decided against it. Something white off to my left caught my eye. I turned my head over that way. Another young chalk white male had stepped out from behind the west side of the lounge and stood smiling, confronting me some 35 feet off to my left. He too, was well armed. Turning back to my right, I could see another older, well armed, chalk white male standing down at the edge of the bunker road. Behind him stood an American three star USAF general and a bird colonel. A few hundred feet behind them, and further down the bunker road, stood another group of five or so, chalk white creatures clustered around a tall and dignified chalk white male. He was taller than most humans, perhaps six feet three inches or taller, but not unusually tall for one of the creatures. Together they made a stunning sight as they all stood there watching me in the hot afternoon sun.

I could hear more muffled commands coming from the sergeants. They were out of sight behind the lounge and behind me to my right. I could hear Anderson shouting anxiously, in muffled sounds, "Sergeant, Smith. The side door to his weather shack can't be held. It's too narrow in there. He'll overpower me for sure. Request permission to join you at the theodolite stand and take him out in the open, head on."

Smith responded immediately, "Request denied. Come forward to the corner of the shack and hold that position at any price. I will assist you when he comes."

Anderson continued, his shouts heavy with emotion, "Sergeant Smith, with respect, we can't hold that gap between the shack and the cable fence. The said airman can escape through that hole there, into that heavy sagebrush. Then he'll run down towards range two to the southeast, there! Once he's out in that heavy sagebrush, he'll shake off our white friends. Then he'll take cover and go to ground. He'll elude us until nightfall. In the darkness he'll escape completely. At night out there, we'll never find him."

Sergeant Smith could be heard shouting back angrily, "Hold that corner as ordered, sergeant! Hold it at any price! Let our white friends worry about covering the gaps!"

I stood there for a few minutes, quietly studying my situation. Then I turned to the young chalk white woman. She had slowly closed the distance between us to a mere 18 feet. Speaking calmly and pleasantly, I said to her, "Well, I see you've brought friends, and some of them seem pretty interested in holding on to the real estate." She seemed to find my statement amusing. After silently laughing, she smiled in return. In the background I could hear the muffled sounds of the sergeants reporting in. Sergeant Smith barked out in muffled sounds, "Brown."

Then Sergeant Brown, answered, "Standing ready to be attacked, sergeant!"

Then Jones, "Standing ready to be attacked, sergeant!"

Then Johnson, and Anderson in turn, "Standing ready to be attacked, sergeant!"

Once again I turned back to the young woman and said, "Well, it looks like I'm quite a bit safer over here by you than I would be if I were back there by my weather shack. Back there I'm afraid I would be in the way, and maybe a little under foot." Once again, the chalk white woman laughed silently for a short while. She gave me another happy smile and looked as if she were going to say something to me, but after a few more minutes, she appeared to decide against it. As I stood there, studying her carefully, she appeared to calm down a great deal."

I continued, still believing that I was speaking to one of my hallucinations, "This is some brain malfunction party I'm having here, but none of you figments of my imagination worry me. What does worry me, though, is that American colonel over there. It looks to me like he's perfectly real. If he is, he sure will put me to work in this hot sun, just to impress that three star general next to him. When that general sees how dirty this place is, that high ranking officer will court martial me for sure. I keep my weather shack clean and military, but I had no idea they were going to send some three star general out here just to check up on me. Somebody must be out to get me really good! I think I'd better get out of here before those officers start playing games with me for real. Now don't be afraid or surprised. I plan to take off running straight past you, right up the valley to the north, there. I'm going to have to brush past you to do it, but don't get angry. I figure you must be well armed to have come in this close, so don't go getting trigger-happy on me. I'm not even going to touch you. I'm just trying to save myself from that three star general over there. There's a good shady hiding spot just over that ridge north of here. If I take off running suddenly, that general and those sergeants will never catch me. You can follow me if you want to. We can both find some shade under that big sagebrush up there, and those officers will never find us. It'll be a simple matter to hide out there until sundown and let my brain cool off. I'll clean my weather shack this evening so it'll pass inspection. If those officers come back tomorrow, I'll pretend that I was sick from the heat today, and lost track of which day they were coming. Then I'll fake some stomach pains and get a week off relaxing down in the Desert Center hospital. You know, if I do this right, I might even have them thinking I'm some kind of hero who got a heat stroke doing his duty out here in the bright sunshine."

The young chalk white woman seemed to find it all very amusing. After laughing some more silently, she smiled at me pleasantly, but refused to step aside. She intentionally moved to her right, to a position that blocked my planned escape route. From over the ridge north of me, two more young chalk white males appeared. Off to my left, another chalk white creature appeared over the ridgeline in the distance. Still another chalk white young girl stepped out from behind the hidden west side of the lounge, plugging another gap in the circle. Then another young chalk white woman stepped out from the hidden east side of the lounge. All of them stood smiling pleasantly at me. I turned back towards the young chalk white woman standing now some 15 feet in front of me, and remarked nervously, "Well, it doesn't look like I'm going to be going much of anywhere does it?"

She smiled in return, as if to agree.

"Well, you know I'm a fun lover," I responded, making light of my difficult situation. "There isn't that much to be said for hiding out in the hot sage on a day like today anyway. Yes, now that I think about it, I've decided to stay right where I am, and let my brain cool off right here in the shade. Standing here in this nice breeze will let my brain cool right down. In a little while all of these hallucinations around me will just float away. If that colonel comes over here and gives me a hard time, well you know I enjoy being the center of attention, even if it is at my own court martial."

The chalk white woman and the rest of the chalk white creatures seemed to find it all very amusing. In the distance off to the east, the general could be heard exclaiming to the colonel, "The guts of that tough young soldier! He's all-alone, cornered, and defenseless. He's got no help coming and he's still going to make a stand there with his back to the wall. That young airman is going to make us come get him! And if we do, that desert-hardened soldier will fight us every inch, tooth and nail! Where did they find a man like that?"

Another gentle wind whispered through the shaded area. It played and swirled through the fine, light sand. It formed the soft amber shifting sand into beautiful whispering drifts and piles and miniature dunes around my feet. As it did so, the young chalk white woman in front of me slowly closed the distance between us to some 10 feet or so. Off to my left, the chalk white eighth grade girl continued her slow, happy dance as she too, slowly closed the distance between us to less than 15 feet. Then as if on command, the pre-teen girl made a quick, sudden move towards the building to my left, giving off a soft meadowlark like sound as she did so. She obviously intended to attract my attention, and I instinctively turned my head in her direction. This exposed my bare right temple to the young woman in front of me. Moving too fast for me to react, she raised the square white object that she held in her hands, pointed it straight at my exposed right temple, and activated the instrument. My mind suddenly seemed to wander and go out of focus. I found myself unable to move my arms or legs. I could move my head only with great difficulty. I tried desperately to shake it off, but I couldn't. Smiling and pleasant, Range Four Harry approached me from my right side. After he had approached to within arm's length, the chalk white woman strode up along side him. He seemed to be measuring something with the instruments in his hands. Then he appeared to communicate something to the young white woman by making a series of soft meadowlark like sounds, intermingled with a few dog-like barks. The young woman, smiled and responded pleasantly, "You must speak English when we are in this close. He speaks only English, and I do not want him frightened."

Range Four Harry responded respectfully, "Yes, teacher. The controls are holding, but he is more intelligent than we expected. You are correct in your desire not to frighten him. We must be very careful. If he becomes agitated, he will use his high intelligence to defeat our controls and break out." He continued, "It is fine with me if the American general and our ambassador come forward now."

A short pause followed. Then the general, the colonel, and the white creatures standing next to them began slowly advancing across the graveled area towards the lounge. Behind them, the second group of white creatures with the tall dignified one in the center also began coming forward. The general and his party were about half way across the graveled area when they stopped. The general called to the sergeants, "Smith. They've got him up here behind the lounge. Bring your men forward and help Harry and the teacher anyway you can."

Sergeant Smith could be heard barking commands to his men, "Johnson, you and Jones cover the west side of the lounge. Stand ready just behind that northwest corner. Anderson, you and I will cover the east side of the lounge. Brown, stand ready by his truck! I don't trust that tricky desert hardened soldier! He should have broken in panic! He should be running by now! He's up to something and I'm not taking any chances!" Then I could hear the sergeants double-timing into position. After a minute or so, sergeants Smith and Anderson could be heard arriving at a position on the eastern side of the lounge. After catching their breath, the two Sergeants slowly stepped into view from around the northeast corner of the building. Smith, speaking slowly and respectfully to the young woman, stated, "Teacher, we are here to assist you and Harry in any manner you wish. Would you like us to take control of the said airman?"

"No," the young woman responded, speaking English. "Step back out of sight behind the lounge. He must not be frightened."

"But we are his kind," sergeant Smith calmly objected. "He should know that we are here beside him, and he's very bull-headed. He may need a good beating so that he obeys his orders, and I'll be happy to give him one."

The young woman responded proudly, obviously showing a high level of feminine pride, "He is not the slightest bit afraid of me, my daughter, or any of my cousins. He has trained himself to relax and stay calm whenever we are around. He is more afraid of you and your officers than he is of us. I am quite certain that he will not need a beating when we are around."

When she had finished, a short pause followed while sergeant Smith considered what to say next. This obviously angered Range Four Harry. Still facing me, and without turning around, he stated in even tones, "You sergeants were told 'No'. Now step back behind the corner of the building as the teacher has ordered."

Upon hearing this, sergeant Smith flinched in obvious fear. He grabbed the arm of the sergeant next to him. Then he immediately stepped back behind the corner of the lounge, dragging the other sergeant with him as he did so. Then he could be heard ordering the other sergeant to transmit similar orders to the two sergeants hidden behind the opposite corner of the lounge. He could be heard saying, "Tell them to remember the teacher has ordered them to stay out of sight behind the lounge. Remember if they disobey the teacher's orders, she will kill them as she killed the others, and there is nothing I can do about it!"

Turning towards me, the teacher stated pleasantly, "Charlie, please step forward three steps, away from the building." Not able to refuse, I stepped forward three steps in much the same manner that a hypnotized man might have. By now, the three star general and his party had reached the corner of the lounge building. Behind him, the tall dignified chalk white male and his party were more than half way across the graveled square. Some members of the chalk white party had broken off, and appeared to be in the process of inspecting my weather shack, my theodolite, and the surrounding buildings.

Turning towards the general and his party, the teacher stated, "I would like the parents and their children to meet Charlie, now."

"Yes, teacher," the general replied respectfully. "Go right ahead with anything you wish." The general's party and the party with the tall dignified male behind him stopped and waited patiently where they were. Another young tall white woman with a thin small son beside her stepped out from behind the hidden western side of the lounge. A second young chalk white woman with a small son and a little girl beside her stepped out from behind the hidden eastern side of the lounge. Her son had a noticeably heavier build than the other children. His build was more like that of an ordinary human child. The teacher addressed the other two women, both of whom appeared to be about her age. "This is Charlie Baker," the teacher stated proudly. "He is just perfect for my pet project. See how gentle he is, and see how easily we can control him."

A short pause followed. Then the young chalk white woman standing to the east, while giggling some, said, "He sure is ugly teacher, but my son just loves to follow him around. When my son was sick last month, he kept asking if he could come out and play with him." A light laughter went through the crowd. Even the general could be heard laughing. Then the young woman continued, "Yes, teacher. Please include my son in your pet project."

The young woman on the west remained standing silently, studying me intently. Then showing remarkable calm, she asked pleasantly, "Did I understand you correctly, teacher? You say he is very intelligent? More intelligent than most other earth men?"

"Yes," replied the teacher. "Charlie uses his intelligence to think things through very carefully before he takes action, as you saw him doing today. I believe that your son will learn a great deal by studying him carefully and seeing how he does things. Charlie is not like the other weather observers. He is very gentle around the children. He does many funny and laughable things that the children and I enjoy. He also keeps his head in an emergency better than any other earth man that we have seen."

The other young woman thought for a minute. Then she turned to her tall thin son, who looked vaguely like a young, thin version of Einstein. She asked, "Are you sure you want to do this? We are a free people. You can say 'No' if you wish. You do not have to do this, you know."

The little boy thought for a minute or so. Then he responded hesitantly, "Yes, mother. It will be fun, and I do not want to be separated from my friends."

"Alright," replied his mother, "You may join the teacher's pet project. Remember! Do not get too close to him, and remember, if anything ever goes wrong, if Charlie ever touches you, I will ask your uncle Harry to kill him."

"Oh, do not worry about anything," laughed the teacher. "Your son will have the time of his life playing around him. Charlie enjoys playing around children, and you saw how easily we have controlled him this afternoon." Then the teacher turned to me and stated, "Charlie, please turn towards the lounge doorway." Not able to refuse, I complied. Then the teacher continued, "Charlie, please walk into the lounge and stand by the desk, facing the telephone." Once again, I complied.

When I reached the southeastern corner of the desk, I stopped, and stood waiting by the desk that held the telephone. Range Four Harry followed in behind me. Using his instruments, he appeared to switch the electronic controls from my right temple to my left temple. After doing this, Harry took up a guard like position near the open front door, remaining always on my left side. Then, upon a command from the teacher, ten or fifteen of the chalk white creatures calmly entered the lounge. Most of them entered the second room in the lounge, but two of them joined Harry in the first room, taking up similar guard-like positions, one on my right and one on my left. The young pre-teen girl remained outside, watching me through the windows. Then the general and the colonel entered the room. They took up standing positions along the wall behind me. After a few minutes, the tall dignified chalk white male entered and took up a standing position alongside the general. The teacher asked the sergeants to take up positions out in the desert so that they also could observe the ceremony through the windows. At last, the teacher entered the room.

She began by inspecting the arrangement of the crowd in an authoritative manner. She felt that the tall white male would be more comfortable if the crowd were rearranged somewhat. She began by having me turn until I faced the eastern wall. Then she had me step sideways and backwards several steps until I was more centrally located. After the crowd had settled down, she began, obviously very proud of her accomplishments so far. Speaking in both a proud and pleasant manner, she began by addressing the crowd, "This is Charlie Baker. He is extremely intelligent. He is the one who saved my little girl's life when she was lost down on range one.

"You must be very cautious and very gentle when you are around him. He is very perceptive of the world so he frightens very easily. In many ways, he frightens far more easily than the other weather observers before him. He likes to sit quietly and enjoy the sights and sounds in the world around him, much as we do, and that has made him the enjoyable person that he is.

"He believes in God. When we come in close, he believes that his God protects him from us. That is why he has not panicked today, even though he is terrified of us. He is so perceptive that he is almost never completely surprised when we come in close.

He is so frightened of us that he refuses to believe that we are real. Even so, he has accomplished something that the general and I have never seen before. All by himself, he has trained himself to calm down and relax whenever I, my cousin, or my daughter, come around. As you all saw today, even though he is terrified of us, he never becomes hysterical, or breaks into panic or runs when we come around. As you all saw today, he has trained himself so well, that we can come in as close as his arms will reach, and he just stands there watching us, singing his favorite songs, thinking things through, and reciting his prayers."

The teacher paused for a few minutes, obviously waiting for her words to sink in. Then the tall, dignified chalk white male, now standing more or less behind me and to my left, spoke to the general on his right. As he spoke, I noticed that he, too, like the teacher and Harry, spoke perfect English, without even a trace of an accent. He said, obviously showing a father's pride, "My daughter has accomplished something truly remarkable. You know general, before now, I would have never thought it possible. If my daughter had tried to approach any of the others, the way she walked right up to Charlie today, they would have panicked and we would have had to kill them all."

"Yes, Mr. Ambassador," replied the general respectfully. "I agree completely with you. Charlie is different from the others. The day he saved your little granddaughter down on range one, he proved himself to be one young tough-nosed quick thinking desert hardened soldier. That brutal young man can handle anything you or your people feel like putting him through. I believe he is just perfect for your daughter's project."

The ambassador nodded politely in agreement. Then he stated, "Now it is time for us to thank him."

The general replied, "I am in total agreement with anything you wish to do, Mr. Ambassador. As I'm certain you already know, we were all happy when he saved your little granddaughter's life, and we have already thanked him plenty. I gave him several days of free medical leave and let him have fun at government expense down in Los Angeles. I'm certain you are also well aware that it was an easy thing for that tough young muscular soldier to trample down some sagebrush and scare off a few rattlesnakes. He is well able to handle anything that lives out on range one. I'm also certain you know well, he was only doing his military duty."

"Yes," replied the ambassador. "But I have only one daughter and only one granddaughter. The others would have panicked, disobeyed your orders, and ran away, leaving my only granddaughter to die in terror out there in the sagebrush. This one overcame his fears. This one came back. This one saved her. I must thank him personally. It is our way."

The teacher ordered me to turn around and face the ambassador. Apparently afraid that I would panic, she also ordered me to stand looking down at the concrete floor in front of him. Slightly hypnotized as I was, I complied immediately. Then the ambassador, speaking in calm even tones, said, "Charlie Baker. Thank you for saving my granddaughter's life. I have only one child and only one grandchild. Your heroic actions have pleased me more than I am able to describe. I have ordered my people to learn your name and to learn to recognize you by sight. You will never have anything to fear from my kind."

I was unable to respond.

The teacher ordered me to turn and face the open front door. Then she too, thanked me, saying, "Thank you, Charlie Baker, for saving my little girl. She is named Playful Butterfly. She means everything to me. I don't know how I could have lived without her."

Then the teacher's little girl came in through the open door. She approached to within 6 feet of me and stated, using perfect English, "Thank you, Charlie Baker, for saving my life and returning me to my parents. I should have thanked you before but I was afraid of you. It was silly of me to be afraid of you. I love to play around you now, and I am not afraid of you any more."

Hypnotized as I was, I was unable to respond.

Then the ambassador turned towards the teacher and stated in fatherly tones, "Yes, daughter. You may proceed with your pet project. I agree that Charlie is a perfect choice."

The teacher smiled in return and answered, "Thank You, Father."

453

Then the ambassador and his party walked out through the open lounge door, turned to the right, and disappeared from view, hidden by the featureless eastern wall of the lounge. Then several of the chalk white creatures from the second room left the building, studying my face closely as they did so. However, several young chalk white women who were in the second room informed the teacher that they were afraid to leave the building because I was very ugly. They were afraid to pass by so closely in front of me. The teacher responded by laughing. Then the teacher ordered me to walk over to the desk, and stand facing the southeastern corner of the room. Then the women thanked the teacher profusely, and hurriedly left the building.

The general and the colonel visually checked the second room to insure that it was empty. Then they left the building and disappeared from view, heading towards the east. They took the sergeants with them as they left. Sergeant Smith could be heard barking orders to the other sergeants, "Brown! Anderson! Johnson! Jones! Abandon your posts and form up with me here on the bunker road!! TODAY, gentleman!!"

Then the two white guards left the room in a military fashion, and fell back towards the east as well, leaving only the teacher and Harry in the room with me. The teacher in a friendly manner while facing me, said, "Thank you, Charlie Baker. You have helped both of our governments more than you will ever know."

Then she too, left the building and disappeared from view, heading back towards the east, leaving only Harry alone in the room with me. In a brotherly manner, Harry said, "Charlie. Please sing one of your favorite songs for me, and please stand there in the corner until you have finished it. You know, the teacher and I always enjoy hearing you sing."

Unable to refuse, I calmly began singing one of my favorite songs. I had just begun when Harry, standing some 10 feet from me, pointed his electronic instrument directly at my exposed left temple and activated the instrument. A gentle shudder seemed to go through my body. Once again my mind wandered and seemed to go into a daze. It took me a few minutes to get control of my thoughts again. When I finally regained control of my thoughts, I was still standing by the desk, singing my song and looking at the corner. I felt numb all over and a little shaky. I seemed to have missed a few lines of my song. I could hear the footsteps of someone outside on the sidewalk, walking away. Even though I was shaky, somewhat numb, and stunned, it was immediately apparent to me that I was no longer hypnotized and that I now had total control over myself.

I stood there by the desk, singing my song. When I had finished, I remained standing there. It took me several minutes to overcome my intense anxiety, inner fears, and to regain control over my muscles again. Finally, I turned around slowly and stood with my back in the corner, facing the empty room with its open front door. Through the windows, out in the distance, perhaps a thousand feet out on the sagebrush covered ridge, I could see the chalk white eighth grade girl. She stood out there, mostly concealed, watching me from a distance. Fearful, confused, and shaky now, I watched her for several minutes. The gentle desert breezes still softly whispered through the open lounge. Still filled with fear and anxiety and a little sick to my stomach, I arranged two of the nearby chairs to form a defensive line in front of me. Still shaking in fear, I picked up my canteen and canteen belt that lay on the desk. I took the canteen from the belt and carefully attached it to my military fatigue belt. The weight of this canteen, along with the weight of the first canteen that I had previously attached to my waist, was too much for my thin fatigue belt. It slipped the friction buckle and fell to the floor, along with my fatigue pants, leaving me standing there in my under shorts. I was too nervous to laugh at the obvious spectacle.

I hurriedly pulled up my pants and re-closed my fatigue belt, leaving only one canteen on it. Then I wrapped the canteen belt around my right hand, intending to use it as a weapon. With my left hand, I took hold of the second canteen and stood waiting to be attacked. After standing there for ten minutes or so, I began to realize that except for me, the lounge really was completely empty. There really wasn't anything in the lounge that was going to attack me. Still, the realization was a long time coming. Keeping my back against the eastern lounge wall, still shaking and feeling numb, I began slowly edging towards the open front door. I began calling out loudly, towards the second room as I did so, "Is anyone there? Am I alone?" Only the gentle desert breezes answered my questions.

I was about half way to the front door when the phone on the desk began to ring. Expecting it to be Dwight, I hurried back to the desk, keeping my back to the wall and facing the open front door as I did so. Picking up the phone, I answered nervously, "Hello, lounge three."

The voice on the other end, sounded almost exactly like my friend Steve. "Charlie," the voice stated pleasantly, "The party is over. You can go back to being 'Yourself' again."

Taken in, and thinking I was speaking to my friend Steve, I began shouting into the phone, "Steve! Thank God it's you! I need your help. I'm trapped out here in the range three lounge. Get the range rats and the power wagons, and come get me NOW! Have Wayne and the guys stay down by the range three gate like you always do. Just bring one power wagon beyond the gate. Bring it around to the front of the lounge so I can jump in. I'm trapped in here. HURRY!"

Laughing pleasantly, the voice on the other end of the line said, "Just stay calm, Charlie. Steve and the range rats are still down at Desert Center. You are totally alone out here, and you are in no danger whatever. We are all pulling out. Everything out here is yours to play with, alone, for the rest of the day."

"Steve? Is that you?" I screamed into the phone, "Steve?" But the person on the other end just slowly hung up. An empty line answered my screams. I slammed down the phone and stood ready to be attacked. After I had caught my breath, steadied my nerves, and a few more minutes had gone by, I decided to try to phone my friend Dwight at Desert Center. Keeping my back in the corner, and facing the open front door, I picked up the phone, and carefully dialed the Desert Center weather station. The phone seemed to be working correctly. However, I noticed that the phone was answered before I had actually heard it ring. I was suspicious, at first, but the person on the other end sounded almost exactly like my good friend Dwight. "Charlie," he answered laughing, "Golly, it's good to hear from you, fella'. You better hurry and get back into base or you'll be missing evening chow at the mess hall. You've had one fine afternoon, guy. The Desert Center base commander has

457

ordered your friend Smokey to have a nice steak dinner waiting for you down at the Wells chow hall, Charlie."

"Dwight?" I shouted into the phone. "Something's happened. I'm trapped out here in the range three lounge. They're outside waiting for me. You got to tell Steve! Dwight, you have to tell the range rats to come get me!"

The voice on the other end responded by laughing pleasantly, "Golly, Charlie. You sure are a card. This is the best practical joke I have ever seen anyone try to play on me. You know that Desert Center base commander was in here at the weather station, just a few minutes ago. Golly, he sure was impressed with your work, Charlie. I personally saw him handing the major a great big award for you. Then he was telling the major how impressed the Pentagon was with the way you have been keeping the ranges clean and ship shape and everything. I am certain the general has ordered your friend Smokey to prepare a really nice big steak dinner for you. I'll just bet he has it waiting for you right now down in the chow hall. The general said they were all so happy with what you did, that you do not even have to lock up or shut down or anything. So, hurry up, get over to your truck, and go head on in to the chow hall, Charlie. Steve and your friends will come out and close everything down tomorrow."

"Dwight?" I shouted, now in disbelief. "Is this really you?"

"Of course, it's me, Charlie," laughed the voice on the other end. "Who else would it be? Hey, I have got to go now, guy. You know I have to be down town in a few minutes to pick up my wife from work, so I have got to hurry. You head on in to chow, Charlie. All of the runs are cancelled for tomorrow. We will laugh some more on

Thursday." With that, the voice on the other end of the phone line slowly hung up, leaving me talking to the dial tone.

Stunned and confused, I stood holding the phone, remembering the perfect English, remembering that Dwight owned two cars, and that Dwight's wife was proud to spend her time being a housewife, who did not work outside her home. I stood watching the open front door for several minutes, trying to decide what to do next. After several minutes, I slowly hung up the phone. It was obvious that once again, I was totally on my own. I quickly assembled my canteens and equipment, and my failing, vegetable courage. With my back against the eastern lounge wall, I began slowly working my way towards the open front door. I kept calling out as I did so, "Is anyone there. Is this place empty? Stand back, all of you. I'm coming out." Only echoes off the empty inner walls answered my calls.

Reaching the open front door, I anxiously moved over to the door to the inner second room. The windows stood open, and the room was empty. Quickly, I closed and locked the open front door. Then I retreated into the second inner room and closed and locked its inner door. Barricaded now into the lounge, I began cautiously and carefully checking outside. The desert seemed empty enough. About 1000 feet out in the desert, out on the sagebrush covered ridge off to the northwest, partially concealed, the eighth grade girl stood motionless, watching me from afar. Up along the mountains to the northeast, perhaps a mile and a half in the distance, I could see the three star general and the colonel standing there in an open, exposed position, also watching me from afar. The general and the colonel obviously intended that I should see them. The ranges appeared to be otherwise deserted.

It had been a long tiring afternoon. By now it was past 4:00 p.m. I was very tired, still shaky, and still feeling a little numb. Feeling temporarily secure barricaded in the lounge as I was, I more or less collapsed into the soft chair to rest. The room was warm and quiet. The chair was very comfortable. I was very tired, and I fell asleep for a short while.

Forty-five minutes or so went by as I slept. It was going on 4:45 p.m. in the afternoon when I was awakened out of my sleep by the sound of footsteps outside on the sidewalk. "Is anyone out there?" I called out, still half asleep, and waking up slowly. The footsteps could be heard double timing away towards the east. As I began to shake the sleepiness from my body and my eyes, off in the distance to the east I could hear one of the sergeants shouting in subdued tones, "Tell the general he's all right. He's still in there sleeping."

Then in the distance off to the east, I could hear sergeant Smith barking back, "Good work, Anderson. Now let's get back up by the general before we upset the teacher." Then the silence of the gentle late afternoon breezes returned.

I sat there relaxing in the chair for a few minutes thinking things through. I still felt a little numb in my body, and I wasn't in any hurry to move. Off in the other room I could hear the phone ringing, but I decided I was better off not answering it, so I just let it ring for a while. It was now 4:55 p.m. in the afternoon. As I sat there watching the afternoon shadows slowly progress across the desert and across the sagebrush outside, I realized that I had a decision to make. Whether I liked it or not, I was going to have to come out of my barricaded lounge, face whatever was outside, and fight my way, if necessary, back into base. There was simply no other way. Drinking the last of the water in one of my canteens, I was now down to just one canteen of water. Not enough to last me through another day. I had no food with me and I was starting to get hungry. The heat of this day was starting to pass and the cooler evening hours were approaching. Another problem was that the lounge had outdoor plumbing. There was simply no other way. I decided that if I was ever going to make my move, I should make it now. I sat there quietly resting for a few more minutes, formulating a plan. I didn't expect my truck to be in working order. After all, the sergeants had spent most of the afternoon keeping me from it. So I expected that I was going to have to spend the night walking back into town. Since it was some 22 miles away, I was going to need more than the one canteen of water that I had with me, if I was going to make it alive. Remembering that I had a third canteen in my weather shack, and a gallon jar of water in my truck, I decided I couldn't leave the range three area without first getting at least two more canteens of water, fighting to get them if I had to.

My mind made up, I slowly stood up, stretched, adjusted my uniform, retied my military boots, wrapped the empty canteen belt around my right hand, and prepared for battle as best I could. Then I began calling out in loud tones through the open windows, "Is anyone out there? If you are, you had better get out of here now. This time I mean business. I'm coming out now, one way or the other. I'm warning you. I'm ready to fight. So if any of you are out there, you better take off running now." Approximately a mile and a half off to the northeast, on the side of the mountain, I could still see the general and the colonel standing there watching me. Behind them stood two sergeants. The other three sergeants were just arriving, having double-timed down the bunker road to the ammunition bunker, and then north along the base of the mountain to where the general and the colonel stood waiting. Since this meant that at least three of the five sergeants would be too tired to pursue me from such a great distance. I decided the time to make my move had arrived. First, I took a minute or so to slowly recite my prayers and get myself ready for action. Then I quickly closed the open windows. Next, after visually checking the first room and the sidewalk outside, to make certain they were empty, I jerked open the inner door and then the front door, stepped outside, and slammed the outer door shut behind me. Once outside in the fresh air I double timed straight north for about 30 feet out into the empty sagebrush, noticing the many boot prints in the soft dirt as I did so. Then I circled west until I was out in the sagebrush perhaps 200 feet west of the lounge. I was shouting out into the empty desert as I did so, "Stay out of my way. Everybody, stay out of my way. I'm going back in to base and none of you are going to stop me. Do you hear me?"

The desert and the sagebrush beyond were quite empty. There was nothing in my way, no sergeants, no chalk white creatures, not even a jackrabbit to slow me down. It took a while for the shock of my solitude to sink in. Once I was some 200 feet or so, west of the range three lounge, I began quickly double-timing south through the sagebrush parallel with the lounge's west wall until I was directly opposite my truck. I stopped for a few minutes to survey the range three area. It was quite deserted. Both the front door and the far side door to my weather shack stood open. Nearer to me, the south door to the generator shack also stood open, although the diesels inside had been shut down. My truck was still in the same position that I had left it earlier in the day. It sat on the gravel inviting me, opposite the northwest corner of the generator shack, facing north with the window on the driver's side rolled down. Partially concealed, out along the sagebrush covered ridge, now some 1200 feet north of me, the chalk white eighth grade girl remained partially concealed, watching me carefully. Out along the base of the mountains to the northeast, perhaps a mile and a half distant from me, the general, the colonel, and the five sergeants stood watching me. They were spread out along the base of the mountain, still obviously intending that I should see them.

I was still certain that I would have to hike back in to town. I was thinking of my truck only as the place where I had stored my extra water. I obviously needed the extra water from my truck, and the extra canteen from my weather shack, if I intended to make it back into town on foot.

I surveyed the range three area carefully. By moving several feet back and forth, I was able to convince myself that the generator shack was empty. Then, to protect myself from any surprises in that area, I suddenly rushed up to the open generator shack door and slammed it closed. Then I retreated back to my open position out in the sagebrush, some 200 feet west of my truck.

Now feeling somewhat more secure, I addressed the problem of retrieving the extra water from my truck and my extra canteen from my weather shack. I spent a few minutes studying the deserted range three area. Deciding it was safe to do so, I approached my truck in a cautious and gingerly manner. My full gallon jar of water still lay in a shaded area on the floor on the passenger side where I had left it earlier in the day. Carefully, I opened the door on the driver's side. I was not expecting my truck to still be in working order. I felt certain that my truck had been left sitting where I had left it, as part of some type of elaborate trap. Carefully, I crawled over the driver's seat and retrieved the gallon jar of water. Returning to the gravel outside, I took a quick drink of water and carefully refilled my canteens. I began feeling safer now that the range three area still appeared to be deserted.

Carrying my two full canteens, I cautiously walked over to my weather shack, shouting loudly as I did so. I paused for a few minutes and carefully surveyed my weather shack from a short distance outside. Feeling a little braver, I gingerly stepped up into my shack, closed and locked the side door. Then I grabbed my third canteen hanging from the hook where I had left it. My hands were still a little numb and shaking. The canteen slipped out of my hands and fell harmlessly to the floor. It took me a few minutes to stop shaking, pick up the canteen, and get control again. Then I quickly stepped back outside and resurveyed my military situation.

The range three area was still deserted. With my nerves still a little numb from fear and my muscles still shaking, it was obvious to me that I would never be able to hike the 22 miles back into town. With no help coming, it was with a certain grimness that I concluded my truck was my only chance for getting back into Mojave Wells. Therefore, I closed and locked up my weather shack. Then, trap or no trap, I cautiously re-approached my truck. It probably took me 10 minutes to convince myself that it was safe for me to again open the door on the driver's side, place my canteens in on the front seat, and climb into the driver's position. When the truck started normally, I was so surprised that it took another few minutes for me to decide what to do next. Finally getting my truck into gear, I began heading slowly back in to town. I was still feeling a little numb all over and my muscles were still shaking, so initially I drove very slowly. For the first fifteen minutes or so, I stayed in low gear and idled along at 10 miles per hour. Then my shakiness began to subside, and I finally got it into second gear. When I got back to the range three gate, I was glad to find it open even though I was certain that I had closed it when I had come out earlier in the day. I continued on in towards base, passing through the section of the road where the sagebrush was unusually high. That section of the trip was unusually frightening and nerve racking, but actually quite uneventful. When the road reached the north side of the runway, it was all I could do to keep myself from just parking my truck and running the rest of the way, straight across the runway, in to base. The last stretch of road, which followed around the eastern end of the runway, past the intersection to the range one road, I found absolutely terrifying. I was certain that my every movement was being watched by something white out in the sagebrush, but nothing actually appeared to be out of place. Still, it was with great relief that I finally arrived at the main gate to the ranges. My hands were still a little numb and very shaky, but otherwise I had no trouble stopping my truck, getting out, opening the main gate, and getting back into my truck. After pulling my truck through the final gate, I stopped and closed the gate behind me. Now, for the first time, I started to relax and breathe easier.

By now, it was almost 7:30 in the evening, well past the normal closing time for the chow hall. My empty stomach was reminding me that I had missed evening chow. I got back in my truck. More out of hunger than anything, I headed on up towards the Mojave Wells chow hall. Now, at last, I began to laugh off my silly nameless fears, the unusual supposed hallucinations that I had experienced in the hot sunshine, and the generally laughable level of my failing vegetable courage. "Remember, I'm the brave one," I laughed to myself. "God help the others," I laughed as I drove slowly across base. By the time I got past the motor pool and into the barracks section I was back to my old self. I was now laughing and singing loudly. "Yes," I said to myself as I took a deep breath and finally got total control of my shaking muscles again, "It's good to be back. Maybe one of these days my hallucinations will kill me but I'm not going to let fear ruin this beautiful day."

When I arrived at the Mojave Wells chow hall, to my surprise, the chow hall was still open. I parked my truck outside and hurried to get inside. I called out to my friend Smokey as I entered the chow hall and carefully closed the screen door behind me. As soon as the screen door had finished closing, I saw my friend Smokey. He was standing nearly frozen in fear behind the far end of the serving line, next to the clean and empty coffee maker. On the serving line, off to his right stood a still warm, sealed steel thermos full of coffee and a large brown sack lunch. He had a half full tray of packaged cracker squares in front of him. He stood there continually rearranging the cracker squares into neat little groups. He didn't look up or react to my presence as I came in. He continued slowly, smoothly, and endlessly rearranging the packages of crackers, as though hypnotized, all the while quietly humming a little tune. Behind him stood the open doorway to the kitchen and the back storage areas of the chow hall. Through the open door I could see the rest of the chow hall. It stood empty, still clean and spotless. From the appearance of the cracker packages, it was immediately obvious to me that Smokey had been standing there for a long time, endlessly rearranging the few packages of crackers in front of him. Seeing that he was in deep trouble, more terrified than any human can handle by himself, I approached him slowly. Then, speaking softly and naturally, I said to him, "Here, Smokey, let me give you a hand with those crackers." He didn't respond but just continued as before. I slowly came around behind the serving line until I was standing next to him, facing him from the side. Understanding his terror, I continued gently, "Here, Smokey, I'll watch your back while you finish arranging those crackers. Don't worry, Smokey. It's me, Charlie. I'm right here beside you, guarding your back." Then I gently placed my hand on the back of Smokey's shoulders.

Smokey, still rearranging the crackers, responded slowly, still humming. When he finally spoke, it sounded as though he were speaking from some place far away, "Is that you, Charlie? Is that you beside me?"

"Yes, Smokey," I responded gently. "It's me Charlie. I'm here in the flesh, big as life. I'm here to protect you, Smokey. I'm here to guard your back while you finish rearranging those crackers. As soon as you finish, Smokey, you and I will take that sack lunch and that thermos of coffee outside. We'll have us a picnic on the grass out behind the chow hall. We'll really have us some fun. Until then, Smokey, I'm right here beside you. I'm right here to protect you."

Smokey didn't respond at first, but continued as before. Then he continued slowly, "It's late, Charlie. You should leave. You should save yourself while I hold them back. They're out there in the back, you know, Charlie. They're out there in the back, behind me."

Smokey's response left me confused. I thought for a minute or so, wondering what to do next. The chow hall had a certain quiet, attractive, deserted beauty. Through the open doorway, the spotless sunlit kitchen stood obviously deserted. The late afternoon sun cast long beautiful shadows through the windows on its south and west sides. The golden red sunshine created beautiful patterns of nearly fluorescent orange highlights on the highly waxed floor. As I studied the red and golden fields where the sunshine played quietly on the highly buffed wax, a certain understanding of Smokey's problem quietly invaded my consciousness. There, on the highly waxed floor, exposed by the late afternoon sunshine, could be seen the boot prints of a young adult and two young children. Off to the left, in the corner by the stove, were another set of adult boot prints, next to a large window which stood open with its screens removed and boot prints in front of it, none of the boot prints could have been made by Smokey.

Not sure what to do next, I turned to Smokey and stated, "You know, Smokey, it looks to me like you could use some more crackers for that pan there in front of you." Then I bent down and began making some loud noises using the sliding aluminum doors to the storage bin that was below the serving line. It seemed to help Smokey. His muscles seemed to begin relaxing and loosening up, so I continued making noise. The storage bin was empty. Standing up again and laughing mildly, I exclaimed, "Shucks, Smokey! That storage bin is empty. What say I just quick jump back there to that back pantry on the right and get some more crackers! Want me to close that open window by the stove while I'm back there?" Without waiting for an answer, I turned towards the open door and began slowly heading into the kitchen beyond. Smokey began loosening noticeably. Raising his voice slightly, and obviously getting a little control over himself, he exclaimed, "No, Charlie. Don't go back there. It isn't safe back there, Charlie."

"Why, Smokey?" I gently asked. "Why isn't it safe back there? What is it that's back there?"

Smokey's muscles continued to loosen noticeably. He began to move his legs some, and started to exercise his arms more, all the time still arranging the crackers. "They're back there, Charlie. Don't go back there. You'll scare them like I did. They'll kill you if you scare them. They told me so. That tall one in the corner, he told me so. He said he'd kill me if I ever scared their children again."

I stopped and waited in the kitchen doorway for a few minutes. The kitchen in the back was obviously deserted. Whoever had been there was long gone. My problem was my need to help Smokey. I paused for a few minutes, thinking things through carefully. Then I continued, "I'm glad you warned me, Smokey. Was he the one who told you to arrange the crackers?"

"Yes," replied Smokey now showing some emotion as he continued to loosen up.

"And you've worn out almost all of those crackers, haven't you?" I continued.

"Yes," replied Smokey, now starting to show deep emotion.

"So they'll understand that you need more crackers, won't they?" I concluded.

Smokey was now becoming too emotional to answer. "Here, Smokey, I'll just get those extra crackers and be right back. Then singing one of my songs loudly over and over, I strolled bravely back into the deserted kitchen, across the highly polished open floor to one of several pantries in the back that held a dozen or so military sized boxes of crackers. Singing loudly to reassure Smokey, I quickly picked a large box from the shelf. Still singing, I strolled bravely back across the open kitchen floor, visiting and closing the open window as I did so. "There's nobody back here but me, Smokey." I shouted out loudly as I closed the window. "This place is as deserted as a church in Green Bay on football Sunday."

As I strolled back through the open kitchen door, I could see that Smokey was becoming very emotional as he progressively got better control of himself. I dropped the big box of crackers down on the floor beside him, making lots of noise as I did so. Then I noisily ripped open the cover and triumphantly announced, "Here, Smokey. Now we've got us lots of crackers!" Then I grabbed a big handful of the small cracker packages and carefully dumped them into the pan in front of Smokey, making loud noises as I did so. Smokey responded at last, by completely breaking down emotionally. Letting go at last, of the cracker packages, he grabbed onto my right arm with both of his arms and hands, and dragging my arm in to his body for security, he began crying and screaming, "Charlie, you've come! Thank God, you've come!"

Putting my left arm around his shoulders, I gave him a big strong, brotherly hug, and answered gently, "Yes, Smokey. It's me. I've come for you." Supporting Smokey with my left arm, and taking the coffee and sack lunch in my right, I helped Smokey out from behind the serving line, across the open chow hall floor to the front door, and out into the sunshine. Reaching the front of my truck, I placed the sack lunch and coffee on the hood and helped Smokey sit down on the front bumper. He sat there for a long time, his head in his hands, crying in agony and in terror, until at last he finally got hold of himself. I stood by him, rubbing the back of his shoulders, pouring him some coffee, and holding it for him so he wouldn't spill it.

"I was coming for you, Charlie," he cried. "I was coming for you like they ordered. I was waiting way up the road towards Willow flats, up by that sergeant they posted up there, just like the general ordered. Along about 4:00 p.m. in the afternoon, they ordered me to come get you. They said you needed your friend Smokey to get you laughing again. I was coming for you, Charlie! God knows I was coming. I took off running towards the chow hall. Without thinking, I disobeyed orders. They told me not to go back into the chow hall. They said just take the truck and come get you, but I came back in to get this coffee and these sandwiches that I had made up for you, and they were in here. They were all over in here, and they were out in the back, looking through the pantry and everywhere. I went to pieces, Charlie. Before I knew what was happening, one of them came up behind me. I became hysterical and began screaming. Then my mind came totally unglued. It was like I was in a dream. I couldn't control anything I was doing. All I could do was obey their orders and stand there,

471

Charlie, like you saw me, until you came. Thank God you came, Charlie. Thank God you came. I don't know how I can ever thank you."

Patting Smokey gently on the back of his shoulders, I responded, "I understand, Smokey. I understand completely." After Smokey finally got hold of himself, laughing, I said, "You know, Smokey, for all the Air Force has put us both through today, we should cook us up a couple of nice steaks, and have us one nice picnic right out here on the grass. There's nobody else on base but us two. Nobody would ever know how much fun we had at Air Force expense. If anyone ever asked about the two missing steaks, just say that I took both of them out to the ranges during the white wolf inspection. What say, eh, Smokey?" Before Smokey could respond, I exclaimed happily, "Great. I'll go get a couple of steaks out of the freezer and get that stove fired up. You finish drinking that coffee and then come on in and show me how to cook them."

Smokey thought things through for a minute. Then a big grin crossed his face. Finally, back to his old self, he began chuckling, and responded, "You sure are something, Charlie. You'd eat your way through a stretch in hell, wouldn't you?"

Laughing, I responded, "You're right, Smokey, but what else is there to do up here until the rest of the men come back from Desert Center? The guards are off the front gate. We got this whole base to ourselves. The two of us are going to have to spend the rest of the night together for our own protection, until we get more guys back here on base. I'm hungry. We might as well spend some of the time eating some of those free government steaks in the freezer."

Laughing out loud at last, Smokey stood up and shouted, "You're right, Charlie! They owe us! They owe us BIG TIME!! Let's go get those steaks. Now don't go thinking I'm chicken, Charlie, because I'm not, but I'll wait here and guard the door while you go in first and make sure the coast is clear."

"Right," I answered happily. I understood completely. Smokey stayed outside for a while, getting control of himself, as I went inside, got the steaks and fired up the stove.

Other Books by Charles James Hall

Millennial Hospitality II, The World We Knew.

Millennial Hospitality III, The Road Home.

Hall Photon Theory (HPT), copyrighted in January 1998 appears in full text in the appendix of *Millennial Hospitality III, The Road Home.*

About the Author

Charles Hall served in the USAF in the mid '60s, here in the states, as well as in Vietnam. His real life experiences while serving as a weather observer provided the background material for this book.